McGraw-Hill Electrical and Electronic Engineering Series

FREDERICK EMMONS TERMAN, *Consulting Editor*

INTRODUCTION TO
ELECTRIC FIELDS

McGraw-Hill Electrical and Electronic Engineering Series

FREDERICK EMMONS TERMAN, *Consulting Editor*

W. W. HARMAN and J. G. TRUXAL

Associate Consulting Editors

BAILEY AND GAULT · Alternating-current Machinery

BERANEK · Acoustics

BRUNS AND SAUNDERS · Analysis of Feedback Control Systems

CAGE · Theory and Application of Industrial Electronics

CUCCIA · Harmonics, Sidebands, and Transients on Communication Engineering

EASTMAN · Fundamentals of Vacuum Tubes

EVANS · Control-system Dynamics

FITZGERALD AND HIGGINBOTHAM · Basic Electrical Engineering

FITZGERALD AND KINGSLEY · Electric Machinery

GEPPERT · Basic Electron Tubes

GLASFORD · Fundamentals of Television Engineering

HAPPELL AND HESSELBERTH · Engineering Electronics

HARMAN · Fundamentals of Electronic Motion

HESSLER AND CAREY · Fundamentals of Electrical Engineering

HILL · Electronics in Engineering

JOHNSON · Transmission Lines and Networks

KRAUS · Antennas

KRAUS · Electromagnetics

LEPAGE · Analysis of Alternating-current Circuits

LEPAGE AND SEELY · General Network Analysis

MILLMAN AND SEELY · Electronics

MILLMAN AND TAUB · Pulse and Digital Circuits

ROGERS · Introduction to Electric Fields

RÜDENBERG · Transient Performance of Electric Power Systems

SEELY · Electronic Engineering

SEELY · Electron-tube Circuits

SEELY · Radio Electronics

SISKIND · Direct-current Machinery

SKILLING · Electric Transmission Lines

SKILLING · Transient Electric Currents

SPANGENBERG · Fundamentals of Electron Devices

SPANGENBERG · Vacuum Tubes

STEVENSON · Elements of Power System Analysis

STORER · Passive Network Synthesis

TERMAN · Electronic and Radio Engineering

TERMAN AND PETTIT · Electronic Measurements

THALER · Elements of Servomechanism Theory

THALER AND BROWN · Servomechanism Analysis

THOMPSON · Alternating-current and Transient Circuit Analysis

TRUXAL · Automatic Feedback Control System Synthesis

INTRODUCTION TO ELECTRIC FIELDS

A Vector Analysis Approach

WALTER E. ROGERS

Associate Professor of Electrical Engineering
University of Washington

New York   Toronto   London

McGRAW-HILL BOOK COMPANY, INC.

1954

INTRODUCTION TO ELECTRIC FIELDS

PREFACE

The purpose of this book is to present Maxwell's equations to the student as a logical summary of some real analytical experience in the use of vector methods of solving problems in electrostatics and magnetostatics. The book was written specifically as a text for a one-quarter undergraduate course which is required of all electrical-engineering students at the University of Washington, power and communication majors alike. Because of this, the arrangement is somewhat less pointed toward waves than are similar treatments intended primarily for communication majors.

Our students reach this course when they are juniors or seniors, and their maturity levels cover a wide range. They have not had any previous experience with formal vector analysis, and most of them have not had a course in elementary differential equations. These factors combine to require a book which proceeds rather slowly and contains a good deal of detail about thinking processes which are new to the student. A perusal of the chapter headings will indicate the pace and the content. Not a treatise, this book is aimed at the average, serious, undergraduate student who is long on effort and short on experience with analytical problems.

I should like to point out to other instructors who use this book that we have found it desirable to schedule a weekly laboratory period in addition to the lecture periods. Some of these are used for fluid mapping, investigations of rubber-sheet models, electrolytic tanks, and graphite sheets, while the remainder are used as problem sessions. The graphic analysis of two-dimensional fields is a case in point. Assistance in getting a laboratory started will be found in the Appendix, which is devoted to a brief discussion of fluid mapping and the construction of rubber-sheet models.

Attention is called to the illustrations. The contour-lighted rubber-sheet models grew from the attempt of an ingenious student, Glenn Walker, to light a model he had constructed with a slit in front of an arc. The fluid maps were modeled and photographed by Professor A. D. Moore at the University of Michigan. He has developed this technique to a point which makes it popular and practical in industry as well as a teaching aid. I cannot thank him enough, but I can point out to those who find them helpful that these illustrations represent several weeks of very hard work on his part.   To my simple request for any suitable negatives which would fit into my proposed list of illustrations, he responded with an enthusiasm which surprised me then, but which would not surprise those who know him, as I do now.   With boundless ingenuity and patient attention to detail, he built special models and developed some new methods in order that the illustrations would be as effective as possible.

With gratitude, I acknowledge the help of my several colleagues who have used the preliminary version in the classroom.   More than thanks must be extended to Dr. John F. Streib of the Physics Department at the University of Washington, who read the entire manuscript and made many helpful suggestions.   However, any errors and omissions which remain are the sole responsibility of the author.

Walter E. Rogers

CONTENTS

TABLE OF SYMBOLS

$\mathbf{F}$	Force vector, newtons	
G	Conductance, mhos	
$\mathbf{H}$	Magnetic-intensity vector, amperes per meter	9.9
H	Magnitude of $\mathbf{H}$	
h_1, h_2, h_3	Metric coefficients	3.9
h	Height, meters	6.5
I	Electric current, amperes	4.1, 4.2
$\mathbf{i}$	Unspecified unit vector	
$\mathbf{i}_1, \mathbf{i}_2, \mathbf{i}_3$	Unit vectors in general orthogonal coordinates	1.14, 3.9
$\mathbf{J}$	Current density, amperes per square meter	4.1
$\mathbf{J}_s$	Surface-current density, amperes per meter of width	9.11
K	Relative dielectric constant, dimensionless	7.1
k	Dielectric susceptibility, farads per meter	7.1
	Unspecified constant	
	An integer	8.13
$\mathbf{L}$	Specified displacement vector, meters	
$d\mathbf{L}, dL$	A small displacement along a specified path, meters	
L	Self-inductance, henries	11.9
$\mathbf{M}$	Magnetic moment, ampere-meters^2	9.5
$\mathbf{M}$	Magnetic moment per unit volume, amperes per meter	9.13
M	Mutual inductance, henries	11.9
m	Mass of electron, 9×10^{-31} kilogram	2.1
	Unspecified scalar quantity	
mmf	Magnetomotive force, amperes	9.9
dN	A small displacement in a direction normal to a surface	3.8
N	Number of turns of a coil	
$\mathbf{n}$	Unit vector normal to a surface	1.9
n	Unspecified scalar quantity	
	Number of turns of a solenoid, per meter of length	9.12
	Number of charges per unit volume	9.3
$\mathbf{P}$	Electric dipole moment, coulomb-meters	3.11
$\mathbf{P}$	Dipole moment per unit volume, coulombs per square meter	7.9

P Magnitude of **P**
Power, watts. 4.9
Pitch of a helix, meters. 9.2

p Power per unit volume, watts per cubic
meter. 4.9

Q Electric charge, coulombs. 2.1

R Distance from a specified point, or perpendicular distance from a line,
meters. 1.13
Resistance, ohms

r Unit vector of cylindrical and spherical
coordinates. 1.13

r Radius of a circle, cylinder, or sphere,
meters

S Specified distance, meters

$d\mathbf{S}$ A small displacement, meters. 3.1

s A unit vector associated with a displace-
ment. 1.7

T Torque vector, newton-meters. 3.11

T Magnitude of T
Period, seconds.   9.2

t Time, seconds

U Velocity vector, meters per second

u_1, u_2, u_3 General orthogonal coordinates. 1.14, 3.9

V Electrostatic scalar potential, potential
difference, volts. 3.3

V_m Maximum value of potential difference
in a specified field, volts

W Energy, joules
Weight of gas, kilograms (Sec. 8.4 only)
Width, meters (Sec. 4.7 only)

w Energy per unit volume, joules per cubic
meter
Density of gas, kilograms per cubic
meter (Sec. 8.4 only)

X A function of x only. 8.11

Y A function of y only. 8.11

Z A function of z only. 8.11

∇ (del, or nabla) Vector operator

∇^{2} (del squared) Laplacian operator. 8.5

α, β (alpha, beta) Used for angle variables,
radians

γ (gamma) Conductivity, mhos per meter   4.3

CHAPTER 1

VECTOR ANALYSIS

1.1 Introduction. Physical problems are usually studied by idealizing them until they fall into a particular branch of applied mathematics. In the study of alternating currents, for example, the most frequent mathematical problem concerns the addition, subtraction, differentiation, and integration of scalar quantities which are sinusoidal functions of time. In order to handle such problems, the engineer learns to use some of the notation and a few of the ideas of a branch of mathematics known as functions of a complex variable. Even though the use of complex numbers seemed difficult and abstract on first contact, most of us have found that the mathematics simplifies the problems and that this result is worth considerably more than the effort expended initially.

The study of physical science is simplified by using the language, notation, and ideas of a branch of applied mathematics known as vector analysis. The most striking characteristic of vector analysis is its shorthand notation, whereby a symbol or two may be used to represent an equation which could occupy a full page in longhand notation. The greatest utility of vector analysis is this: It allows us to keep physical problems in their original, general form through the greater part of their solution. This permits us to make physical statements without the introduction of coordinate systems, delaying this and the other algebraic and arithmetical details to the last possible moment.

We must learn a language, and it will help us tremendously if we can learn it well enough to think in it, in the same sense that an accomplished linguist is said to be able to think in several languages. In the study of a new language we start by stating a few of the rules of grammar and, picking up a small vocabulary, proceed to describe our common experiences of everyday life in the new language. We shall study the language of vector analysis in the same way. It takes time to become accustomed to its shorthand notation, and as with any shorthand, skill comes with practice.

It is first necessary to define the quantities we shall use and the symbols needed to represent them. We must then set up a few rules for such things as addition, subtraction, and multiplication. We shall treat these simply as rules or instructions, rather like the postulates of Euclidean geometry. To do much more than this would make this book a study of mathematics instead of an introductory book about electric fields.

1.2   Vectors, Scalars, and Fields.   Vector quantities, or *vectors*, are those which are not completely described until a direction has been specified.   By contrast, the word *scalar* is used to distinguish, rather loosely, those quantities with which we do not associate a direction.   Forces, velocities, and accelerations are vector quantities, while temperature, mass, and volume are scalar quantities.   Of the scalars, numbers are the simplest kind.

To be more specific, vector quantities are those which we can represent on a map or model by a *directed line segment*, where the length of the line represents the magnitude, the orientation of the line represents the direction, and an arrow indicates the sense.   In addition to this we shall reserve the term *vector* for those quantities which obey the rules of addition, subtraction, and multiplication soon to be specified. Not everything which can be represented by a line segment is sufficiently well behaved to obey all our rules.

A *field* is a region of space with which we associate a physical quantity. There is something going on in the region that we want to investigate and describe.   We use the word *field* rather than the word *region* to indicate that we are thinking about the region in terms of the scalar or vector quantities which we might measure there.

To distinguish the vector quantities from the scalars, heavy or boldface type will be used.   Thus the symbol **V** may represent the velocity of wind, which we may find is 10 miles per hour in a westerly direction at some particular place and time.   To indicate the scalar magnitude of a vector quantity, we shall frequently enclose the vector symbol in square brackets.   The choice of $|\mathbf{V}|$ rather than V is a way of making it a little clearer where this scalar quantity came from.

$$\mathsf{A\ B\ C\ D\ E\ H}$$

$$\mathsf{a\ b\ c\ d\ i\ j\ k\ n\ r\ \theta\ \phi}$$

FIG. 1.1   Simulating boldface type in hand lettering.

On the typewritten page, vector quantities are frequently underlined, or occasionally overlined.   This method may be carried over to hand lettering.   However, boldface type may be simulated in hand lettering, quickly and effectively, by adding a stroke to the letters as illustrated in Fig. 1.1.   Because there are other reasons for underlining things, some find that this system avoids confusion in taking notes, working problems, or writing on the blackboard.   The person new at vector analysis seldom realizes the importance of methodical methods of distinguishing clearly and consistently between vector and scalar quantities.   The method used is unimportant, but the attention paid to this detail is one of the marks of experience.

1.3 Addition of Vectors. The sum of two vectors is frequently called the resultant rather than the sum to remind us that vectors are to be added differently from scalars. The magnitude and direction of the sum of two vectors is obtained by representing them as directed line segments and then following a set of instructions known as the parallelogram law. To add **B** to **A**, we are to lay the beginning of **B** at the end of **A**. Then

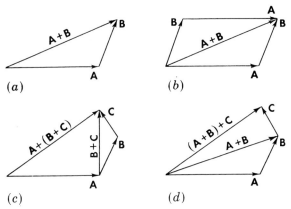

(*a*) (*b*)

(*c*) (*d*)

F<small>IG</small>. 1.2 Addition of vectors. Parts *a* and *b* illustrate how the parallelogram law arises from the law that the sum of two vectors is independent of the order in which they are added. Parts *c* and *d* extend this law to three vectors.

the sum, **A** + **B**, is given in magnitude and direction by the line segment which joins the beginning of **A** to the end of **B**, as shown in Fig. 1.2*a*. The same result is obtained if the order of the operations is reversed. When this is done and the figures are superimposed, the parallelogram of Fig. 1.2*b* is formed.

In formal language, the statement that the sum of vectors is independent of the order in which they are added is known as the *commutative* law of addition. In equation form, we write this law as

$$\mathbf{A} + \mathbf{B} = \mathbf{B} + \mathbf{A} \qquad \text{Commutative law} \qquad (1)$$

The sum of several vectors may be obtained by a repetition of the instructions for adding two of them, and they may be paired, two by two, in any manner. Using parentheses to indicate the order of performing the operations, as in scalar algebra, we can write this rule as an equation, illustrated in Fig. 1.2*c* and *d*,

$$\mathbf{A} + (\mathbf{B} + \mathbf{C}) = (\mathbf{A} + \mathbf{B}) + \mathbf{C} \qquad (2)$$

associative law

The corresponding rule in scalar algebra is

$$A + (B + C) = (A + B) + C \tag{3}$$

and is known as the *associative* law of addition.

We need to know about these apparently obvious properties and to recall the probably forgotten formal terminology in order to increase our awareness and appreciation of the few differences which do exist between scalar and vector algebra, along with the many similarities.

1.4   Multiplication of a Vector by a Scalar, and Subtraction of Vectors. In ordinary arithmetic, multiplication may be thought of as a process of addition, and addition as a process of counting. In fact, we first learn

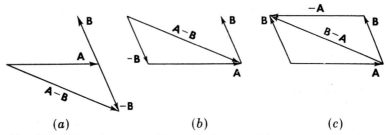

(a) (b) (c)

Fig. 1.3   Subtraction of vectors. The operation **A** − **B** is equivalent to adding −**B** to **A**. The result is independent of the order in which the operations are performed, as demonstrated in *a* and *b*. A comparison of *c* with *a* and *b* demonstrates that **B** − **A** = −(**A** − **B**).

to add by counting, and to multiply by adding. In vector algebra, we can repeat this line of reasoning when multiplying a vector by a scalar. A line segment 10 inches long is equivalent to the sum of 10 parallel line segments, each 1 inch long. One 7-pound force applied at a point is equivalent to seven 1-pound forces applied at the same point, if the direction of each of the 1-pound forces is the same as the direction of the 7-pound force. We may think of this either as a process of addition or of multiplication. To make a rule, we state that when a vector is multiplied by a positive scalar the operation changes the magnitude of the vector but does not change its direction.

We can deal with all negative scalars by considering only the scalar −1. The length of a line segment is a quantity which is essentially positive. The result of the scalar multiplication (-1)**A** is a vector having the same magnitude as **A** but the opposite direction. Graphical *subtraction of vectors* thus becomes a process of reversing the direction of the vector to be subtracted and then following the rule for addition, as illustrated in Fig. 1.3.

The rules for the removal of parentheses in the multiplication of vector quantities by a scalar, and vice versa, are the same as in scalar algebra.

The distributive law of algebra

$$n(A + B + C) = nA + nB + nC \tag{1}$$

has the counterparts

$$n(\mathbf{A} + \mathbf{B} + \mathbf{C}) = n\mathbf{A} + n\mathbf{B} + n\mathbf{C} \tag{2}$$

and

$$(m + n)\mathbf{A} = m\mathbf{A} + n\mathbf{A} \tag{3}$$

in vector algebra.

Those who had some previous experience with the theory of alternating currents may have learned to call some scalar quantities which are sinusoidal functions of time by the name vectors. However, the voltages and currents of alternating-current circuit theory are *complex scalars*, or *phasors*. The use of complex numbers gives the easiest way to account for the relative positions in time of sinusoidal functions of time. These cannot be said to have a direction in space in the same sense as the vectors with which we are presently concerned. While the complex scalars obey the parallelogram law of addition, they do not obey the rules for scalar and vector multiplication soon to be established for vectors. Further, we do not associate multiplication of a vector quantity by the scalar $\sqrt{-1}$ with the process of rotation of the line segment which has been drawn to represent the vector quantity.

1.5 The Scalar Product of Two Vectors. Two operations on vectors are called multiplication. One has a scalar result, and the other a vector result. Neither corresponds to the rule for multiplication of complex numbers which involves the product of the magnitudes and the sum of the angles.

The scalar product of two vectors is defined as the scalar quantity which is the product of the magnitudes and the cosine of the angle between them. The shorthand notation for this type of product, applied to the two vectors $\mathbf{A}$ and $\mathbf{B}$, is $\mathbf{A} \cdot \mathbf{B}$. Our definition may be written as an equation

$$\mathbf{A} \cdot \mathbf{B} = AB \cos \alpha \tag{1}$$

where α is the angle between the two vectors. Because of the dot between the vector symbols, the scalar product is also known as the *dot product*. The word *dot* is easier to say than *scalar*, but we shall consistently call this operation by the longer name in order to remind us that the result is a scalar and not a vector. Until we have attained considerable familiarity with all these new terms, we shall need every helpful suggestion.

When $\mathbf{F}$ is the force, and $\mathbf{L}$ the vector which represents the displacement, the scalar product $\mathbf{F} \cdot \mathbf{L}$ is the work done by the force. There is no reason to restrict the use of this type of product to vectors having these

units of force and distance; it is useful for other kinds of vectors, too.   It
is also interesting to observe that when two vectors are perpendicular,
their scalar product is zero.   On the other hand, if the scalar product of
two vectors is zero, either the magnitude of one is zero, or the two are
perpendicular.   This is easily visualized for the force **F** and the path **L**,
and is occasionally used in dealing with other kinds of vectors.

The scalar product behaves itself algebraically and no special interpretations are required.   For contrast with the vector product, yet to be
defined, we point out that the scalar product obeys the commutative law

$$\mathbf{A} \cdot \mathbf{B} = \mathbf{B} \cdot \mathbf{A} \tag{2}$$

Not immediately obvious, but easily demonstrated, is the distributive law

$$\mathbf{A} \cdot (\mathbf{B} + \mathbf{C}) = \mathbf{A} \cdot \mathbf{B} + \mathbf{A} \cdot \mathbf{C} \tag{3}$$

The frequently used extension of Eq. (3) is

$$(\mathbf{A} + \mathbf{B} + \cdots) \cdot (\mathbf{M} + \mathbf{N} + \cdots) = \mathbf{A} \cdot \mathbf{M} + \mathbf{A} \cdot \mathbf{N} + \cdots$$
$$+ \mathbf{B} \cdot \mathbf{M} + \mathbf{B} \cdot \mathbf{N} + \cdots + \cdots \tag{4}$$

The scalar product of a vector with itself is interesting and is sometimes
called the square of a vector.

$$\mathbf{A} \cdot \mathbf{A} = A^2 \tag{5}$$

1.6   Unit Vectors.   Vectors whose magnitude is unity are called unit
vectors, and one's first thoughts turn to such things as 1-pound forces,
1-knot velocities, and 1-meter displacements as good and correct examples.   However, in dealing with scalar quantities algebraically, we agree
on a system of measuring units and then put the quantities into our equations as pure numbers.   This we can do with vector quantities also, and
when we reflect on the significance of a unit vector, we see that it can
capably play the role of specifying a direction and that we need not associate any measuring stick with it at all.   Like the pure number *one*, a
dimensionless unit vector is a very useful quantity, and it serves as a
pointer.   Further, we can always obtain a dimensionless unit vector from
any other vector quantity by dividing it by its magnitude, as we are
instructed to do by the equation

$$\mathbf{a} = \frac{\mathbf{A}}{|\mathbf{A}|} \tag{1}$$

From another view, we see that we can write the identity

$$\mathbf{A} = |\mathbf{A}|\mathbf{a} \tag{2}$$

in which all the units of measurement, as well as the number of them, are
lumped together in the scalar $|\mathbf{A}|$.   This leaves to the unit vector **a** only
the role of describing the direction of **A**.

Now the consistent use of lower-case letters to indicate only unit vectors, and never a vector whose magnitude is not unity, is one of the peculiarities of this book. In others, unit vectors call for lower-case letters, but not all lower-case vectors are unit vectors. In turning to any reference work using vector-analysis notation, it is necessary for the reader to discover what particular system is used to distinguish unit vectors; there is no standard.

1.7 The Component of a Vector, and Component Vectors. When one of the vectors of a scalar product is a unit vector, the result is subject to a special interpretation. The equation

$$\mathbf{F} \cdot \mathbf{s} = F \cos \alpha$$

Component of the Vector

gives the magnitude of the effective force $\mathbf{F}$ in the direction of the unit vector $\mathbf{s}$, when α is again the angle between them. The scalar product of a vector and a unit vector is known as the *component of the vector* in the direction specified by the unit vector. More than a shorthand, perhaps, we can think of the symbols as a *set of instructions telling us that it is our task to find the component of the given vector in the direction of the unit vector. This is the most frequently performed calculation and the commonest symbol in vector analysis.* It replaces the equivalent direction cosine symbols of analytic geometry. If on the other hand, we desire to know the component of a vector in some direction, one of the ways of doing this will be to find a unit vector in that direction and then to evaluate their scalar product.

$\hat{a} \cdot \hat{b} = \cos \angle_{ab}$

The scalar product of two unit vectors is equal to the cosine of the angle between them, and it is quite handy to find the cosine of certain angles in just this way. In fact it is very easy to obtain the trigonometric formula for the cosine of the sum and difference of two angles from the scalar product of two unit vectors. This is set up in one of the problems at the end of this chapter, and it is the sort of thing that caused Oliver Heaviside to remark that vector analysis was more basic than trigonometry.

When we know the component of a vector in a given direction, we can associate this scalar magnitude with a vector in that direction, and the corresponding vector quantity is known as the *component vector*. The component of the vector $\mathbf{A}$ in the direction of the unit vector $\mathbf{i}$ is the scalar quantity $\mathbf{A} \cdot \mathbf{i}$. The component vector in the direction of $\mathbf{i}$ is $(\mathbf{A} \cdot \mathbf{i})\mathbf{i}$. This is usually written without the parentheses as $\mathbf{A} \cdot \mathbf{i}\,\mathbf{i}$, the parentheses being unnecessary as we have not and will not define a vector operation without a symbol between them. When we also desire the component perpendicular to $\mathbf{i}$ and in the plane of $\mathbf{A}$ and $\mathbf{i}$, one of the ways of finding it is by subtraction, $\mathbf{A} - \mathbf{A} \cdot \mathbf{i}\,\mathbf{i}$ as in Fig. 1.4.

In these figures, observe that, as far as possible, dimensions are treated

Component Vector $\mathbf{A} \cdot \hat{i}\hat{i}$

as scalar quantities, and dimension lines have arrows on both ends as in engineering-drawing practice. Vector quantities are drawn heavier and have, of course, only one arrowhead.

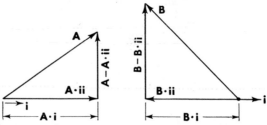

FIG. 1.4 Components and component vectors. The components are scalars. The sum of the component vectors is the original vector. The two parts of the figure compare the component vectors for angles greater and less than 90°.

1.8   The Vector Product of Two Vectors. A frequent calculation in physical science involves finding a quantity proportional to the product of the magnitudes of two vectors and the sine of the angle between them. Examples are the problems of finding the moment of a force, the force on a current-carrying conductor in a magnetic field, and the area of a parallelogram. In some cases by defining, and in other cases by keeping, the vector nature of these quantities, we may describe them without reference to a system of coordinates.

The shorthand notation for the vector product of the vectors **A** and **B** is **A** × **B**, read "**A** cross **B**." This is a vector quantity whose magnitude is the product of the magnitudes of the given vectors, **A** and **B** and the sine of the smaller angle between them. We are directed to evaluate the magnitude of the vector product from the formula

$$|\mathbf{A} \times \mathbf{B}| = AB \sin \alpha \tag{1}$$

The direction of **A** × **B** is the direction of advance of a right-hand screw as it turns (through the smaller angle) to carry **A** toward **B** as in Fig. 1.5a. To the surprise of people who have turned lots of screws, this statement is not a clear description of a direction to everyone. The direction of **A** × **B** is perpendicular to both **A** and **B**, and hence to their plane, and has the sense given by the thumb of the right hand when the fingers are pointed in the direction in which **A** must be turned to carry **A** toward **B**, through the smaller angle. In future discussions, we shall refer to this simply as the *right-hand rule*.

The commutative law of multiplication does not hold for the vector product. If we follow our instructions carefully each time, we observe that

$$\mathbf{A} \times \mathbf{B} = (-1)(\mathbf{B} \times \mathbf{A}) \tag{2}$$

This is the second important difference between scalar algebra and vector algebra. The first was that the sum of the magnitudes is not the magnitude of the sum, in general. With careful regard for the order of operations, however, the distributive law holds for the vector product. That is,

$$(\mathbf{A} + \mathbf{B} + \cdots) \times (\mathbf{M} + \mathbf{N} + \cdots) = \mathbf{A} \times \mathbf{M} + \mathbf{A} \times \mathbf{N} + \cdots$$
$$+ \mathbf{B} \times \mathbf{M} + \mathbf{B} \times \mathbf{N} + \cdots + \cdots \quad (3)$$

Presented without proof, this reasonable rule is not obvious. Reference to texts on vector analysis will reveal a surprising variety of methods of demonstration.

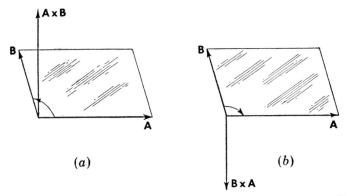

(a)　　　　　　　　(b)

Fig. 1.5   The vector product of vectors is perpendicular to both of them. The sense of the product is determined by the right-hand rule. The magnitude is numerically equal to the area of a parallelogram. Interchanging the order of operations changes the sense of the product.

In addition to the advantage in the shorthand, the utility of the vector product is illustrated in the relative simplicity with which it finds the perpendicular to a surface at a point in that surface. All we need to do is to find two vectors which lie in the surface at that point, and then find their vector product, as in Fig. 1.5. Another use for the vector product is as a test for parallel vectors. If two vectors are parallel, their vector product is zero. If the vector product is zero, on the other hand, either the magnitude of one of the vectors is zero, or the two are parallel.

1.9 Surfaces as Vectors. The position of a surface in space lends itself well to treatment as a vector. There is an infinity of line segments or vectors which lie in the surface, and hence no uniquely defined direction in the surface itself. The perpendicular to the surface or *normal* is uniquely defined at every point in the surface. As previously mentioned in introducing the concept, the normal can be found by taking the vector product of any two nonparallel vectors which lie in the surface at the point in question. As a matter of convenience we shall have frequent occasion to describe a plane area as a vector whose magnitude is the magnitude of the area, and whose direction is perpendicular to the surface, as specified by a unit vector **n** (for normal). For a curved surface, as in Fig. 1.6, the differential area dA is a plane area in the limit.

When the area we are describing as a vector forms a part of a closed surface, we shall assign the *outward* normal as the *positive* direction. For areas which do not form a part of a closed surface, we shall recognize that an ambiguity exists in the sense of the normal and shall remove it when the need arises.

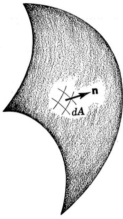

FIG. 1.6   The position of a surface in space may be described in terms of a unit vector **n**, perpendicular to the surface at every point.

1.10   The Relation of Vectors to a Coordinate System. Cartesian Coordinates.

Most of our problems will require us to describe the magnitude and direction of a vector quantity in a region of interest in terms of a system of coordinates. It will help to discuss briefly the similar problem of relating a purely scalar quantity to a system of coordinates. One such quantity is the temperature throughout a region, such as that in the various parts of an electric motor. We can measure these temperatures by installing a number of thermocouples. Each thermocouple will specify the temperature which exists at one point in the machine. In describing the temperature of the machine, we must describe the location of the point of measurement, as well as the temperature which is found at that point. There may or may not be any simple relationship between the numbers which we use to describe the location of the thermocouple, and the number which we use to describe the temperature which we found at that point. A description, simple or complicated, of the temperature which exists at every point in a region of interest is a description of a scalar field. Since we cannot conceive of two different temperatures being measured simultaneously at any point, we shall have occasion to call such a field a *single-valued scalar function of position*.

In a similar way, we shall be dealing with the problem of describing the magnitude and the direction of vector quantities as we find them, or measure them, at every point in a region of interest. To every point in the region, we assign a set of numbers which describes its position, and to every point we assign another set of numbers which describes the magnitude and direction of the vector quantity. Again, there may or may not be any simple relationship between the two sets of numbers. A description, simple or complicated, of the magnitude and direction of a vector quantity found at all points in a region is a description of a vector field.

Let us think now about describing such a vector quantity as the velocity of the wind. To do a thorough job of it, we are going to have to specify the magnitude and the direction of the wind at every point in such a region of interest as the first few miles above the surface of an ocean. In order to specify the location of the points, we shall resort to the use of three numbers in connection with each point, describing latitude, longitude, and height above the surface of the earth. We should be greatly surprised to find any correlation at all between the magnitude and direction of the wind at a point, and the latitude, longitude, and height of that point. Such a correlation might occur, however. One particular day we might find a gentle westerly wind blowing over a wide range of latitude and longitude, increasing uniformly with the altitude. GREAT IS OUR GOOD FORTUNE in being able to describe this wind in the form of an equation relating the direction and the magnitude, in miles per hour, to the coordinates of the point of measurement:

$$\mathbf{V} = (10 + z)\mathbf{i}$$

where z = altitude in miles
    $\mathbf{i}$ = a unit vector pointing east

Most of the time, we are going to confine ourselves to simple vector quantities in which there is a definite correlation between the magnitude and direction of the vector and the numbers, or *coordinates*, used to represent the position of the point of observation. We must recall that such relations are fortunate, if not accidental, and above all we must not confuse the vector itself with the number set used to describe the location of a point.

There are as many ways of describing the direction of a vector as there are of describing the direction of a line segment. In pointing out our intention to describe areas as vectors, in Sec. 1.9, we suggested that a direction could be specified by the perpendicular to a surface. An even more common way of specifying the direction of a line is to describe it as the intersection of two surfaces. When the two intersecting surfaces are planes, their line of intersection is straight. More generally, two surfaces intersect in a curve. We shall find it convenient to use both kinds of surfaces, depending on the nature of the vector to be described.

Three surfaces which are mutually perpendicular define three mutually perpendicular lines of intersection all passing through a single point. When the three surfaces are planes, the three lines of intersection form *cartesian coordinate axes*, and their point of intersection is known as the origin. Now a cartesian coordinate system is certainly familiar, but the process of thinking of the coordinate axes as the intersection of three planes is not so familiar. We shall elaborate on such a thought process shortly.

In the cartesian coordinate system, we may erect three mutually perpendicular *unit* vectors lying in the coordinate axes. We refer to the three axes as x, y, and z, and call the corresponding unit vectors **i**, **j**, and **k**. In order to distinguish between up and down, we must specify which directions are positive. The sense of the unit vectors corresponds to the direction of *increasing* coordinates. For consistent results, we must also define a *right-hand coordinate system* as one in which

$$\mathbf{i} \times \mathbf{j} = \mathbf{k} \qquad \mathbf{j} \times \mathbf{k} = \mathbf{i} \qquad \mathbf{k} \times \mathbf{i} = \mathbf{j} \qquad (1)$$

as in Fig. 1.7.

Regardless of the position of any point in space with respect to the origin, we may pass through that point three planes which are parallel to the planes forming the origin of coordinates. We may erect *at the point* three mutually perpendicular unit vectors which have the same direction as those at every other point in space, as long as we use cartesian coordinates. These three reference directions provide a useful way of describing the direction of any vector quantity which we may find at the point in question.

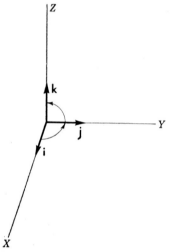

Let **A** be any vector, such as a force, whose magnitude and direction are known at a point in space. At that point, then, we now have four vectors; the vector to be described, and the three unit vectors. We shall describe the vector of interest in terms of the sum of three vectors whose directions correspond to the directions of the unit vectors. To do this is to break the vector of interest up into three component vectors which can be added together again to describe the vector of interest. We have defined the scalar product of a vector and a unit vector as the component of the vector in the direction of the unit vector. Taking the scalar product of the vector **A** with each of the unit vectors, and multiplying each of the results by the corresponding unit vector, gives the three component vectors which lie parallel to the three unit vectors. Adding the results gives

Fig. 1.7   A right-hand system of unit vectors. $\mathbf{i} \times \mathbf{j} = \mathbf{k}$, $\mathbf{j} \times \mathbf{k} = \mathbf{i}$, $\mathbf{k} \times \mathbf{i} = \mathbf{j}$. Note the cyclic order.

$$\mathbf{A} = (\mathbf{A} \cdot \mathbf{i})\mathbf{i} + (\mathbf{A} \cdot \mathbf{j})\mathbf{j} + (\mathbf{A} \cdot \mathbf{k})\mathbf{k} \qquad (2)$$

More frequently, the scalar values in the brackets are replaced by a scalar symbol and a subscript which denotes the direction of the unit vector, to write

$$\mathbf{A} = A_x \mathbf{i} + A_y \mathbf{j} + A_z \mathbf{k} \qquad (3)$$

where $A_x = \mathbf{A} \cdot \hat{\imath}$
$A_y = \hat{A} \cdot \hat{\jmath}$
$A_z = \hat{A} \cdot \hat{k}$

At first glance the business of using three vectors to represent one vector quantity would seem complex. The advantages lie in performing the operations of addition, subtraction, and multiplication. The rules for these various operations permit the simplifications listed below.

1. To add or subtract vectors, we may add or subtract their components separately. In equation form,

$$\mathbf{A} \pm \mathbf{B} = (A_x \pm B_x)\mathbf{i} + (A_y \pm B_y)\mathbf{j} + (A_z \pm B_z)\mathbf{k} \qquad (4)$$

2. The scalar product of two vectors is numerically equal to the sum of the algebraic products of the corresponding components:

$$\mathbf{A} \cdot \mathbf{B} = A_x B_x + A_y B_y + A_z B_z \qquad (5)$$

3. The vector product of two vectors may be written in terms of the unit vectors and the products of the components in the form of the determinant:

$$\mathbf{A} \times \mathbf{B} = \begin{vmatrix} \mathbf{i} & \mathbf{j} & \mathbf{k} \\ A_x & A_y & A_z \\ B_x & B_y & B_z \end{vmatrix} \qquad (6)$$

4. The magnitude of a vector is equal to the square root of the sum of the squares of its three rectangular components:

$$|\mathbf{A}| = \sqrt{A_x{}^2 + A_y{}^2 + A_z{}^2} \qquad (7)$$

The proof of these statements utilizes the distributive laws and the basic definitions of scalar and vector products. The details are left to the student as an instructive problem.

1.11   Equality of Vectors. Two vectors are equal if they have the same magnitude and the same direction. While this is the simplest statement of the conditions of equality, we do not ordinarily apply it literally as a test for equality. It is not always convenient to compute and compare the magnitudes and directions separately. As a test for equality, we recognize that if $\mathbf{A} = \mathbf{B}$, then $\mathbf{A} - \mathbf{B} = 0$. For practical use, an equivalent statement of the conditions of equality is: "Two vectors are equal if their difference is zero."

To find the difference of two vectors, we may subtract them graphically, as in Sec. 1.4, or by algebraic manipulation. As an illustration of the latter method, let us test the following two vectors for equality:

$$\mathbf{A} = x\,\mathbf{i} + y\,\mathbf{j} + z\,\mathbf{k}$$
$$\mathbf{B} = y\,\mathbf{i} + x\,\mathbf{j} + z\,\mathbf{k}$$

Their difference is

$$\mathbf{A} - \mathbf{B} = (x - y)\mathbf{i} + (y - x)\mathbf{j} + (z - z)\mathbf{k}$$

The difference will be zero, and the vectors $\mathbf{A}$ and $\mathbf{B}$ are therefore equal at all points in the plane $x = y$. At all other points, the vectors $\mathbf{A}$ and $\mathbf{B}$ are not equal, though they do have the same magnitude everywhere.

From this procedure, we observe that two vectors are equal if all their components are equal.   As a test for equality, however, this is sometimes difficult to apply.   The difficulty arises when the references vectors have different directions at different points, as in the polar-coordinate system discussed in the following section.

The condition for equality of vectors says nothing about the position of the point with which the vector is associated.   A vector is not altered by moving it from one point to another, keeping its direction unchanged. The concept of equality of vectors is not the same thing as *equivalence of effect*.   A concentrated force vector applied at the center of a simple beam does not produce the same deflection or stress as an equal force vector applied at a different point.

1.12   Vectors in Plane Polar Coordinates.   Many problems are more easily handled by using coordinate systems other than cartesian.   In the methods of describing direction in these other coordinate systems, there are some details which need careful examination.   We also need to know how to change from one coordinate system to another.   If we look at two-dimensional systems first, the three-dimensional problem will be more than half completed.

To describe the location of a point in a plane, two numbers are needed. In cartesian coordinates, these two numbers are the perpendicular distances to two perpendicular reference axes.   In plane polar coordinates, the two numbers used to locate a point are the distance to a point called the origin, and the angle between the line from the origin to the point, and a reference line.   By drawing a sketch, Fig. 1.8a, we write the following relationships between the two systems:

2 dimensional Cartesian to Polar Conversion

$$R = \sqrt{x^2 + y^2} \tag{1}$$
$$\theta = \text{arc tan } \frac{y}{x} \quad \text{(quadrant by inspection)} \tag{2}$$
$$x = R \cos \theta \tag{3}$$
$$y = R \sin \theta \tag{4}$$

To describe a vector which we find in a plane, we have to describe its direction as well as its magnitude.   In cartesian coordinates we specify directions at every point in a plane by drawing two lines through the point parallel to the reference axes.   We then draw two unit vectors at the point in the direction of increasing coordinates.   We describe the vector quantity which we find at the point in terms of its components, or its component vectors, with respect to these two unit vectors.   In Fig. 1.8b, the line segments represent a vector quantity $\mathbf{V}$ and its component vectors $\mathbf{V}_x$ and $\mathbf{V}_y$, for two different points.   At the point Q, the component vector $\mathbf{V}_x$ has a direction opposite to that of the reference unit vector

i, and this is equivalent to a negative x component, V_x, as remarked in Sec. 1.4.

In plane polar coordinates, we handle this matter of describing directions somewhat differently. At each point in a plane, we erect two unit vectors, **r** and **θ**. The first is directed along the line from the origin to the point, in the direction which *increases* the coordinate or measure number R. The other unit vector is directed perpendicular to **r** and has a sense

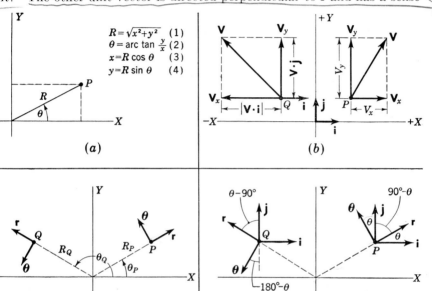

$$R=\sqrt{x^2+y^2} \quad (1)$$
$$\theta = \arctan \tfrac{y}{x} \quad (2)$$
$$x=R \cos \theta \quad (3)$$
$$y=R \sin \theta \quad (4)$$

(a)

(b)

(c)

(d)

Fig. 1.8 Coordinate transformations in a plane. (a) Relations between the plane polar and the cartesian coordinates of a point; (b) components and component vectors in cartesian coordinates; (c) the unit vectors in plane polar coordinates; (d) the angles between the unit vectors in the two systems.

which matches the direction of motion which is required to *increase* the coordinate θ. These reference vectors are shown for two points in Fig. 1.8c. In contrast to the reference vectors in cartesian coordinates, these do not have constant directions.

When we are given a vector in terms of its components in cartesian coordinates, and wish to find its corresponding components in plane polar coordinates, we proceed as follows. Given $\mathbf{V} = V_x \mathbf{i} + V_y \mathbf{j}$, we find the component along the unit vector **r** from the scalar product

$$V_R = \mathbf{V} \cdot \mathbf{r}$$

Then

$$V_R = V_x \mathbf{i} \cdot \mathbf{r} + V_y \mathbf{j} \cdot \mathbf{r} \tag{5}$$

Similarly,

$$V_\theta = V_x \mathbf{i} \cdot \mathbf{\theta} + V_y \mathbf{j} \cdot \mathbf{\theta} \tag{6}$$

The resulting vector expression in plane polar coordinates is

$$\mathbf{V} = V_R \mathbf{r} + V_\theta \mathbf{\theta}$$

which in terms of Eqs. (5) and (6) is

$$\mathbf{V} = (V_x \mathbf{i} \cdot \mathbf{r} + V_y \mathbf{j} \cdot \mathbf{r})\mathbf{r} + (V_x \mathbf{i} \cdot \mathbf{\theta} + V_y \mathbf{j} \cdot \mathbf{\theta})\mathbf{\theta} \tag{7}$$

We have now reduced the transformation problem to that of finding the scalar products of the unit vectors in the two coordinate systems, and this we have seen is equal to the cosine of the angle between them. By superimposing Fig. 1.8b and c, we can evaluate these scalar products as in Fig. 1.8d. Observing the angles between the unit vectors in the figure, and writing the scalar products as the cosine of the angle, we have

$$\mathbf{i} \cdot \mathbf{r} = \cos \theta \tag{8}$$
$$\mathbf{j} \cdot \mathbf{r} = \sin \theta \tag{9}$$
$$\mathbf{i} \cdot \mathbf{\theta} = -\sin \theta \tag{10}$$
$$\mathbf{j} \cdot \mathbf{\theta} = \cos \theta \tag{11}$$

When these relations are substituted into Eq. (7), we have a general expression for transforming from plane cartesian to plane polar coordinates.

$$V_x \mathbf{i} + V_y \mathbf{j} = (V_x \cos \theta + V_y \sin \theta)\mathbf{r} + (-V_x \sin \theta + V_y \cos \theta)\mathbf{\theta} \tag{12}$$

In this expression the two components of the vector in plane polar coordinates are

$$V_R = V_x \cos \theta + V_y \sin \theta \tag{13}$$

and

$$V_\theta = -V_x \sin \theta + V_y \cos \theta \tag{14}$$

Reversing the process to find the cartesian components when we are given the plane polar components gives the following result when relations (1) to (4) are used:

$$V_R \mathbf{r} + V_\theta \mathbf{\theta} = \frac{V_R x - V_\theta y}{\sqrt{x^2 + y^2}} \mathbf{i} + \frac{V_R y + V_\theta x}{\sqrt{x^2 + y^2}} \mathbf{j} \tag{15}$$

The use of cartesian coordinates to describe the direction of the physical vectors we observe in nature is so much a part of our experience that we are apt to be blinded to some of the interesting features of life in another coordinate system. To see some of the implications of a polar coordinate system, let us imagine a lonely group of islands on which a civilization has arisen without discovering the compass or the possibility of using the stars in navigation. There is a high mountain on the largest, most central island of the group, which forms a natural beacon. As the civilization extended to the other islands, the mountain beacon has been used as the only guide in navigation. Directions have come to be known as:

1. Away from home (positive), and homeward (negative)
2. Perpendicular to homeward, with a positive sense established by the navigator's rule of "right returning"

The locations of all points are described in terms of their distance from home, and the angle between the homeward line of direction and the average position in which the sun comes up.   The streets have been laid out according to these directions, with the avenues straight lines pointing homeward, and the streets circular arcs intersecting the avenues at right angles.   The altars face homeward, and the reference marks below the weathercocks have been oriented in these directions.

Weather-observation stations are established on the islands of the group, each reporting to the central station on the island known as home. To us who have been raised on a diet of cartesian coordinates, the weather information requires a good deal of interpretation.   Smooth sailing and good weather seem to occur when each of the stations reports the wind as coming from a different direction.   Rather terrible storms have accompanied identical reports from each station that the wind was "perpendicular" to homeward.   There is a legend concerning a disastrous day on which the mountain beacon blew off its top in a volcanic eruption, after which all stations reported the wind as "away from home."

The reference vectors which are used to describe direction have a different direction at each point of observation.   To compare the reports, or the description of a vector quantity observed at two different places, requires that each report be resolved into corresponding components at the point of comparison.

1.13   Vectors in Cylindrical and Spherical Coordinates.   It will be well to restate some of the ideas about the description of vectors in cartesian coordinates before proceeding to two other commonly used systems.   Cartesian coordinates have their origin at the point of intersection of three mutually perpendicular plane surfaces.   The three planes which intersect at the origin have the equations

$$x = 0 \qquad y = 0 \qquad z = 0$$

Through any point in space we may pass three planes which are parallel to these planes, having the equations

$$x = \text{a constant} \qquad y = \text{a constant} \qquad z = \text{a constant}$$

Coincident with the lines of intersection of each pair of these three planes, we may erect three mutually perpendicular unit vectors $\mathbf{i}$, $\mathbf{j}$, and $\mathbf{k}$.   We may then describe a vector at this point of intersection of the three planes in terms of its components along the directions of these three unit vectors.

The three mutually perpendicular surfaces whose intersections form a system of *cylindrical coordinates* are shown in Fig. 1.9.   The plane surfaces $z = 0$, and $z = $ a constant, are the same as in cartesian coordinates. The second surface is a plane perpendicular to the z planes, and is called the θ plane, where θ is the angle between the line of intersection of the z and θ planes, and some reference line in the z plane, commonly the x axis when both cartesian and cylindrical coordinates appear on the same diagram. The third surface, everywhere perpendicular to the first two, is a circular cylinder whose axis is perpendicular to the z planes at the origin. In this cylinder the variable R is a constant. Through every

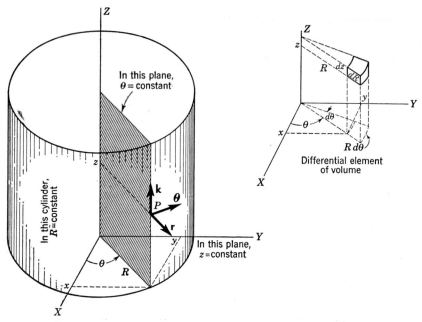

FIG. 1.9 Cylindrical coordinates. The unit vectors lie in the lines of intersection of three pairs of coordinate surfaces. The differential element of volume is shown at the right in the figure.

point in space, we may pass three mutually perpendicular surfaces, having the equations

$$R = \text{a constant} \qquad \theta = \text{a constant} \qquad z = \text{a constant}$$

Parallel to the lines of intersection of these three planes, we erect three mutually perpendicular unit vectors $\mathbf{r}$, $\mathbf{\theta}$, and $\mathbf{k}$. At this point of intersection we may describe a vector in terms of its components along the directions of these three unit vectors. The unit vectors form a right-hand system as in Sec. 1.10, Eq. (1).

$$\mathbf{r} \times \mathbf{\theta} = \mathbf{k} \qquad \mathbf{\theta} \times \mathbf{k} = \mathbf{r} \qquad \mathbf{k} \times \mathbf{r} = \mathbf{\theta}$$

The differential element of volume has sides of lengths dR, $R\,d\theta$, and dz. The areas of its faces are $dR\,dz$, $R\,d\theta\,dz$, and $R\,dR\,d\theta$. The volume is

$$dv = R\,dR\,d\theta\,dz$$

The transformations previously given in Sec. 1.12 for plane polar and cartesian coordinates hold also for cylindrical coordinates, since the third variable and the unit vector in the z direction are identical in the two systems. It is well to remember that the variable R represents the distance of the point in question from the z axis, and not the distance from the origin, as in the spherical coordinate system to follow.

In spherical coordinates, the three coordinate surfaces are
1. The sphere, $R = $ a constant
2. The cone, $\theta = $ a constant
3. The plane, $\phi = $ a constant

as shown in Fig. 1.10. The coordinates of a point P are
1. Its distance from the origin, O, represented by the line segment $OP = R$
2. The angle θ between the z axis and R
3. The angle ϕ between the x axis and the projection of R onto the xy plane

Through every point in space we may pass three such surfaces, and in their lines of intersection erect three mutually perpendicular unit vectors, $\mathbf{r}$, $\mathbf{\theta}$, and $\mathbf{\phi}$. Each of these unit vectors is pointed in the direction which corresponds to an increase in the respective coordinate, and they form a right-hand system

$$\mathbf{r} \times \mathbf{\theta} = \mathbf{\phi} \qquad \mathbf{\theta} \times \mathbf{\phi} = \mathbf{r} \qquad \mathbf{\phi} \times \mathbf{r} = \mathbf{\theta}$$

The differential element of volume has sides of lengths dR, $R\,d\theta$, and $R \sin\theta\,d\phi$. The areas of its faces are $R\,dR\,d\theta$, $R \sin\theta\,dR\,d\phi$, and $R^2 \sin\theta\,d\theta\,d\phi$. The volume is

$$dv = R^2 \sin\theta\,dR\,d\theta\,d\phi$$

Figure 1.10 reveals the following relations between cartesian and spherical coordinates:

$$\left.\begin{aligned}
x &= R \sin\theta\cos\phi \\
y &= R \sin\theta\sin\phi \\
z &= R \cos\theta \\
R &= \sqrt{x^2 + y^2 + z^2} \\
\theta &= \text{arc cos} \frac{z}{\sqrt{x^2 + y^2 + z^2}} \\
\phi &= \text{arc tan} \frac{y}{x} \quad \text{(quadrant by inspection)}
\end{aligned}\right\} \qquad (1)$$

When we are given a vector in terms of its components in cartesian coordinates

$$\mathbf{V} = V_x\mathbf{i} + V_y\mathbf{j} + V_z\mathbf{k}$$

the corresponding components in spherical coordinates are found from the scalar products

$$\left.\begin{array}{l} V_R = \mathbf{V} \cdot \mathbf{r} = V_x \mathbf{i} \cdot \mathbf{r} + V_y \mathbf{j} \cdot \mathbf{r} + V_z \mathbf{k} \cdot \mathbf{r} \\ V_\theta = \mathbf{V} \cdot \mathbf{\theta} = V_x \mathbf{i} \cdot \mathbf{\theta} + V_y \mathbf{j} \cdot \mathbf{\theta} + V_z \mathbf{k} \cdot \mathbf{\theta} \\ V_\phi = \mathbf{V} \cdot \mathbf{\phi} = V_x \mathbf{i} \cdot \mathbf{\phi} + V_y \mathbf{j} \cdot \mathbf{\phi} + V_z \mathbf{k} \cdot \mathbf{\phi} \end{array}\right\} \quad (2)$$

The scalar product of the unit vectors in Eq. (2) is equal to the cosine of the angle between them, and we can find these angles by an examination

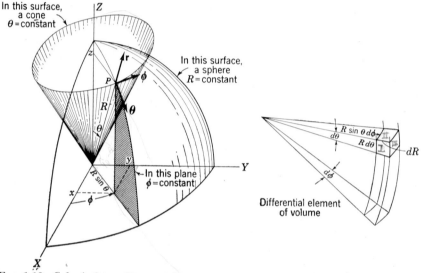

Fig. 1.10 Spherical coordinates. The unit vectors lie in the lines of intersection of three pairs of coordinate surfaces. The differential element of volume is shown at the right in the figure.

of their relative positions in Fig. 1.10. Students without considerable previous experience in this matter are urged to verify each of the statements to follow by reference to the figure. The unit vectors $\mathbf{r}$ and $\mathbf{\theta}$ lie in the plane ϕ = a constant. The angle between $\mathbf{r}$ and $\mathbf{k}$, lying in the z axis, is θ, so that

$$\mathbf{k} \cdot \mathbf{r} = \cos \theta \quad (3)$$

The angle between $\mathbf{r}$ and the xy plane is $90° - \theta$; hence the projection of $\mathbf{r}$ onto the xy plane has the magnitude of $\sin \theta$. This projection of $\mathbf{r}$ makes the angle ϕ with $\mathbf{i}$ in the x axis, and the angle $90° - \phi$ with $\mathbf{j}$ in the y axis, giving us the relations

$$\mathbf{i} \cdot \mathbf{r} = \sin \theta \cos \phi \quad (4)$$
$$\mathbf{j} \cdot \mathbf{r} = \sin \theta \sin \phi \quad (5)$$

The projection of the unit vector $\mathbf{\theta}$ onto the xy plane has the magnitude $\cos \theta$. This projection of $\mathbf{\theta}$ onto the xy plane lies parallel to the projection of $\mathbf{r}$ on the xy plane and thus makes the same angles with the x and y axes. Hence the relations corresponding to Eqs. (4) and (5) are

$$\mathbf{i} \cdot \mathbf{\theta} = \cos \theta \cos \phi \tag{6}$$
$$\mathbf{j} \cdot \mathbf{\theta} = \cos \theta \sin \phi \tag{7}$$

The angle between $\mathbf{\theta}$ and $\mathbf{r}$ is 90°, which makes the angle between $\mathbf{k}$ and $\mathbf{\theta}$ equal to $90° + \theta$. Hence

$$\mathbf{k} \cdot \mathbf{\theta} = - \sin \theta \tag{8}$$

The unit vector $\mathbf{\phi}$ is parallel to the xy plane, and perpendicular to $\mathbf{k}$ and the z axis. It makes the angle ϕ with the y axis and the angle $90° + \phi$ with the x axis. Thus we write

$$\mathbf{i} \cdot \mathbf{\phi} = - \sin \phi \tag{9}$$
$$\mathbf{j} \cdot \mathbf{\phi} = \cos \phi \tag{10}$$
$$\mathbf{k} \cdot \mathbf{\phi} = 0 \tag{11}$$

When the relations (3) to (11) are substituted into Eq. (2), we have the following expressions for the spherical components of a vector in terms of its cartesian components:

$$V_R = V_x \sin \theta \cos \phi + V_y \sin \theta \sin \phi + V_z \cos \theta$$
$$V_\theta = V_x \cos \theta \cos \phi + V_y \cos \theta \sin \phi - V_z \sin \theta \tag{12}$$
$$V_\phi = -V_x \sin \phi + V_y \cos \phi$$

The transformation which expresses the cartesian components in terms of the spherical components is left as a problem.

1.14 A Summary. Without reference to a system of coordinates, the algebra of vectors may be summarized in a few simple statements:

1. Vectors are added according to the parallelogram law.

2. The scalar product of two vectors has the *scalar* result

$$\mathbf{A} \cdot \mathbf{B} = AB \cos \alpha$$

3. The vector product of two vectors has a *vector* result whose magnitude is

$$|\mathbf{A} \times \mathbf{B}| = AB \sin \alpha$$

and whose direction is given by the right-hand rule.

4. The component of a vector in a given direction is found from its scalar product with a unit vector in that direction.

These things are the *essence*, as opposed to the *details* involved in numerical calculations. Arising from the use of coordinate systems, these details are more difficult to summarize.

Before collecting and listing the most frequently used relationships in the coordinate systems, we should observe that it is possible to condense the list considerably if we can write a single relationship which is valid in all three of the coordinate systems we shall use. To do this we can use numbers as subscripts to represent the components and the unit vectors. We shall denote the components of the vector $\mathbf{A}$ as A_1, A_2, and A_3, and the respective unit vectors as $\mathbf{i}_1$, $\mathbf{i}_2$, and $\mathbf{i}_3$. To this system of notation we give the name *general orthogonal coordinates*. To go from the general form to the specific form we may use the accompanying table.

SUMMARY OF NOTATION

Coordinate system	Components			Unit vectors		
General orthogonal.........	A_1	A_2	A_3	$\mathbf{i}_1$	$\mathbf{i}_2$	$\mathbf{i}_3$
Cartesian.................	A_x	A_y	A_z	$\mathbf{i}$	$\mathbf{j}$	$\mathbf{k}$
Cylindrical..............	A_R	A_θ	A_z	$\mathbf{r}$	$\boldsymbol{\theta}$	$\mathbf{k}$
Spherical................	A_R	A_θ	A_ϕ	$\mathbf{r}$	$\boldsymbol{\theta}$	$\boldsymbol{\phi}$

With this condensation, we proceed to summarize the details in performing the basic operations on vectors in a coordinate system.

Addition: $\mathbf{A} + \mathbf{B} = (A_1 + B_1)\mathbf{i}_1 + (A_2 + B_2)\mathbf{i}_2 + (A_3 + B_3)\mathbf{i}_3$

Magnitude: $\quad |\mathbf{A}| = \sqrt{(A_1{}^2 + A_2{}^2 + A_3{}^2)}$

Scalar product: $\quad \mathbf{A} \cdot \mathbf{B} = A_1 B_1 + A_2 B_2 + A_3 B_3$

Vector product: $\quad \mathbf{A} \times \mathbf{B} = \begin{vmatrix} \mathbf{i}_1 & \mathbf{i}_2 & \mathbf{i}_3 \\ A_1 & A_2 & A_3 \\ B_1 & B_2 & B_3 \end{vmatrix}$

For transforming from one coordinate system to another, a table of the scalar products of the cartesian unit vectors with the others is useful.

THE SCALAR PRODUCTS OF THE UNIT VECTORS

	Cylindrical			Spherical		
	$\mathbf{r}$	$\boldsymbol{\theta}$	$\mathbf{k}$	$\mathbf{r}$	$\boldsymbol{\theta}$	$\boldsymbol{\phi}$
$\mathbf{i}$	$\cos\theta$	$-\sin\theta$	0	$\sin\theta\cos\phi$	$\cos\theta\cos\phi$	$-\sin\phi$
$\mathbf{j}$	$\sin\theta$	$\cos\theta$	0	$\sin\theta\sin\phi$	$\cos\theta\sin\phi$	$\cos\phi$
$\mathbf{k}$	0	0	1	$\cos\theta$	$-\sin\theta$	0

The relationships between the coordinates are summarized below.

From cartesian to cylindrical   *From cartesian to spherical*

$$R = \sqrt{x^2 + y^2}$$

$$\theta = \text{arc tan } \frac{y}{x}$$

$$z = z$$

$$R = \sqrt{x^2 + y^2 + z^2}$$

$$\theta = \text{arc cos } \frac{z}{\sqrt{x^2 + y^2 + z^2}}$$

$$\phi = \text{arc tan } \frac{y}{x}$$

From cylindrical to cartesian   *From spherical to cartesian*

$$x = R \cos \theta$$
$$y = R \sin \theta$$
$$z = z$$

$$x = R \sin \theta \cos \phi$$
$$y = R \sin \theta \sin \phi$$
$$z = R \cos \theta$$

The elementary operations so far described are thought to be just barely sufficient to allow us to begin our study of electric fields. Many important and useful operations on vectors have not been included in this introductory chapter. Some of those which have been omitted are listed below, while others will be introduced as they are needed.

1. *Division* by a vector quantity is an operation not defined.

2. While the *derivative* of a vector is introduced at the outset when one is studying vector analysis for use in mechanics, we shall not have occasion to use this concept until Chap. 10. Until that time we shall confine ourselves to the derivatives of the scalar components of vectors.

3. The *triple products* such as $\mathbf{A} \cdot (\mathbf{B} \times \mathbf{C})$ and $\mathbf{A} \times (\mathbf{B} \times \mathbf{C})$ are important in vector analysis but will not be used enough in this book to warrant their discussion. Should a question arise, the operations inside the parentheses are to be performed first.

REFERENCES

1. Heaviside, Oliver: "Electromagnetic Theory," Dover Publications, New York, 1950. Chapter III of Vol. I is entitled "The Elements of Vectorial Algebra and Analysis." The introductory pages contain a fascinating discussion of the historical introduction of vector methods. The private paper by Gibbs, to which Heaviside refers, will be found in the collection listed as reference 2.
2. "The Collected Works of J. Willard Gibbs," Vol. II, Part II, pp. 17–90, Yale University Press, New Haven, 1948.
3. Wilson, E. B.: "Vector Analysis," Yale University Press, New Haven, 1901. Based on the lectures of J. Willard Gibbs, this text discusses the elements of vector algebra in considerable detail.
4. Lass, Harry: "Vector and Tensor Analysis," McGraw-Hill Book Company, Inc., New York, 1950.
5. Phillips, H. B.: "Vector Analysis," John Wiley & Sons, Inc., New York, 1933.
6. Ware, Lawrence A.: "Elements of Electromagnetic Waves," Pitman Publishing Corp., New York, 1949.

PROBLEMS

1.1 By a simple sketch, demonstrate graphically that

(a) $\mathbf{A} + \mathbf{B} = \mathbf{B} + \mathbf{A}$

(b) $\mathbf{A} + \mathbf{B} + \mathbf{C} = (\mathbf{A} + \mathbf{B}) + \mathbf{C} = \mathbf{A} + (\mathbf{B} + \mathbf{C})$

(c) $\mathbf{A} + (\mathbf{B} - \mathbf{A}) = \mathbf{B}$

(d) $(m + n)\mathbf{A} = m\mathbf{A} + n\mathbf{A}$

(e) $n(\mathbf{A} + \mathbf{B}) = n\mathbf{A} + n\mathbf{B}$

1.2 Given:
$$\mathbf{A} - \mathbf{B} = \mathbf{i} + \mathbf{j} + \mathbf{k}$$
$$\mathbf{A} + \mathbf{B} = 5\mathbf{i} - 3\mathbf{j} + 3\mathbf{k}$$

Find **A** and **B**.

1.3 The line segments
$$\mathbf{A} = \mathbf{i} + 2\mathbf{j} + 3\mathbf{k}$$
$$\mathbf{B} = 3\mathbf{i} + 2\mathbf{j} + \mathbf{k}$$

extend from the origin. Find the length of the line joining their ends, and describe its direction.

1.4 The line segments $\mathbf{R}_1$, $\mathbf{R}_2$, $\mathbf{R}_3$ extend from the origin and form three edges of a parallelepiped. Demonstrate graphically that their vector sum forms a diagonal.

1.5 By means of a sketch, demonstrate that the displacement of a point from the origin of cartesian coordinates is a vector quantity **R**, and that its magnitude and direction are related to the coordinates of the point by the equation

$$\mathbf{R} = x\,\mathbf{i} + y\,\mathbf{j} + z\,\mathbf{k}$$

1.6 What is the restriction on the unit vectors $\mathbf{i}_1$, $\mathbf{i}_2$, $\mathbf{i}_3$ which allows us to write the following formula?

$$|\mathbf{A}| = \sqrt{A_1{}^2 + A_2{}^2 + A_3{}^2}$$

1.7 Without the use or implication of a coordinate system, write a formula for finding the component of the vector **A** along the vector **B**.

1.8 By expansion, show that

$$(F_x\,\mathbf{i} + F_y\,\mathbf{j} + F_z\,\mathbf{k}) \cdot (S_x\,\mathbf{i} + S_y\,\mathbf{j} + S_z\,\mathbf{k}) = F_x S_x + F_y S_y + F_z S_z$$

1.9 Find the component of $\mathbf{A} = \mathbf{i} + \mathbf{j} + \mathbf{k}$ along the line joining the points

(a) 1, 1, 1 and 0, 1, 1

(b) 1, 1, 0 and 0, 1, 1

1.10 Find the component of $\mathbf{A} = 3\mathbf{i} + 2\mathbf{j} + \mathbf{k}$ along the line $y = 2x$, $z = 0$.

1.11 If $\mathbf{B} \cdot \mathbf{a} = \mathbf{C} \cdot \mathbf{a}$, can we infer that $\mathbf{B} = \mathbf{C}$? Sketch and discuss.

1.12 The vectors $\mathbf{a} = \mathbf{i} \cos \alpha + \mathbf{j} \sin \alpha$ and $\mathbf{b} = \mathbf{i} \cos \beta + \mathbf{j} \sin \beta$ are unit vectors in the xy plane which make angles α, β with the x axis. From $\mathbf{a} \cdot \mathbf{b}$, find the trigonometric formula for $\cos (\alpha - \beta)$.

1.13 Write the expression for two unit vectors making angles α and β above and below the x axis. From the scalar product, find the trigonometric formula for $\cos (\alpha + \beta)$.

1.14 Find the cosine of the angle between the vectors

$$\mathbf{F} = \mathbf{i} + \mathbf{j} + \mathbf{k} \qquad \text{and} \qquad \mathbf{G} = \mathbf{i} - 2\mathbf{j} + 3\mathbf{k}$$

1.15 From Fleming's left-hand rule for the force on a current-carrying conductor in a magnetic field, formulate an expression utilizing the vector product of two vectors. (Current is a scalar quantity.)

1.16 In order to determine the area of a parallelogram whose sides are 3 and 5 units in length and are at an angle of 30°, set up the sides as vectors and find their vector product.

1.17 By expansion, show that

$$(A_x\,\mathbf{i} + A_y\,\mathbf{j} + A_z\,\mathbf{k}) \times (B_x\,\mathbf{i} + B_y\,\mathbf{j} + B_z\,\mathbf{k}) = \begin{vmatrix} \mathbf{i} & \mathbf{j} & \mathbf{k} \\ A_x & A_y & A_z \\ B_x & B_y & B_z \end{vmatrix}$$

1.18 In order to find a unit vector perpendicular to the plane $x + y + z = 3$, find two vectors in the plane and take their vector product.

1.19 With the help of Fig. 1.10, evaluate the vector products

(a) $\mathbf{k} \times \mathbf{r}$

(b) $\mathbf{k} \times \mathbf{\theta}$

(c) $\mathbf{k} \times \mathbf{\phi}$

1.20 Write the expression for two unit vectors in the xy plane, making angles α and β with the x axis. Take β first below and then above the x axis, in order to obtain the trigonometric formulas for $\sin(\alpha + \beta)$ and $\sin(\alpha - \beta)$ from the vector product of the unit vectors. Resolve any possible ambiguity in sign by carefully examining the sense of the vector part of the vector product.

1.21 Given $\mathbf{A} \cdot \mathbf{i} = 0$, and $\mathbf{A} \times \mathbf{i} = \mathbf{k}$. Find $\mathbf{A}$.

1.22 Given

$$\mathbf{A} = 3\mathbf{i} + 4\mathbf{j}$$
$$\mathbf{A} \times \mathbf{B} = 0$$
$$\mathbf{A} \cdot \mathbf{B} = -50$$

Find $\mathbf{B}$.

1.23 A vector 10 units long extends from the origin of cartesian coordinates, making equal angles with the x and y axes and an angle of 45° with the z axis. Find the cartesian components of the given vector.

1.24 Express the magnitude and direction of the velocity of a freely falling object, released from rest, as a vector quantity which is a function of the position of the object.

1.25 A ping-pong ball is connected to a fixed point by a rubber band. Describe the force exerted on the ball by the rubber band, as a vector function of the position of the ball. Use spherical and then cartesian coordinates.

1.26 Considering only the spin, describe the velocity of a point in the earth as a vector function of its position. Compare the expressions in all three coordinate systems.

1.27 Describe as a vector, the direction of current in a helix or single-layer solenoid. This is also the direction taken by the hand in winding a coil of wire onto a spool. Choose the most appropriate coordinate system, and justify your choice.

1.28 A phonograph turntable is driven by a constant torque **T**. As a vector quantity, describe the horizontally applied force necessary to stop the turntable, as a function of position of the point of application of the force. Set up the problem in cylindrical coordinates and transform to rectangular.

1.29 Describe the forces experienced by a bug of mass m as it slowly explores the entire surface of a phonograph turntable which is rotating at constant angular velocity. Include the force of gravity. Set up the problem in cylindrical coordinates and transform to rectangular.

1.30 Consider the magnitude and the direction of the vector

$$\mathbf{M} = (1 - x)\mathbf{i} + (2 - y)\mathbf{j} - z\,\mathbf{k}$$

Describe the surface generated by the locus of all points in which this vector is a constant in magnitude. What is the relation between the direction of the vector and the surfaces of constant magnitude? Can this vector conceivably describe Prob. 1.25?

CHAPTER 2

ELECTROSTATIC FIELDS FROM THE VIEWPOINT
OF COULOMB'S LAW

In this chapter, we begin the study of electric-force vectors from the viewpoint which is the least abstract, that of Coulomb's law. In order to aid in visualizing the vectors we are studying, we shall investigate some pictorial representations called field maps. We shall extend our ideas about adding vectors into one of the ways of integrating vectors. We shall find that the Coulomb's-law approach, though physically satisfying, leads to serious mathematical difficulties. Pointing out the source of some of these difficulties will guide us toward other approaches involving more subtleness and less brute force.

2.1 Electric Forces and Charges. A part of the science of mechanics is the study of the forces of attraction between all material objects. These forces, called gravitational forces, have been found to obey an inverse-square law. Established by Newton and others from observations of the periods and the size and shape of the planetary orbits, the inverse-square law was brought to the laboratory level by Cavendish. In measuring the constant of proportionality, Cavendish used a delicate torsion balance invented by Coulomb.

Under certain conditions, material objects exert forces on one another which are many times greater than those which can be attributed to gravitational forces, and forces of repulsion are observed as well as forces of attraction. These forces are called electric forces, and the bodies which experience the forces are said to be charged.

We think of all physical substances as being ultimately divisible into atoms, and the atoms as composed of several more basic subatomic particles which are characterized by their effective inertia (mass) and the way they respond to electric forces (charge). When our attention is focused on the electric forces alone, we speak of the forces experienced by charges, leaving out of the picture and the terminology any thought of an object, or a particle, or a mass associated with the charge. When we study the motion of an object or a charged particle, it is necessary to consider its mass and its velocity, as well as its charge.

Of the subatomic charged particles, the electron is most easily enticed to leave the atom and subject itself to the study of the physicist and the control of the engineer. Its charge is the smallest found in nature, and in our MKS system of measuring charges; we find that its magnitude is 1.6(10^{-19}) coulomb. With its mass, we associate a very much smaller number, 9(10^{-31}) kilogram. The ratio of the charge to the mass is a very large number, and in a suggestive way, this ratio indicates the overwhelming difference in the magnitude of the electric and gravitational forces experienced by such particles. Before the nature of these properties was understood as well as it is today, the charge resulting from an excess of electrons was considered as a negative charge. Though accidental, the choice seems to be with us to stay. We think of positively charged objects in terms of a deficiency of electrons from a normally neutral collection of atoms.

Mathematically, however, it is convenient to ignore the idea that electric charge comes in a minimum-size package, and to consider electric charge as continuously divisible into volume-, surface-, and line-charge densities. We do this in the mathematical treatment of solids, fluids, and gases, too, when we speak of their densities. In neither case do we imply that we shall continue to do this when making a microscopic examination so detailed that the fine structural details can be discerned. The volume-charge distribution may be thought of as a jelly, and the surface- and line-charge densities as extremely thin coats of paint. A point charge is a rather dense volume-charge distribution, in a region so small in extent that all other distances under consideration are essentially infinite in comparison.

The unit of measurement of electric charge is called the coulomb. Historically, the unit of electric charge was defined in terms of the forces between point charges at rest. In the MKS rationalized system of units, internationally adopted in 1935, the units of electric and magnetic quantities are not defined until one can see the whole picture of the interrelations between the various quantities, and then the units are chosen to simplify the expressions which are most frequently used in practical problems. The unit of electric charge is defined in terms of the unit of electric current, as measured by a carefully constructed instrument at the Bureau of Standards. We shall consider the details later. For now, it will suffice to consider the coulomb as the charge represented by 6.25(10^{18}) electronic charges.

2.2 Coulomb's Law. Experimental observations of the forces between two point charges reveal the following facts. Like charges repel, and unlike charges attract. The force acts along the line between the charges. The magnitude of the force is inversely proportional to the square of the distance between them and depends on the medium in which the charges are placed. When the medium surrounding the charges is essentially infinite in extent, we may express these facts in the scalar equation

$$F = k \frac{Q_1 Q_2}{R^2}$$

(1)

where Q_1 and Q_2 = magnitude of charges

R = separation of charges

k = a constant which depends on the medium in which the test is made

In the MKS rationalized system of units, the constant of proportionality k is written as $1/4\pi\epsilon$. The symbol ϵ denotes a property of the medium, most commonly termed its *permittivity*. Other names are dielectric constant and capacitivity. The permittivity of a vacuum, or free space, is found experimentally to be $1/[36\pi(10^9)]$ and is denoted by adding the subscript to make the symbol ϵ_0. The permittivity of all other physical substances is somewhat larger than that of vacuum, but in the case of all gases the difference is slight. At the outset, we shall consider all our experiments as being performed in a vacuum or a gas and shall consider material substances in connection with another subject.

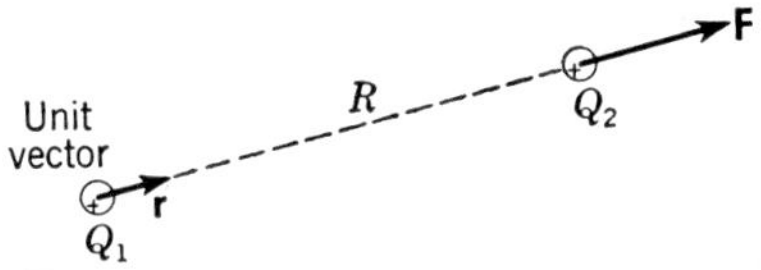

To write Coulomb's law as a vector equation, we may consider the force experienced by the charge Q_2, due to the presence of charge Q_1, as acting along a unit vector **r** drawn from Q_1 toward Q_2, as shown in Fig. 2.1. When

FIG. 2.1 Illustrating notation in the vector formulation of Coulomb's law, Eq. 2.1(2).

the charges are alike, this will indicate a force in the **r** direction, and when the charges are unlike, the minus sign will indicate a reversal of direction of the force. This gives us the vector equation

$$\mathbf{F} = \frac{Q_1 Q_2}{4\pi\epsilon_0 R^2} \mathbf{r}$$

(2)

where $\mathbf{F}$ = force, newtons

R = separation of charges, meters

Q_1 and Q_2 = magnitude of charges, coulombs

By our choice of notation in Eqs. (1) and (2), we are erecting the origin of a system of spherical coordinates at the location of Q_1. As our problems grow to include more elaborate charge distributions, it will be necessary to use coordinate systems which are more appropriate to the specific problem under study.

While we have no great interest in the force between two point charges as such, we want to examine some of the consequences of the inverse-square-law nature of electric forces. Before proceeding to other viewpoints, however, we must add an additional experimental observation regarding Coulomb's law. When more than two point charges are present, any one of them will experience a force which is the vector sum of all the individual forces as given by Coulomb's law. As in circuit theory, this is called *linear superposition*.

As a laboratory experiment, Coulomb's law is exceedingly crude. It is through indirect experiments that we know the truth of the inverse-square law. The nature of the indirect observations will unfold as we proceed.

2.3 Electric Field Intensity. A thoughtful examination of the expression for Coulomb's law shows that there is no unique quantity in the force experienced by a test charge. The force experienced by the charge Q_2, in Fig. 2.1, can be produced by any of an infinite number of combinations of Q_1 and R, as long as the ratio Q_1/R^2 is held constant. From the viewpoint of the charge Q_2, the force experienced is a function of its position in space and is not associated with any particular point charge.

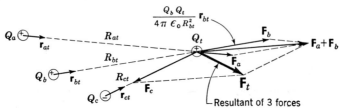

FIG. 2.2   The total force experienced by the test charge Q_t is the vector sum of the forces due to each of the point charges Q_a, Q_b, and Q_c.   In this figure the sum of the vectors is obtained by successive applications of the parallelogram law.

We may endow a test charge with the ability to experience and measure the forces but not with the ability to describe just what it is that is causing the force at any one point in space.

Let us pick out a particular positive point charge, whose magnitude is extremely small, and imagine that we can instruct him to travel throughout all space and then return and report to us the magnitude and direction of the forces which he experienced wherever he went. The story he tells when he returns is a description of the electric field of force, as experienced by our particular pet test charge which we label Q_t. In pursuing the limited kinds of fields of force due to charges at rest, we require that the exploring reporter Q_t observe the forces of the field while *standing still*, as we are not yet interested in the forces he experiences while he is moving.

At any point in space, Q_t is going to observe forces caused by every other point charge in the universe, and the force he reports will be the *vector* sum of all the forces, each of which is given by Coulomb's law. Labeling all the other charges by other subscripts, and using the notation of Fig. 2.2, we write

$$\mathbf{F}_t = \frac{Q_a Q_t}{4\pi\epsilon_0 R_{at}{}^2} \mathbf{r}_{at} + \frac{Q_b Q_t}{4\pi\epsilon_0 R_{bt}{}^2} \mathbf{r}_{bt} + \cdots + \frac{Q_n Q_t}{4\pi\epsilon_0 R_{nt}{}^2} \mathbf{r}_{nt} \qquad (1)$$

From this expression we factor the magnitude of the test charge

$$\mathbf{F}_t = Q_t \left(\frac{Q_a}{4\pi\epsilon_0 R_{at}{}^2} \mathbf{r}_{at} + \frac{Q_b}{4\pi\epsilon_0 R_{bt}{}^2} \mathbf{r}_{bt} + \cdots + \frac{Q_n}{4\pi\epsilon_0 R_{nt}{}^2} \mathbf{r}_{nt} \right) \qquad (2)$$

Of this expression for the force on the test charge, that factor which is entirely due to its position in space, and not to its own characteristic charge, is the term in brackets. This is the part in which we are primarily interested, as it represents the force on the test charge, divided by the magnitude of the test charge. We shall call this quantity the *electric field intensity* and denote it by the symbol **E**. Field intensity is force evaluated on a per-unit basis. From Eq. (2) we have a formula for computing this vector quantity at any point in space, for any number of point charges. We can shorten it a little by using the summation sign Σ, provided that we remember that these are vector quantities and that they must be added according to the parallelogram law, or by resolving them into components and adding the components separately. The *defining equation* for **E** is

$$\mathbf{E} = \frac{\mathbf{F}_t}{Q_t} \qquad (3)$$

and the formula by which we can compute its value due to any number of point charges is

$$\mathbf{E} = \sum \frac{Q_n}{4\pi\epsilon_0 R_{nt}{}^2} \mathbf{r}_{nt} \qquad (4)$$

The units of electric-field intensity are the units of force, divided by the units of electric charge. In the system we are using this is newtons per coulomb. In the older CGS system it would be dynes per statcoulomb. For those who like to think of their forces measured in pounds, we could just as well deal in pounds per coulomb by making the numerical conversions. There are about 4 newtons to a pound, since 1 newton equals 0.224 pounds.

Example 1. A numerical example of an evaluation of Eq. (4) is shown in Fig. 2.3. To simplify the arithmetic, three equal charges have been chosen having a magnitude which will produce a field intensity of unit magnitude at a distance of 1 meter. The three charges are arranged in a line and are 1 meter apart. The field is evaluated at a distance of 1 meter from one of the end charges. The vector summation is obtained graphically by successive applications of the parallelogram law.

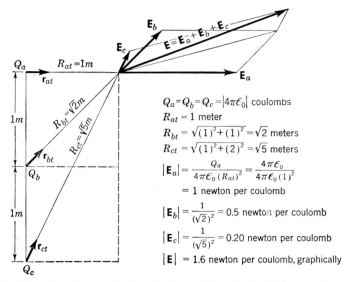

$Q_a = Q_b = Q_c = |4\pi\epsilon_0|$ coulombs

$R_{at} = 1$ meter

$R_{bt} = \sqrt{(1)^2 + (1)^2} = \sqrt{2}$ meters

$R_{ct} = \sqrt{(1)^2 + (2)^2} = \sqrt{5}$ meters

$|\mathbf{E}_a| = \dfrac{Q_a}{4\pi\epsilon_0 (R_{at})^2} = \dfrac{4\pi\epsilon_0}{4\pi\epsilon_0 (1)^2}$

$\quad\quad = 1$ newton per coulomb

$|\mathbf{E}_b| = \dfrac{1}{(\sqrt{2})^2} = 0.5$ newton per coulomb

$|\mathbf{E}_c| = \dfrac{1}{(\sqrt{5})^2} = 0.20$ newton per coulomb

$|\mathbf{E}| = 1.6$ newton per coulomb, graphically

FIG. 2.3   Example of a graphical evaluation of the electric field intensity at a point in the field of three equal point charges, equally spaced along a line.

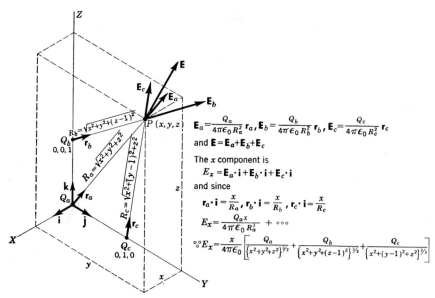

$\mathbf{E}_a = \dfrac{Q_a}{4\pi\epsilon_0 R_a^2}\, \mathbf{r}_a,\, \mathbf{E}_b = \dfrac{Q_b}{4\pi\epsilon_0 R_b^2}\, \mathbf{r}_b,\, \mathbf{E}_c = \dfrac{Q_c}{4\pi\epsilon_0 R_c^2}\, \mathbf{r}_c$

and $\mathbf{E} = \mathbf{E}_a + \mathbf{E}_b + \mathbf{E}_c$

The x component is

$E_x = \mathbf{E}_a \cdot \mathbf{i} + \mathbf{E}_b \cdot \mathbf{i} + \mathbf{E}_c \cdot \mathbf{i}$

and since

$\mathbf{r}_a \cdot \mathbf{i} = \dfrac{x}{R_a},\, \mathbf{r}_b \cdot \mathbf{i} = \dfrac{x}{R_b},\, \mathbf{r}_c \cdot \mathbf{i} = \dfrac{x}{R_c}$

$E_x = \dfrac{Q_a x}{4\pi\epsilon_0 R_a^3} \quad + \circ \circ \circ$

$\therefore E_x = \dfrac{x}{4\pi\epsilon_0}\left[\dfrac{Q_a}{\{x^2+y^2+z^2\}^{3/2}} + \dfrac{Q_b}{\{x^2+y^2+(z-1)^2\}^{3/2}} + \dfrac{Q_c}{\{x^2+(y-1)^2+z^2\}^{3/2}}\right]$

FIG. 2.4   Example of the evaluation of one of the components of the electric field intensity at a general point in the field of three point charges, arranged at three corners of a square.

Example 2. The next type of problem requires us to find the field intensity due to three point charges arranged at the corners of a square, as in Fig. 2.4. This time we are to obtain an expression for the field intensity which will be valid anywhere. Taking advantage of the little bit of symmetry in the arrangement of the charges, we erect a system of cartesian coordinates so that we can locate the field points in terms of these coordinates. When this has been done we evaluate the various distances from the charges to the field point and obtain the vector expressions for the individual contributions of the field intensity due to each point charge. To add the individual contributions, we resolve them into components and add the components separately. The steps for the analysis of one of the components accompany the figure.

Now examples like these soon become tedious. There is nothing challenging here, and we should dwell on this sort of detail only long enough to satisfy ourselves that we are familiar with the notation and the steps required. Given enough time, and enough patience to get the arithmetic right, we should be confident in our ability to work any sort of problem involving any number of point charges. In sections to follow, we consider continuously distributed charges, and there we can use the calculus to perform the additions for us.

One word of caution must be appended. Because of the fact that the distance R appears in the denominator of all expressions for the field intensity due to a point charge, we must anticipate the field will be infinite when R is zero. This arises from our mathematically convenient, but physically questionable, assumption that we could concentrate a finite amount of charge in a region of zero volume.

2.4   The Field of a Uniformly Charged Line.   Let us consider a charge configuration in which the charges are spread out on a straight line, like the enamel on a fine straight wire. To tell how much charge we have in a given place, we speak of the charge per meter of the line length just as a manufacturer of enameled wire computes its cost in terms of the number of gallons of paint used per mile of wire. We will represent this quantity by the symbol λ, a linear-charge density. To find the field intensity at a point in space due to this arrangement of charge, the first thing we must do is to reduce the problem to a number of equivalent point charges. Then we shall find the field produced by each of the point charges and add the vectors by resolving them into components.

This problem lends itself nicely to analysis in cylindrical coordinates because an analysis in any plane $\theta =$ a constant holds in all such planes. The use of cartesian coordinates would not take advantage of the fact that the symmetry makes this a two-dimensional rather than a three-dimensional problem. In the analysis of fields, the proper choice of a coordinate system is really more than half the battle. In Fig. 2.5 the geometry of the problem is illustrated. The origin of coordinates has been taken at the center of the line, to which we have assigned the length $2a$. The coordinates of the point P, at which we are finding the field, are R and z, quantities which are constants in this analysis.

To reduce the line charge to an array of point charges, we consider the infinitesimal length of line dL in meters. The charge on this length of line is found by multiplying its length by the charge per unit length, $\lambda\, dL$. This is the magnitude of the equivalent point charge playing the

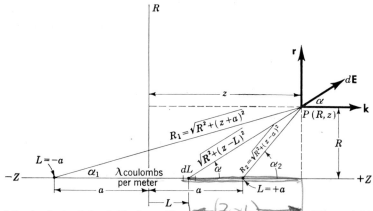

FIG. 2.5   Analysis of the field of a uniformly charged line. Each differential length of the line dL, and the charge it carries, is treated as a point charge. The total field intensity is the vector sum of all the individual contributions $d\mathbf{E}$. The summation is obtained by resolving into components and adding the components by integration.

role of Q in Coulomb's law. The square of the distance from this equivalent point charge to P is $R^2 + (z - L)^2$. Substituting these values into the expression for the field intensity due to a point charge, and indicating that this is a differential part of the total field intensity by using the differential symbol $d\mathbf{E}$, we have

$$|d\mathbf{E}| = \frac{\lambda\, dL}{4\pi\epsilon_0[R^2 + (z - L)^2]} \tag{1}$$

The vector $d\mathbf{E}$ is directed along the line from dL to P. Now every little dL on the line makes a similar contribution to the field intensity vector at P, and they are not all parallel. To add them up, we must first resolve them into components along the unit vectors $\mathbf{r}$ and $\mathbf{k}$. To find these components

$$dE_z = d\mathbf{E} \cdot \mathbf{k} = dE \cos \alpha \qquad \text{and} \qquad dE_R = d\mathbf{E} \cdot \mathbf{r} = dE \sin \alpha \quad \text{(2), (3)}$$

We are not yet ready to add, because $\cos \alpha$ and $\sin \alpha$ are variables.

$$\cos \alpha = \frac{z - L}{[R^2 + (z - L)^2]^{1/2}} \qquad \text{and} \qquad \sin \alpha = \frac{R}{[R^2 + (z - L)^2]^{1/2}} \quad \text{(4), (5)}$$

$$dE_z = \frac{\lambda}{4\pi\epsilon_0} \frac{(z - L)\, dL}{[R^2 + (z - L)^2]^{3/2}} \tag{6}$$

and

$$dE_R = \frac{\lambda}{4\pi\epsilon_0} \frac{R\, dL}{[R^2 + (z - L)^2]^{3/2}} \tag{7}$$

These purely scalar expressions in the single variable L may be summed by integration between the limits $L = -a$ and $L = +a$. One of the ways of evaluating the integrals is to use a table of integrals, and to find them there quickly we substitute $x = z - L$ and $dx = -dL$. This changes Eqs. (6) and (7) to the shorter form, where the integration has been indicated:

$$E_z = \frac{-\lambda}{4\pi\epsilon_0} \int_{x=z+a}^{x=z-a} \frac{x\, dx}{(R^2 + x^2)^{3/2}} \tag{8}$$

and

$$E_R = \frac{-\lambda R}{4\pi\epsilon_0} \int_{x=z+a}^{x=z-a} \frac{dx}{(R^2 + x^2)^{3/2}} \tag{9}$$

From a table of integrals,

$$E_z = \frac{-\lambda}{4\pi\epsilon_0} \left[\frac{-1}{(R^2 + x^2)^{1/2}} \right]_{x=z+a}^{x=z-a} \tag{10}$$

and

$$E_R = \frac{-\lambda R}{4\pi\epsilon_0} \left[\frac{x}{R^2(R^2 + x^2)^{1/2}} \right]_{x=z+a}^{x=z-a} \tag{11}$$

When the limits have been substituted and the minus signs taken inside

$$E_z = \frac{\lambda}{4\pi\epsilon_0 R} \left[\frac{R}{\{R^2 + (z - a)^2\}^{1/2}} - \frac{R}{\{R^2 + (z + a)^2\}^{1/2}} \right] \tag{12}$$

and

$$E_R = \frac{\lambda}{4\pi\epsilon_0 R} \left[\frac{z + a}{\{R^2 + (z + a)^2\}^{1/2}} - \frac{z - a}{\{R^2 + (z - a)^2\}^{1/2}} \right] \tag{13}$$

In Eq. (12), the numerator and denominator have been multiplied by R to show the similarities to Eq. (13) in the factor outside the brackets. Returning again to the figure, we see that Eqs. (12) and (13) can be written in the shorter trigonometric form

$$E_z = \frac{\lambda}{4\pi\epsilon_0 R} (\sin \alpha_2 - \sin \alpha_1) \tag{14}$$

and

$$E_R = \frac{\lambda}{4\pi\epsilon_0 R} (\cos \alpha_1 - \cos \alpha_2) \tag{15}$$

The form of Eqs. (14) and (15) suggests now that these results could have been obtained with less formidable algebraic expressions if the angle variable α had been used in the analysis. This is true, and in one of the problems at the end of this chapter the student will be asked to repeat the analysis in this way. The proper choice of variable in problems like these is largely a matter of experience, and guided by this present experience we shall evaluate similar problems in sections to come by means of this angle variable.

The form of the results we have obtained is not very illuminating without further study. It would help if we had a picture or diagram which would assist our understanding, and we shall picture this field later in this chapter. Right now we are focusing our attention on the methods of analysis rather than the over-all picture of the results. In fact, there is little practical application for this particular field except as one of the simpler illustrations of the analysis of distributed charges. We cannot assume that these results apply to a charged conducting wire of finite radius, for we have no assurance that the charge distribution would be uniform in that case.

When the line is infinitely long, however, the results simplify a good deal. The z component vanishes, and in the limit the component perpendicular to the line gives us, as a approaches infinity,

$$E = \frac{\lambda}{2\pi\epsilon_0 R}\,\mathbf{r} \tag{16}$$

Of course, no real line is infinitely long, but practically, the results are the same whenever the distance to both ends of the line is very much greater than the perpendicular distance to the line R. Equation (16) and the field it describes will be treated as an important building block in our further studies. The expression is similar to that for the field of a point charge, the primary difference being that it is an inverse first-power relationship with distance instead of an inverse square. Further, we are cautioned to remember that in Eq. (16) we imply cylindrical coordinates rather than spherical.

Unfortunately, there are not very many other cases in which charges distributed along a line can be handled with simple integrals. When the charges are distributed along a curved line, an analysis is extremely difficult. Even in the apparently simple case of a circle, uniformly charged, the general expression involves elliptic integrals, so we shall not pursue it in this introductory book. On the axis of the circle, however, results are obtained more easily than in the example illustrated in this section, and so that case has been included in the problems at the end of this chapter.

Equations (12) to (15) are in a form which becomes indeterminate on the axis of the line, where $R = 0$. Where z is greater than a, however, Eq. (1) gives the magnitude of the z component and can be integrated

without further ado.   This, too, is not difficult, and the results are asked
for in the problems.

2.5   The Field of an Infinite Sheet of Charge.   We have seen that
the description of the field of an infinitely long line is simpler than that of
a field due to a line of finite length, because the former has no component
parallel to the line.   In analyzing the field due to charges distributed
uniformly over the surface of a plane sheet, we shall take advantage of

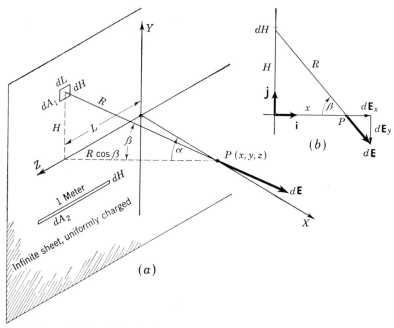

Fig. 2.6   For analysis of the field due to an infinite sheet, uniformly charged.   (a)
Isometric view for visualization of the problem; (b) a two-dimensional view for
analysis as an extension of the field of a uniformly charged line, infinitely long.

the simplifications which result from making the sheet infinitely large and
shall apply the results in a practical case only to those regions which are
relatively remote from the edges of a finite sheet.

In finding the field due to a distributed charge by extending the known
results for a single point charge, we could reduce the problem again to
summing the contributions to the field which are made by an infinite
number of point charges.   Let the sheet be covered with a uniform
surface-charge density of σ coulombs per square meter, as we speak of the
coverage of paint in gallons per thousand square feet.   Referring to
Fig. 2.6a, we need to find the contribution at the point P, due to each
equivalent point charge on each differential surface element such as dA_1.
The area of this surface element is $dL\,dH$.   (We are using L for length

and H for height to avoid confusing the location of dA_1 with the location of the point P. After integrating and substituting limits, L and H will disappear.) The charge which this surface element carries is $\sigma\, dL\, dH$, and this corresponds to the Q in Coulomb's law. The distance from the equivalent point charge to the point P, at which we are evaluating the field, is given by $R^2 = x^2 + H^2 + L^2$. Calling the differential contribution to the field intensity $d\mathbf{E}$, and substituting into the expression for the field intensity due to a point charge, we obtain

$$|d\mathbf{E}| = \frac{\sigma\, dL\, dH}{4\pi\epsilon_0(x^2 + H^2 + L^2)} \tag{1}$$

The differential vectors are not parallel, and therefore the magnitude of their sum is not the sum of the magnitudes. Again it will be necessary to break the differential vectors up into components which can be added separately. To sum each of the three components, a double integration would be required.

However, if we look at the problem a little differently, and think of the infinite sheet of charge as being formed of a number of differential line charges, we can take advantage of our previous results to reduce the work required to integrate Eq. (1) over the sheet. We can do this by considering the charge which appears on the differential area dA_2 in the figure. This has unit length and width of dH. The area is dH, and the charge it carries is the product of σ, its charge per unit area, and its area, dA. The result is the charge per unit length, corresponding to λ in Eq. 2.4 (16) for the field of a uniformly charged line, infinitely long. This was

$$\mathbf{E} = \frac{\lambda}{2\pi\epsilon_0 R}\, \mathbf{r} \tag{2}$$

This procedure reduces the problem to two dimensions as shown in the two-dimensional sketch in Fig. 2.6b. Here, $R^2 = x^2 + H^2$, and we may now write Eq. (2) as

$$|d\mathbf{E}| = \frac{\sigma\, dH}{2\pi\epsilon_0 R} \tag{3}$$

The x component of $d\mathbf{E}$ is

$$dE_x = d\mathbf{E}\cdot\mathbf{i} = \frac{\sigma\, dH\,\cos\beta}{2\pi\epsilon_0 R} \tag{4}$$

There are two more lessons from our previous experiences which we should apply here. The first is to recognize that it will not be necessary to evaluate E_y because for every line charge at $+H$ which produces a downward dE_y there is a corresponding line charge at $-H$ producing an equal upward component, so that when the individual contributions are summed the resulting E_y will be zero. The second is the experience of

Sec. 2.4 that an angle variable may give a simpler expression to integrate than does the coordinate variable.

To accomplish the change of variable, we observe that only H and R are functions of β, since x is a constant for any one field point. From the figure, $H = x \tan \beta$, and therefore $dH = x \sec^2 \beta \, d\beta$. Also $R = x \sec \beta$. Substituting these values into Eq. (4), all the trigonometric functions cancel, leaving only

$$dE_x = \frac{\sigma \, d\beta}{2\pi\epsilon_0} \tag{5}$$

Integrating between the limits of $-\pi/2$ and $+\pi/2$ gives

$$E_x = \frac{\sigma}{2\epsilon_0} \tag{6}$$

On the side of the sheet for which x is positive, the field is directed along $+\mathbf{i}$, and on the other side of the sheet where x is negative, the field is directed along $-\mathbf{i}$. To avoid having two expressions for the two sides of the sheet, and to divorce our analysis from our choice of a coordinate system, we can express our results in terms of the unit vector $\mathbf{n}$, directed away from the surface of the sheet.

$$\mathbf{E} = \frac{\sigma}{2\epsilon_0} \mathbf{n} \tag{7}$$

Field of a sheet of charge

This result is somewhat surprising in that the field intensity is completely independent of the distance from the sheet of charge. The field is constant in magnitude and direction, and because of this it is called a *uniform field*. It extends on both sides of the sheet of charge and is discontinuous at the sheet of charge, where its direction reverses completely in passing through that surface. We can think of half the charge producing the field on each side of the sheet because of the factor of 2 in the denominator of Eq. (4), if it will help us to remember it. This leads us to inquire about the possibility of confining the field to one side of the surface.

If we erect a second sheet of charge, parallel to the first and carrying an equal charge distribution of the opposite sign, the fields due to the two sheets of charge will be in the same direction in the region between the two sheets, but in opposite directions everywhere else. In the region between the sheets, the vector sum of the two fields is

$$\mathbf{E} = \frac{\sigma}{\epsilon_0} \mathbf{n} \tag{8}$$

and is directed from the positively charged sheet toward the negatively charged sheet. Elsewhere the field is zero. The field is discontinuous at

each sheet, in that it begins abruptly on one of them, and ends as abruptly on the other.

This is an important field, and because of its uniformity it is perhaps the simplest kind. It forms another important building block in our study of fields.

2.6   The Field Map of a Single Point Charge.   As an aid to visualization of fields, we frequently resort to maps or pictures of fields, and much of the terminology and methods of analysis of fields has come from such

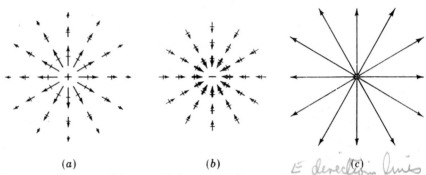

(a)   (b)   (c)

Fig. 2.7   Three possible ways of drawing field maps of point charges. In *a*, for a positive charge, the length of the line segment represents the magnitude of the vector. In *b*, the width of the line segment represents the magnitude of the vector field intensity for a negative point charge. In *c*, the lines show only the direction and the symmetry; the length of the line has no significance.

maps.   Let us try to map the field vector **E** which results from a single point charge located at the origin of spherical coordinates. We have a very simple relationship between the magnitude of the vector and the coordinates of the point of observation

$$\mathbf{E} = \frac{Q}{4\pi\epsilon_0 R^2}\mathbf{r} \tag{1}$$

At any point P, whose coordinates are R, θ, and ϕ, we are to substitute the value of R into Eq. (1), to obtain both the magnitude and direction of **E**. The field is three-dimensional, so we must satisfy ourselves on paper by drawing a plane section of it obtained by passing any plane through the origin. A three-dimensional picture would suggest a tennis ball with pins projecting radially from its surface.

The two-dimensional section in Fig. 2.7*a* has been constructed by drawing line segments whose length is proportional to the magnitude of the **E** vector, and arranging them to point in the direction of the **E** vector. This has been done at 36 selected points lying on three circles of increasing radius. The difficulties in completing a map of this type are quite evident. The longest line segments are needed on the inner circles, where there is no room to draw a long line.   Any length of line chosen to suit points on the inner circle rapidly becomes too short at greater distances from the origin.   Regardless of the number of lines which we try to draw to represent the field at points near the origin, relatively large spaces are left in the picture at large distances from the origin.   We might think of letting the thickness of the line represent the magnitude of the vector, as in Fig. 2.7b, but again we need to put thick lines where there is the least room for them.

One of the ways out of this difficulty is to avoid attempting to represent the magnitude of the vector by a line segment, and instead to draw lines which represent only the direction of the vector.   Such a sketch as this appears in part c of the figure.   Here the length of the line signifies nothing other than the limits of the space allowed for the figure.   If we had more space, we would continue the lines on out to infinity.   When the lines on a field map are continuous and are not intended to represent the magnitude of the vector, but only its direction, we may call them *direction lines*.

The technique of representing a vector field by a map or diagram of lines which show only direction has many ramifications.   Among these is the observation that the symmetry of the field can be indicated by a symmetrical arrangement of the direction lines.   Another is that the number of lines passing through a region is an indication of the relative magnitude of the vector in that region.   This in turn suggests proportioning the number of lines to the magnitude of the charge present.   Of these several lines of thought we now select the matter of determining direction and investigate it in detail.   We shall not slight the others.

Some readers with previous experience would expect the lines, here called *direction lines*, to be called *lines of force;* while others would be looking for the term *flux lines*.   These are partly matters of individual preference, partly custom, and also emphasis.   The emphasis here is on the fact that this technique may be used on vector quantities which are not forces, or which have nothing to do with electrostatic fields.   Other general terms in use are *stream lines* and *field lines*.   Our preference for the term direction lines arises from our desire to emphasize that these lines are intended basically to show only direction and that anything else which they show is a welcome bonus.

2.7   Direction Lines in Two Dimensions.   To map vector fields, let us explore the use of lines or curves which have the same direction as the vector quantity at every point in the field.   Another way of saying this is to state that the vector quantity is always tangent to the direction lines.   The relationship between the slope of the curve and the components of a two-dimensional vector $\mathbf{E}$ is shown in Fig. 2.8a.   At any point P, the slope of the curve is given equally well by dy/dx or E_y/E_x.

When we know the components of the vector in terms of the coordinates of the point with which it is associated, we can equate the two expressions

$$\text{at any Point } P, \text{ the slope} = \frac{dy}{dx} = \frac{E_y}{E_x} \tag{1}$$

This is a differential equation satisfied by a family of curves meeting our requirements. If we can solve this differential equation, it may be easier to map the field by drawing the family of curves than by making point-by-point calculations.

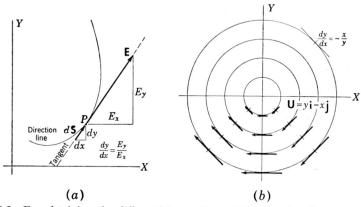

(a)   (b)

FIG. 2.8   For obtaining the differential equation of the direction lines of a vector which lies in a plane.   Part *a* shows the direction line, the vector to which it is tangent at the point *P*, and the simple relation between the slope of the direction line and the components of the vector.   In *b* is shown an example of the solution of the differential equation of the direction lines of a given vector field.

As an example of the simplest kind, let us map the two-dimensional vector

Circle

$$\mathbf{U} = y\,\mathbf{i} - x\,\mathbf{j} \tag{2}$$

Here, as in Eq. (1),

$$\frac{dy}{dx} = \frac{U_y}{U_x} \tag{3}$$

and $U_y = -x$, while $U_x = y$.   Substituting these components into Eq. (3),

$$\frac{dy}{dx} = \frac{-x}{y} \tag{4}$$

Cross-multiplying separates the variables

$$y\,dy = -x\,dx \tag{5}$$

Integrating both sides,

$$\frac{y^2}{2} + \text{a constant} = \frac{-x^2}{2} + \text{a constant} \tag{6}$$

This we can write in the more familiar form

Circle

$$x^2 + y^2 = C^2 \tag{7}$$

which is the equation of a family of circles centered at the origin. The particular circle passing through a point of specific interest is given by substituting the coordinates of the point into Eq. (7) and solving for C, here the radius of the circle. The vector under study, $\mathbf{U}$, has the magnitude

$$|\mathbf{U}| = \sqrt{y^2 + x^2} \tag{8}$$

which is directly proportional to the distance of the point from the origin. In Fig. 2.8b, the vector quantity is represented in the lower half while only the direction lines are shown in the upper half.

Physically, this vector could be the velocity of a point in a revolving disk, while the direction lines could be associated with the locus of spots on the disk.

The simplicity of this example should not lead us to expect that we can obtain the equation of the direction lines easily, even though they lie in a plane. In examples to follow, we shall find that the solution of such equations is not a simple matter at all. Regardless of this, however, Eq. (1) defines the slope of the direction lines, and sometimes a good deal of information can be obtained about a curve just from a study of its slope. Such a study may even guide us toward an intelligent guess as to the form of the equation of the curve.

2.8   The Field Map of a Uniformly Charged Line of Finite Length. To prepare a map of the field of a uniformly charged line of finite length by using direction lines, we equate the slope of the lines to the ratio of the components, as in the previous section. Here

$$\frac{dR}{dz} = \frac{E_R}{E_z} \tag{1}$$

From the results of Sec. 2.4, in which we obtained the components of the field intensity vector as Eqs. (12) and (13),

$$\frac{dR}{dz} = \frac{[(z + a)/R_1] - [(z - a)/R_2]}{(R/R_2) - (R/R_1)} \tag{2}$$

in which R_1 and R_2 are the distances to the ends of the line as shown in Fig. 2.5

$$R_1 = \sqrt{(z + a)^2 + R^2} \tag{3}$$

$$R_2 = \sqrt{(z - a)^2 + R^2} \tag{4}$$

In a preliminary attempt to separate the variables of Eq. (2), we could cross-multiply and expand to obtain

$$R_1 R \, dR - R_2 R \, dR = R_2(z + a) \, dz - R_1(z - a) \, dz \tag{5}$$

Beyond this point, without some hint as to the possibilities, algebraic manipulation becomes difficult because of the radical nature of R_1 and R_2.

One of the characteristics of differential equations is that there is no satisfactory recipe or formula for driving the answer out of them. Hints as to the nature of the family of curves whose derivative may be thrown into the form of Eq. (2) are available from a thorough examination of the trigonometry and analytic geometry of the physical problem from which Eq. (2) was obtained. However, there is another approach in the study of the *symmetry* of the physical problem which not only gives a hint as

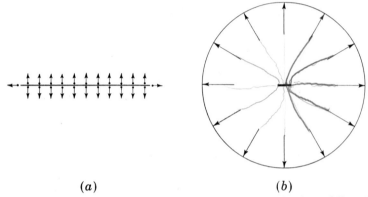

(a)   (b)

Fig. 2.9 A study of the symmetry in the field of a uniformly charged line of finite length. (a) Very near the line the field is perpendicular to the line; (b) at distances very remote from the line, the field is normal to the surface of a sphere, like that of a point charge. This suggests that the direction lines might be hyperbolas.

to the nature of the direction lines, but illustrates a method of thinking which we shall use frequently and shall ultimately call "satisfying the boundary conditions."

At points very near the charged line, the radial component overwhelms the axial component, so that the direction of the field is along **r**. On the extended axis of the line, however, the radial component vanishes. At great distances from the line, the field cannot be greatly different from that of a point charge. Rough sketches of these two viewpoints are shown in Fig. 2.9a and b. Aided by the figures, we observe that following a direction line from the charges outward to infinity must involve starting along **r** and finishing up in a direction asymptotic to radial lines from the origin. Of the simple geometric curves, this suggests a family of hyperbolas. A hyperbola is the locus of a point whose distances to two focal points differ by a constant. If the direction lines should turn out to be hyperbolas and if the focal distance should happen to be R_1 and R_2, we should be able to arrange our differential Eq. (2) in terms of R_1 and R_2 and their derivatives.

Squaring both sides of Eqs. (3) and (4) and differentiating yields

$$R_1\, dR_1 = (z + a)\, dz + R\, dR \tag{6}$$

and

$$R_2\, dR_2 = (z - a)\, dz + R\, dR \tag{7}$$

We now see that Eq. (5) can be arranged as suggested by the right-hand sides of Eqs. (6) and (7):

$$\frac{(z + a)\, dz + R\, dR}{R_1} = \frac{(z - a)\, dz + R\, dR}{R_2} \tag{8}$$

and that these are the derivatives of R_1 and R_2.

$$dR_1 = dR_2 \tag{9}$$

Integration of both sides gives the equation of the family of curves

$$R_1 - R_2 = C \tag{10}$$

which are indeed hyperbolas with their focal points at the ends of the line.

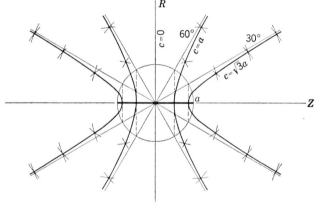

FIG. 2.10   A map of the direction lines in the field of a uniformly charged line of finite length.   The direction lines are confocal hyperbolas, with foci at the ends of the charged line.   To show the spherical symmetry at great distances from the line, the hyperbolas which have been drawn are asymptotic to equally spaced lines drawn from the center of the charged line.   The construction lines have been shown to illustrate how the field can be mapped without point-by-point calculations.

A field map should portray whatever symmetry pertains to the field, and in this case there is spherical symmetry at infinite distances from the center of the line.   This requires that the few representative members of the family of hyperbolas which are actually drawn on the map should be selected from symmetrically spaced asymptotes.   If it were not for this, we would be tempted to select those which cut the charged line at equally spaced intervals.   In drawing the field map in Fig. 2.10, only graphic techniques were employed.   A sufficient number of construction lines are shown to portray the relation of the hyperbolas and their intercepts to the asymptotes. For our present needs this is preferable to exploring the analytic geometry in any more detail. It further illustrates the idea that, if the equation of the direction lines can be found, the actual preparation of a field map need not involve extensive numerical calculations.

2.9 The Field of Equal and Opposite Line Charges. The field of a two-wire line is of obvious importance to all electrical engineers, whether their interest is primarily in the power aspects or in a communication problem. The field has a surprisingly important mathematical significance, too, and warrants a detailed analysis.

We shall use the notation of Fig. 2.11a and cartesian coordinates. From our previous analysis of a single line charge, the field at any point

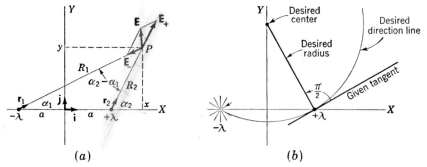

(a)   (b)

Fig. 2.11   (a) Analysis of the field of two line charges, infinitely long and having opposite polarity; (b) method of construction of the field map by utilizing the symmetry at points very near the line charges, along with the information that the direction lines are families of circles passing through the line charges.

P, due to the positively charged line, is

$$\mathbf{E}_+ = \frac{\lambda}{2\pi\epsilon_0 R_2}\,\mathbf{r}_2 \tag{1}$$

while that due to the negatively charged line is

$$\mathbf{E}_- = \frac{-\lambda}{2\pi\epsilon_0 R_1}\,\mathbf{r}_1 \tag{2}$$

The total field is the vector sum of the two contributions, which can be written at once as

$$\mathbf{E} = \frac{\lambda}{2\pi\epsilon_0}\left(\frac{\mathbf{r}_2}{R_2} - \frac{\mathbf{r}_1}{R_1}\right) \tag{3}$$

This is the simplest form in which we can place a description of the magnitude and direction of this vector field. Though neat, terse, and adequate for numerical computations at any specific point, Eq. (3) does not give us an over-all picture of the field. To aid our visualization, let us go through the details of obtaining the equation of the direction lines in a coordinate system so that the field can be mapped.

Resolving Eq. (3) into components along the x and y axes gives

$$E_y = \mathbf{E} \cdot \mathbf{j} = \frac{\lambda}{2\pi\epsilon_0} \left(\frac{y}{R_2^2} - \frac{y}{R_1^2} \right) \tag{4}$$

and

$$E_x = \mathbf{E} \cdot \mathbf{i} = \frac{\lambda}{2\pi\epsilon_0} \left(\frac{x-a}{R_2^2} - \frac{x+a}{R_1^2} \right) \tag{5}$$

For the slope equation

$$\frac{dy}{dx} = \frac{E_y}{E_x} \tag{6}$$

we have the result

$$\frac{dy}{dx} = \frac{(y/R_2^2) - (y/R_1^2)}{[(x-a)/R_2^2] - [(x+a)/R_1^2]} \tag{7}$$

Cross-multiplying,

$$\frac{(x-a)\,dy}{R_2^2} - \frac{(x+a)\,dy}{R_1^2} = \frac{y\,dx}{R_2^2} - \frac{y\,dx}{R_1^2} \tag{8}$$

Associating terms with the same denominator,

$$\frac{(x-a)\,dy - y\,dx}{R_2^2} = \frac{(x+a)\,dy - y\,dx}{R_1^2} \tag{9}$$

Now, expressing R_1^2 and R_2^2 in terms of x and y,

$$\frac{(x-a)\,dy - y\,dx}{(x-a)^2 + y^2} = \frac{(x+a)\,dy - y\,dx}{(x+a)^2 + y^2} \tag{10}$$

The numerators suggest the derivatives of the ratios

$$d\left(\frac{y}{x \pm a} \right) = \frac{(x \pm a)\,dy - y\,dx}{(x \pm a)^2} \tag{11}$$

In Eq. (10), we divide numerator and denominator by $(x-a)^2$ on the left and by $(x+a)^2$ on the right, to obtain

$$\frac{\dfrac{(x-a)\,dy - y\,dx}{(x-a)^2}}{1 + \left(\dfrac{y}{x-a} \right)^2} = \frac{\dfrac{(x+a)\,dy - y\,dx}{(x+a)^2}}{1 + \left(\dfrac{y}{x+a} \right)^2} \tag{12}$$

These have the form of

$$\frac{du}{1+u^2} = \frac{dv}{1+v^2} \tag{13}$$

which are the derivatives of arc tan u and arc tan v.

$$d(\text{arc tan } u) = d(\text{arc tan } v)$$

therefore

$$\text{arc tan } u = \text{arc tan } v + C \tag{14}$$

In terms of the angles of Fig. 2.11a, we observe that arc tan $u = \alpha_2$ and arc tan $v = \alpha_1$.

$$\alpha_2 - \alpha_1 = C \tag{15}$$

As a point P moves on a direction line, α_2 and α_1 may vary, but their difference must remain a constant. Further, $\alpha_2 - \alpha_1$ is the angle between R_1 and R_2. The locus of a point moving under this restriction is a circle passing through the charges. While the equation of the family of circles may be obtained by equating the tangents of both sides of Eq. (15), expanding the left-hand side by a trigonometric identity, and after relating the tangents to the coordinates, completing the square; the field may be mapped without all this algebra.

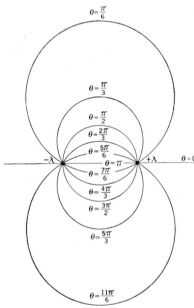

Very near each of the line charges, the contribution from the nearest line will overwhelm that from the other line, and in this region the field must have the same symmetry as does the field of the nearest line alone. This is illustrated at $-\lambda$ in Fig. 2.11b. The centers of the circles, and their radii, are then obtained graphically as shown in Fig. 2.11b at $+\lambda$. On the field map, Fig. 2.12, the direction lines are labeled with the polar angle which their tangent makes with the

Fig. 2.12   Direction lines in the field of equal and opposite line charges. The direction lines are labeled with the angle which they make with the plane of the charged lines at the positive line charge.

x axis at the positively charged line, as was shown in Fig. 2.11b.

In those fields in which it is possible to obtain the equation of the direction lines in the form of a relatively easily constructed curve, mapping the field is reduced to graphical construction methods. The student may correctly conclude that, even here, mapping the field may be a task equal to or greater than its analysis as a vector quantity. This is indeed true, and a good portion of the difficulty arises from the necessity of relating the vector quantity to a coordinate system, to say nothing of solving the resulting differential equation. When these methods fail, there are other ways of obtaining the equations of the direction lines. We shall examine one of them briefly in Chap. 5 in connection with the subtle approach of Gauss's law.

2.10   Direction Lines in Three Dimensions.   Field mapping is usually restricted to those parts of the field in which the vectors lie in a plane, and where the direction lines are plane curves. The reason for this lies in the difficulty of representing three-dimensional fields on two-dimensional paper. It is not very much harder to set up the differential equation of the direction lines in three dimensions than in two. The approach is slightly different, and we cannot capitalize on the results quite as quickly. A geometric interpretation of the results is interesting and illuminating.

As in Sec. 2.7 and Fig. 2.8a, we associate two vector quantities with each point in the field. The first of these is the vector quantity under study $\mathbf{E}$ and the other is a differential line segment $d\mathbf{S}$, lying in that particular direction line which passes through the point. These two vector quantities are parallel and differ only in their scalar magnitudes. In equation form we may state this equality as

$$d\mathbf{S} = m\mathbf{E} \tag{1}$$

in which m is the scalar, or scale factor, by which the magnitude of $\mathbf{E}$ must be multiplied in order to make its magnitude equal to that of $d\mathbf{S}$ at the particular point in question. To obtain our differential relationships, we resolve each of the vectors into their three components at the point in question. In cartesian coordinates the results are

$$d\mathbf{S} = dx\,\mathbf{i} + dy\,\mathbf{j} + dz\,\mathbf{k} \tag{2}$$

and

$$\mathbf{E} = E_x\,\mathbf{i} + E_y\,\mathbf{j} + E_z\,\mathbf{k} \tag{3}$$

Substituting into Eq. (1)

$$dx\,\mathbf{i} + dy\,\mathbf{j} + dz\,\mathbf{k} = mE_x\,\mathbf{i} + mE_y\,\mathbf{j} + mE_z\,\mathbf{k} \tag{4}$$

By equating the equal components of the equal vectors, we obtain three scalar equations

$$dx = mE_x \qquad dy = mE_y \qquad dz = mE_z \tag{5}$$

Solving each of these for m,

$$m = \frac{dx}{E_x} \qquad m = \frac{dy}{E_y} \qquad m = \frac{dz}{E_z} \tag{6}$$

From this we may select any pair of the equalities

$$\frac{dx}{E_x} = \frac{dy}{E_y} \qquad \frac{dx}{E_z} = \frac{dz}{E_x} \qquad \frac{dy}{E_u} = \frac{dz}{E_z} \tag{7}$$

To save space we write a dual equality having the same meaning as Eq. (7) and termed the *symmetric form:*

Cartesian Form

$$\boxed{\frac{dx}{E_x} = \frac{dy}{E_y} = \frac{dz}{E_z}}$$

(8)

Equation (8) states simply that the respective components of the two vector quantities have a fixed ratio at every point in space. For a two-dimensional case, the appropriate relationship from Eq. (7) would be used.

Before we move on to discussing the solution of Eq. (8), it is well to obtain the similar expressions in the two other coordinate systems we have been using. Referring to Fig. 1.9, which depicts cylindrical coordinates, we see that the differential line segment $d\mathbf{S}$ has the following components:

$$d\mathbf{S} = dR\,\mathbf{r} + R\,d\theta\,\boldsymbol{\theta} + dz\,\mathbf{k}$$

(9)

Resolving the $\mathbf{E}$ vector into its components and substituting into Eq. (1) we obtain

$$dR\,\mathbf{r} + R\,d\theta\,\boldsymbol{\theta} + dz\,\mathbf{k} = mE_R\,\mathbf{r} + mE_\theta\,\boldsymbol{\theta} + mE_z\,\mathbf{k}$$

(10)

Proceeding as was detailed in Eqs. (5) to (7), we obtain the symmetric form analogous to Eq. (8)

$$\frac{dR}{E_R} = \frac{R\,d\theta}{E_\theta} = \frac{dz}{E_z}$$

(11)

In spherical coordinates, after referring to Fig. 1.10, we write

Spherical Form

$$\boxed{\frac{dR}{E_R} = \frac{R\,d\theta}{E_\theta} = \frac{R\sin\theta\,d\phi}{E_\phi}}$$

(12)

From the restricted and purely utilitarian viewpoint of mapping those parts of a field which lie in a plane, Eqs. (8), (11), and (12) form a useful collection of formulas from which we may select an appropriate pair of equalities. But we really have much more than this.

These relations are capable of giving us the equation of the direction lines of a general, three-dimensional field. A geometrical interpretation of how the mathematics does this for us carries us back again to a pre-viously mentioned facet on the problem "How shall we describe a direction?" When we first examined coordinate systems we observed that a line of direction may be described by the line of intersection of two sur-faces. In spherical coordinates, for example, we erected our unit vectors in the lines of intersection of the sphere, the cone, and the plane illustrated in Fig. 1.10.

Any two of the equalities given in the symmetric form of Eqs. (8), (11), and (12) are satisfied by two families of geometric surfaces. The direc-tion lines lie in the lines of intersection of the surfaces. In cartesian coordinates, for example, the two differential equations of (8)

$$\frac{dx}{E_x} = \frac{dy}{E_y} \quad \text{and} \quad \frac{dx}{E_x} = \frac{dz}{E_z}$$

have as their solutions the functions

$$F_1(x,y,z) = C_1 \quad \text{and} \quad F_2(x,y,z) = C_2 \qquad (13), (14)$$

where C_1 and C_2 are the arbitrary constants arising from the solution of the differential equations. There is a particular value of the parameters C_1 and C_2 at each point in space. Equations (13) and (14) represent two families of surfaces, and all points which satisfy both Eq. (13) and

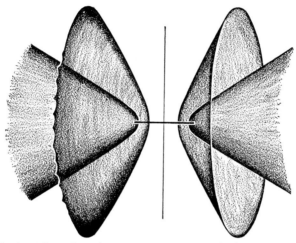

Fig. 2.13   Confocal hyperboloids of revolution in the field of a uniformly charged line of finite length, obtained by rotating the hyperbolas of Fig. 2.10 about the axis of the line charge.   The direction lines lie in the intersection of the hyperboloids and the planes, θ = a constant.

Eq. (14) lie in the lines of intersection of the two families of surfaces. These lines of intersection are our direction lines.

In this light, let us examine the field of a line charge of finite length. In Sec. 2.8, we obtained a two-dimensional equation of the direction lines in the field of a uniformly charged line of finite length and found them to be hyperbolas. From the three-dimensional view, the equation $R_2 - R_1 = C$ is not the equation of a line, but the equation of a hyperboloid of revolution as in Fig. 2.13. The direction lines are the lines of intersection of the hyperboloids and any of the planes, θ = a constant. From the three-dimensional viewpoint, the direction lines of this field are given by the parametric equations

$$\left.\begin{array}{r} R_2 - R_1 = C_1 \\ \theta = C_2 \end{array}\right\} \qquad (15)$$

In the field of the two-wire line, mapped in Sec. 2.9, the direction lines are given by the parametric equations

$$x^2 + \left(y - \frac{a}{\tan C_1}\right)^2 = \left(\frac{a}{\sin C_1}\right)^2 \\ z = C_2 \Bigg\} \tag{16}$$

The first of these equations results from expressing Eq. 2.9 (15), which was $\alpha_2 - \alpha_1 = C$, in terms of the coordinates from an inspection of the

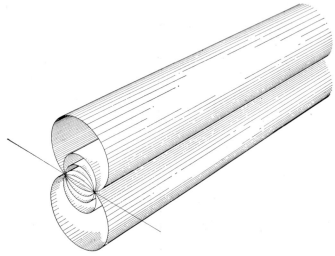

FIG. 2.14 The cylindrical surfaces which contain the direction lines in the field of equal and opposite line charges. The cylinders intersect at the charged lines. The direction lines lie in the lines of intersection of the cylinders and the planes perpendicular to the axis.

radii and centers of the circles as was shown in Fig. 2.11b. The first of the equations of (16) is a family of cylinders as depicted in Fig. 2.14, and the direction lines we have mapped lie in the lines of intersection of the cylinders and the planes given by the second of the Eqs. (16).

Let us now use Eq. (8) to make a frontal attack on the problem of obtaining the equation of the direction lines in the field of a point charge located at the origin, using cartesian rather than spherical coordinates. The spherical coordinate expression for the field intensity is

$$\mathbf{E} = \frac{Q}{4\pi\epsilon_0 R^2}\, \mathbf{r} \tag{17}$$

When this is resolved into cartesian components the results are

$$\mathbf{E} = \frac{Q}{4\pi\epsilon_0 R^2}\left(\frac{x}{R}\mathbf{i} + \frac{y}{R}\mathbf{j} + \frac{z}{R}\mathbf{k}\right) \tag{18}$$

Substituting the components into Eq. (8),

$$\frac{dx}{(Qx)/4\pi\epsilon_0 R^3} = \frac{dy}{(Qy)/4\pi\epsilon_0 R^3} = \frac{dz}{(Qz)/4\pi\epsilon_0 R^3} \qquad (19)$$

The common factors indicate what might have been anticipated, that the direction of the field is independent of the magnitude of the charge and of whether or not it is a square-law field. Simplifying Eq. (19),

$$\frac{dx}{x} = \frac{dy}{y} = \frac{dz}{z} \qquad (20)$$

Selecting two from the three possibilities, we write

$$\frac{dx}{x} = \frac{dy}{y} \quad \text{and} \quad \frac{dx}{x} = \frac{dz}{z} \qquad (21)$$

Integrating both sides and including the arbitrary constant,

$$\log_e x = \log_e y + \log_e C_1 \quad \text{and} \quad \log_e x = \log_e z + \log_e C_2 \qquad (22)$$

In antilogarithmic form

$$x = C_1 y \quad \text{and} \quad x = C_2 z \qquad (23)$$

These equations describe, respectively, all planes containing the z axis and all planes containing the y axis. The direction lines lie in the intersection of these two families of planes, and all such lines are straight lines passing through the origin. To find the direction line which passes through the point 1, 2, 3, for example, substitution of the given coordinates into Eq. (23) gives

$$C_1 = \tfrac{1}{2} \quad \text{and} \quad C_2 = \tfrac{1}{3} \qquad (24)$$

and these values select from the families of planes the specific planes

$$x = \frac{y}{2} \quad \text{and} \quad x = \frac{z}{3} \qquad (25)$$

All points which satisfy both the relations of Eq. (25) lie on the same direction line passing through the point 1, 2, 3.

The same attack starting with Eq. (12) in spherical coordinates gives an apparent difficulty

$$\frac{dR}{E_R} = \frac{R\,d\theta}{0} = \frac{R \sin\theta\,d\phi}{0} \qquad (26)$$

The terms with the zero denominator seem to give an infinite result, but since the first ratio is not zero except at the origin, Eq. (26) can only be satisfied in general by equating $d\theta$ and $d\phi$ to zero. The differential equations

$$d\theta = 0 \quad \text{and} \quad d\phi = 0 \qquad (27)$$

have the solutions

$$\theta = C_1 \quad \text{and} \quad \phi = C_2 \qquad (28)$$

describing the families of cones and planes, illustrated in Fig. 1.10, which intersect in straight lines through the origin.

The pairs of differential equations (8), (11), and (12) are evidently satisfied by a variety of surfaces. This is more generality than we need, and leads us to inquire as to whether or not there is a more limited and unique way of describing the direction lines. There is such a way, and it, also, is associated with a family of surfaces. These are the surfaces which are perpendicular to the direction lines, and we shall study them in the next chapter.

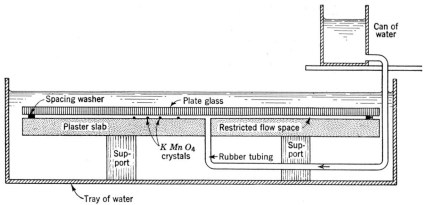

Fig. 2.15   Diagram of the construction and operation of a fluid-flow model for obtaining the direction lines in the field of a single line charge. Water enters the restricted flow channel between a plaster slab and a covering sheet of plate glass by means of a hole in the center of the slab. As the water flows to the outer edges, the stream is dyed by crystals of potassium permanganate, as shown in the plan view of Fig. 2.16. For further details, see Appendix 2.

2.11 Fluid-flow Maps. Of several methods of making physical models of fields, that called fluid-flow mapping is certainly the most photogenic. As a result of several new techniques invented by Professor A. D. Moore at the University of Michigan, this rather old method of mapping fields is receiving much attention. Professor Moore prepared special models of many of the fields we shall study and has supplied most of the photographs. Well within the reach of the budget and facilities of the most limited laboratory, fluid-flow maps are recommended as classroom study aids. His instructions for their preparation appear in Appendix 2.

A moving film of water is made visible by dyeing it with slowly dissolving crystals of potassium permanganate sprinkled in the flow space before assembly. The construction features for the simplest map are shown in Fig. 2.15. Water leaves an elevated can and enters the restricted flow region between a smooth plaster slab and a covering sheet of plate glass

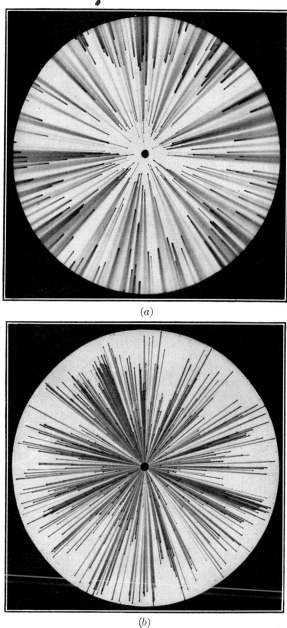

(a)

(b)

Fɪɢ. 2.16 Fluid-flow maps of the fields of line charges. In a, water enters at the hole, while in b, water leaves at the hole. The stream is dyed by the stationary crystals of potassium permanganate sprinkled in the channel before assembly. (*This and other fluid-flow maps modeled and photographed by Professor A. D. Moore at the University of Michigan.*)

by means of a hole in the center of the plaster slab. The water then flows radially to the edges, and the path of the stream is marked by the colored water as in Fig. 2.16a, which is a photograph of the model in operation.

We shall use maps like these solely to aid our visualization of fields, resisting the temptation here to explain the analogies between the velocity of a slowly moving incompressible fluid and the electrostatic

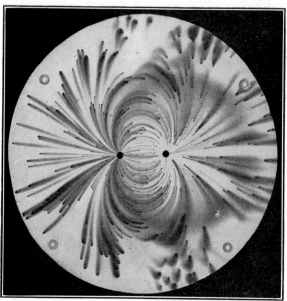

FIG. 2.17   Fluid-flow map of the direction lines in the field of equal and opposite line charges, infinitely long.

field.   After we have discussed Laplace's equation and Poisson's equation in Chap. 8, the explanation will be easier.   We shall recognize, however, that one of the more valuable uses for these models is in the study of more complicated fields which can be studied only with great difficulty in purely mathematical terms.

In Fig. 2.16 are two maps of the direction lines in the field of a uniformly charged line, infinitely long.   It happens also that they represent the field of a point charge, when the difference between the two-dimensional character of the map and the three-dimensional character of the field of a point charge is kept in mind.   In one case water enters at the hole in the center of the slab, and in the other case the flow direction is reversed. This gives us the opportunity to treat one case as a positive charge and the other as a negative charge, associating the flow from a hole which is a *source* with the positive charge, and the flow into a hole which is a drain or *sink* with the negative charge.

Using equal source and sink, the map of Fig. 2.17 represents the field of two lines carrying equal and opposite, uniform charge densities. (It does not correctly represent the field of equal and opposite point charges, because the direction lines in that field are not circles.) Because the physical model cannot be infinite in extent, this map is only approximate, but in those parts of the picture near the center and away from the arbitrary circular edges of the flow, it is a rather good approximation. The direction lines are close enough to circular to assure us that they really

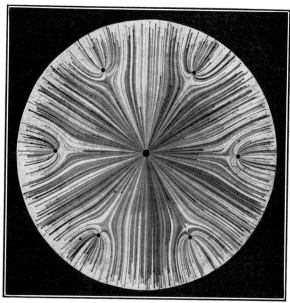

FIG. 2.18   Fluid-flow map of the direction lines in the electrostatic field of a triode vacuum tube without space charge. Modeled as the field of seven line charges in a cylindrical boundary, the central circle represents the cathode, the six symmetrical circles represent the grid wires, while the outer boundary represents the plate.

are circular in the actual field configuration. Upon close inspection of the photograph, a distortion in the direction lines can be seen in the upper part of the picture to the right of the center. This arises from the flow around a small air bubble entrapped in the flow space. Also, the two small circles on the center line are additional holes in the slab which were plugged temporarily. At the outer edges, four washers are visible which maintain the spacing between the plaster slab and the plate glass.

Figure 2.18 is a map of a more elaborate field than we shall study mathematically in this book. It represents the direction lines of the electrostatic field in a simplified triode vacuum tube without space charge, by treating it as the field due to a central charged line (to represent the cathode), six symmetrically spaced lines (to represent the grid), and a circular outer boundary to represent the plate.

Figure 2.19 is a map of the direction lines in the field of a uniformly charged line of finite length. These lines are indeed hyperbolas, asymptotic to radial lines from the center of the charged line, as was determined mathematically. The boundaries of the sink at the center are elliptical, and no attempt is made to represent the field within the ellipse. To represent the field quite near the charged line would require that the

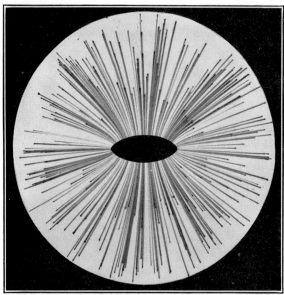

FIG. 2.19   Fluid-flow map of the direction lines in the field of a uniformly charged line of finite length, also drawn in Fig. 2.10.   The finite line charge extends between the focal points of the central ellipse.   No attempt has been made to map the field quite near the line charge.   The central ellipse is an equal-pressure region, and its boundaries are perpendicular to the direction lines.

sink have finite length and zero width; but if it did, no water could pass through it.   Accordingly, the boundaries of the sink were made to coincide with the surfaces which are orthogonal to the direction lines.   The success of the results will be explained when we examine these orthogonal surfaces in the next chapter.

The relative spacing of the colored-water paths which represent the direction lines of the field is determined by the random location of the crystals of potassium permanganate, and not by the nature of the field itself.   This reminds us that in these maps the direction lines are intended to represent only direction and not the magnitude of the vector quantity. Even with random spacing, however, the direction lines are close together where the field is most intense, and as was stated previously, we shall pursue this matter of the relative density of the direction lines in some detail in Chap. 5.

2.12 A Summary and a Criticism. Of greatest importance is the concept of electric-field intensity. This vector quantity is the force, per unit of test charge, experienced by a vanishingly small positive test charge, placed (in our imagination) at a point in a field. Of less importance are the formulas we have used so far for computing its value for a given configuration of charges.

For a finite number of point charges, whose positions are known, the electric-field intensity may be computed from the vector sum, Eq. 2.3(4):

$$\mathbf{E} = \sum \frac{Q_n}{4\pi\epsilon_0 R_n{}^2} \mathbf{r}_n$$

In order to add the individual vector contributions to $\mathbf{E}$ properly, they may first be resolved into components, and the components added separately. For continuous distributions of charge along a line, over a surface, or within a volume, it is convenient to treat the charge distribution as an infinite number of vanishingly small point charges and to perform the vector addition by a vector integration.

$$\mathbf{E} = \int \frac{\lambda\,dL}{4\pi\epsilon_0 R^2}\,\mathbf{r} + \int \frac{\sigma\,dA}{4\pi\epsilon_0 R^2}\,\mathbf{r} + \int \frac{\rho\,dv}{4\pi\epsilon_0 R^2}\,\mathbf{r} \tag{1}$$

To evaluate these integrals properly, they must first be resolved into three mutually perpendicular components, and the scalar integrals evaluated separately. The notation of this integral formula for computing the value of the electric-field intensity is usually shortened by writing only the last integral, but in doing so, we imply the longer form.

$$\mathbf{E} = \int \frac{\rho\,dv}{4\pi\epsilon_0 R^2}\,\mathbf{r} \tag{2}$$

The literature of field theory is filled with expressions like this one, and it is a good idea to get used to looking at them and thinking about what they mean. They are not intended to be either confusing or profound, but rather a neat shorthand summary of the things we have been talking about in this chapter. The integral directly above is intended to convey this simple idea: "If you know where the charges are located, you can compute the field intensity which they produce by treating them as a number of individual point charges, and by adding their individual contributions according to the parallelogram law. Or, alternatively, you can resolve the individual contributions into components and add the components as scalars."

Among other examples, we have used the methods symbolized by this equation to evaluate the electric field intensity for an infinitely long, uniformly charged line and for a uniform sheet of charge, infinite in extent. Together with the point charge, these provide three important building blocks which we shall use again and again in our analysis of fields:

Point charge: $\qquad\qquad\qquad\qquad\mathbf{E} = \dfrac{Q}{4\pi\epsilon_0 R^2}\,\mathbf{r}$ $\qquad$ 2.3(4)

Uniform line charge, infinitely long: $\qquad\mathbf{E} = \dfrac{\lambda}{2\pi\epsilon_0 R}\,\mathbf{r}$ $\qquad$ 2.4(16)

Uniform sheet of charge, infinite in extent: $\mathbf{E} = \dfrac{\sigma}{2\epsilon_0}\,\mathbf{n}$ $\qquad$ 2.5(7)

There are similar relations in illumination. The light intensity produced by a point source is proportional to the inverse square of the distance from the source. An infinite array of fluorescent lights in a line would produce an intensity of illumination inversely proportional to the distance from the source. An infinite sheet of light sources would produce a uniform intensity of light regardless of the distance from the sheet. A good approximation to an infinite sheet of light sources is a field of snow in bright sunlight.

When equal and opposite charge distributions are present, we find that the field tends to become confined to restricted regions of space. The two equal and opposite, uniform, plane sheets of charge provided definite boundaries which confined the field entirely to the space between the sheets. In general, surfaces which carry charges provide either a discontinuity or a definite boundary for the field. Later we shall focus our attention on these *boundary conditions*.

As an aid to visualizing fields, field maps are useful. The lines on these field maps are commonly called lines of force, stream lines, or flux lines. In this book, however, they will usually be called direction lines to emphasize the fact that they indicate only the direction of the vector quantity and not its magnitude. As an aid to plotting field maps, the equation of the direction lines is useful, and it may be obtained by solving a system of differential equations. In cartesian coordinates the differential equations are

$$\frac{dx}{E_x} = \frac{dy}{E_y} = \frac{dz}{E_z} \qquad\qquad 2.10(8)$$

Writing down a differential equation is easier than solving it. However, for the purpose of fixing in the mind the definition of direction lines as a family of curves which are tangent to a vector at every point in a field, there is probably nothing more straightforward than the differential equation because of its close association with the idea of defining a plane curve by its slope.

The examples presented have not exhausted the possibilities of the analysis of fields through the Coulomb's-law approach. We could continue on in the same fashion, breaking each charge configuration down into point charges, finding the differential contribution of each point charge to the field at every point in space, resolving the differential vectors into their components and adding the results individually, and finally recombining the components to express the field as a function of the coordinates of the point of observation. But very shortly, the mathematical processes would begin to require more and more of our energy and attention—so much so, in fact, that we would be apt to lose sight of our original purpose, even if we were very fond of mathematics. Coulomb's law does not yield much to brute-force tactics.

We inquire with good reason as to whether or not there are other ways of obtaining the same results with less difficulty mathematically. Most of us recall that similar problems in dealing with forces in mechanics became a good deal easier when approached by the method of the conservation of energy, but not all of us are able to explain why the energy idea made the problems so much easier. A part of our mathematical difficulties have arisen from the need to break the vectors up into components, and from the everlasting necessity of obtaining the field by a process of integration. What we need is some sort of scalar idea about fields, whose individual contributions can be added as scalars instead of vectors. In addition to this, we should be very thankful for a procedure in which the field could be obtained by a process of differentiation, as we find it so very much easier than integration. Closely related to energy, the name of the concept we are seeking is *potential*, and we examine it in the next chapter.

More serious than the mathematical difficulties is the fact that we have had to know the location of the charges before we could determine the field. Ultimately we shall have to find a viewpoint capable of telling us where the charges are when we connect a system of conductors to a source of electrical energy.

REFERENCES

1. Boast, Warren B.: "Principles of Electric and Magnetic Fields," Harper & Brothers, New York, 1948. Contains many examples of the use of Coulomb's law in electrostatics. Does not use vector-analysis notation.
2. Morris, Max, and Brown, O. E.: "Differential Equations," Prentice-Hall, Inc., New York, 1945. See Chap. VII for methods of solving the differential equations of the direction lines of a vector.
3. Smythe, William R.: "Static and Dynamic Electricity," pp. 7–9, McGraw-Hill Book Company, Inc., New York, 1939. Obtains the equation of the direction lines in the field of two point charges as a solution to a differential equation.

For references on fluid-flow maps, see Appendix 2.

PROBLEMS

The five problems whose numbers are accompanied by an asterisk form a suggested minimum of experience in applying the subject matter of this chapter.

2.1 In a form similar to Eq. 2.9(3), set up the vector expression for the electric-field intensity in the region surrounding equal point charges of the same polarity. Do not attempt to simplify the expression algebraically, but resolve it into components and find the axis of symmetry of the field.

2.2 Repeat Prob. 2.1 for unequal point charges of unlike polarities.

2.3 Four point charges of equal magnitude are located at the corners of a square. Two of the charges are positive and two are negative, with those of the same polarity at opposite corners. Compute the magnitude and direction of the force on each charge, finally presenting the results in a form independent of a coordinate system.

*2.4 Obtain the vector expression for the field intensity on the axis of a charged ring of radius a, carrying a uniform linear-charge density of λ coulombs per unit length. Use cylindrical coordinates with the axis of the ring on the z axis. Rearrange your results in terms of the total charge on the ring.

*2.5 Extend the results of Prob. 2.4 to the field of a circular disk carrying a uniform surface-charge density of σ coulombs per square meter. Rearrange your results in terms of the total charge of the disk.

*2.6 Find the field due to an infinite sheet of charge by extending the results of Prob. 2.5.

2.7 Integrate Eqs. 2.4(6) and (7) by a change of variable from L to α. To begin, observe that

$$z - L = R \cot \alpha$$

and by differentiating both sides, obtain

$$dL = \frac{R \, d\alpha}{\sin^2 \alpha}$$

*2.8 As outlined at the end of Sec. 2.4, obtain the field intensity on the extended axis of a uniformly charged line of finite length, where z is greater than a, and $R = 0$.

2.9 Sketch the fields associated with Eqs. 2.5(7) and (8). By inspection, choose a suitable coordinate system and write the equation of the direction lines.

2.10 Write the equation of the direction lines in the field of a uniformly charged line, infinitely long.

*2.11 Find the equation of the direction lines of the field of the hypothetical vector

$$\mathbf{A} = \frac{1}{x}\mathbf{i} + 2\mathbf{j}$$

and sketch the field.

2.12 A uniformly charged line extends from the origin to $z = -\infty$. Find the field intensity at any point $P\ (R,\theta,z)$.

2.13 Show that the equation of the direction lines in the field of a semi-infinite line, Prob. 2.12, is a family of parabolas. (It may be easier to solve the differential equation by a change of variable, $u^2 = R^2 + z^2$ to eliminate R and dR.)

2.14 In the field of equal and opposite line charges, infinitely long, the x component of the field intensity is zero along two hyperbolas through the line charges. Obtain the equation of the hyperbolas.

2.15 That family of curves everywhere perpendicular to a given family of curves is termed the orthogonal trajectories. In the field of equal and opposite line charges, infinitely long, show that the orthogonal trajectories of the direction lines are the family of circles whose equation is

$$\frac{R_1}{R_2} = \text{a constant}$$

2.16 When a conducting cylinder of unit radius is placed in a unit uniform field, the components of the field intensity outside the cylinder are given by the equations

$$E_R = (\cos \theta) \frac{1 + R^2}{R^2} \quad \text{and} \quad E_\theta = (\sin \theta) \frac{1 - R^2}{R^2}$$

Find the equation of the direction lines (see Fig. 6.19).

CHAPTER 3

POTENTIAL AND POTENTIAL GRADIENT

In the previous chapter, we found that the Coulomb's-law viewpoint of fields involved a number of mathematical difficulties. One of these arose from the necessity of resolving the vector quantities into components and summing the contributions separately. In general, this requires that three integrals be evaluated. In this chapter we shall use the energy relations of electrostatic fields to find another way of handling these problems. The energy relations provide a *scalar* concept known as *potential*, whose evaluation for a given configuration of charges involves a scalar rather than a vector summation. The vector field intensity can be obtained from the scalar potential by a process of differentiation, an operation called *finding the gradient*. A geometric interpretation of potential will aid us in mapping and visualizing fields.

3.1 Work, and the Line Integral of a Vector. Before relating the vector quantities of the electrostatic field to the scalar concept of energy, we need to examine briefly the details involved in computing the work done by a force. The forces of the electrostatic field belong to a restricted class of forces, and to emphasize their special nature, we begin with a more general type of force which is not found in electrostatic fields.

If **F** is a force and $d\mathbf{S}$ a differential displacement tangent to the path of motion, then the differential work done by the force is given by the scalar product

$$dW = \mathbf{F} \cdot d\mathbf{S} \tag{1}$$

The total work done by the force along a specified path between two points, a and b, is found by adding up the differential contributions (by means of an integral when it is mathematically feasible). This operation is symbolized by the notation

$$W = \int_a^b \mathbf{F} \cdot d\mathbf{S} \tag{2}$$

in which the lower limit is the starting point and the upper limit is the finishing point on the specified path, as in Fig. 3.1. In general, the work done by a force depends on the path, a statement which can be demonstrated by a simple example.

In the left part of the figure is a rough map of a force which is directed

64

along the x axis, and whose magnitude increases with the distance y from the x axis.   On this map, the length of the line segment represents the magnitude of the force.   The equation of this vector force is

$$\mathbf{F} = y\,\mathbf{i} \tag{3}$$

We shall compute the work done by this force between the points a and b located as shown in the figure, along two paths which present no mathematical difficulties.   The first path is parabolic; the second is the straight line ab connecting the two points.   Along any path, it is usually easiest

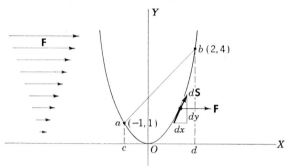

FIG. 3.1   Illustration for examples of evaluating the work done by a force vector along several paths.   The vector $\mathbf{F} = y\,\mathbf{i}$ is mapped at the left by letting the length of the line represent the magnitude.   Parabolic and straight-line paths are shown at the right.   Here the line integral and the work done depend on the path.

to evaluate the scalar product required by Eq. (1) by first resolving the line segment $d\mathbf{S}$ into its component vectors

$$d\mathbf{S} = dx\,\mathbf{i} + dy\,\mathbf{j} + dz\,\mathbf{k} \tag{4}$$

The scalar product is then

$$\mathbf{F} \cdot d\mathbf{S} = F_x\,dx + F_y\,dy + F_z\,dz \tag{5}$$

For the particular vector force of this example, described by Eq. (3)

$$\mathbf{F} \cdot d\mathbf{S} = y\,dx \tag{6}$$

Along the parabolic path shown in the figure, y and x are related by the equation

$$y = x^2 \tag{7}$$

Substituting Eq. (7) into Eq. (6),

$$\mathbf{F} \cdot d\mathbf{S} = x^2\,dx \tag{8}$$

The total work along the parabolic path is the line integral

$$W = \int_a^b x^2\,dx \tag{9}$$

Integrating and indicating the location of the points a and b by their x coordinates

$$W = \left[\frac{x^3}{3} \right]_{x=-1}^{x=2} \tag{10}$$

The numerical value of this is

$$W = 3 \text{ units of work} \tag{11}$$

Now along the straight line connecting the points a and b of the figure, x and y are related by

$$y = x + 2 \tag{12}$$

Substituting Eq. (12) into Eq. (6),

$$\mathbf{F} \cdot d\mathbf{S} = (x + 2)\, dx \tag{13}$$

Integrating Eq. (13),

$$W = \left[\frac{x^2}{2} + 2x \right]_{x=-1}^{x=2} \tag{14}$$

which has the numerical result

$$W = 7.5 \text{ units of work} \tag{15}$$

Presented purely as an illustration, these numerical values have no particular significance, as it is possible to choose paths which give any numerical result from zero to infinity in this example.   The zero result occurs on the path $acdb$.   Along ac and db, $\mathbf{F} \cdot d\mathbf{S} = 0$, because $\mathbf{F}$ and $d\mathbf{S}$ are perpendicular.   Along cd, $\mathbf{F} \cdot d\mathbf{S} = 0$ because $\mathbf{F}$ is zero.

Let us now take the path of integration as a closed path.   For example, we shall first permit the force to act along the straight line from a to b. On this part of the path it will do 7.5 units of work as found in Eq. (15). If the line of action then is continued along the parabola from b to a, the work done will be negative.   Physically, it will be necessary for an external force to do work along this part of the closed path.   We have computed the magnitude as 3 units in Eq. (11).   The net work done around this closed path is $7.5 - 3 = 4.5$ units of work.

When a line integral is evaluated around a closed path, the operation is signified by a circle through the integral sign.   For the closed path $abdca$ in Fig. 3.1, the line integral could be computed by breaking the path up into parts and computing the sum

$$\oint \mathbf{F} \cdot d\mathbf{S} = \int_a^b \mathbf{F} \cdot d\mathbf{S} + \int_b^d \mathbf{F} \cdot d\mathbf{S} + \int_d^c \mathbf{F} \cdot d\mathbf{S} + \int_c^a \mathbf{F} \cdot d\mathbf{S} \tag{16}$$

In general, the results of this operation will depend on the path and on the direction in which the path is traversed.

While we have illustrated the evaluation of a line integral in terms of a force vector, it may also be performed in the same way on any vector quantity.   The scalar result of the operation symbolized by $\int \mathbf{A} \cdot d\mathbf{S}$ is

known as the line integral of the vector **A**. We may *properly* call the
result by the name of *work* only in the special case of a force vector.   If
A is a velocity in meters per second, the line integral has the units of
square meters per second and should not be called work.   In general,
not only will the value of the line integral depend on the path, but the
units of the scalar result will depend on the units of the vector quantity.

The scalar quantity which results when the line integral of a vector is
evaluated around a closed path is known, in general, as *circulation*.   We
shall examine the rather inept terminology and the concept itself at some
length in Chap. 10.

3.2   Potential Difference as Related to Energy.   We here study the
potential energy of a simple charge configuration consisting of a positive
point charge Q and a vanishingly small positive test charge Q_t as illus-

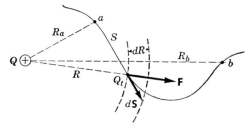

FIG. 3.2   For analysis of the potential energy of a vanishingly small test charge Q_t
in the field of a positive point charge Q.

trated in Fig. 3.2.   If the two point charges are allowed to move apart
under the influence of the forces of repulsion, the potential energy which
is released is equal to the work done by the forces of the field.   In order
to compute the work done by the forces of the field we shall have to
evaluate a line integral, as in the previous section.

Referring to the figure, the potential energy at point a is *greater* than
the potential energy at point b by the amount of work which can be done
by the forces of the field along the path from a to b.   In Eq. form:

$$\text{Potential energy at } a - \text{potential energy at } b = \int_a^b \mathbf{F} \cdot d\mathbf{S} \qquad (1)$$

To remove the dependence of this relationship on the magnitude of the
test charge, we may proceed in a manner identical to that which we used
in defining the field-intensity vector by the equation

$$\mathbf{E} = \frac{\mathbf{F}}{Q_t} \qquad (2)$$

Dividing both sides of Eq. (1) by Q_t and using Eq. (2),

$$\frac{\text{Potential energy at } a}{Q_t} - \frac{\text{potential energy at } b}{Q_t} = \int_a^b \mathbf{E} \cdot d\mathbf{S} \qquad (3)$$

$$\hat{r} \cdot d\vec{s} = dR$$

The *entire* left-hand side of this equation is known as the *potential difference* between points a and b, which we shall denote by the symbol $V_a - V_b$.

$$V_a - V_b = \int_a^b \mathbf{E} \cdot d\mathbf{S} \tag{4}$$

In the field of a point charge the field intensity was written from Coulomb's law as

$$\mathbf{E} = \frac{Q}{4\pi\epsilon_0 R^2}\,\mathbf{r} \tag{5}$$

To evaluate the right-hand side of Eq. (4) using Eq. (5), we first observe that $\mathbf{r} \cdot d\mathbf{S} = dR$; then

$$V_a - V_b = \int_{R_a}^{R_b} \frac{Q\,dR}{4\pi\epsilon_0 R^2} \tag{6}$$

Since R is the only variable, the limits of integration have been changed to the R coordinates of points a and b. Evaluating the integral, substituting limits, and writing the positive quantity first,

$$V_a - V_b = \frac{Q}{4\pi\epsilon_0}\left(\frac{1}{R_a} - \frac{1}{R_b}\right) \tag{7}$$

This equation means that, in the field of a point charge, the potential difference between two locations depends only on the relative distances of the two locations from the point charge. In the analysis of the previous section, it was necessary to associate the line integral with a particular path before the integral could be evaluated. Here that step is completely unnecessary. The line integral, and the potential difference between the two points, is completely independent of the path between the two points. *This condition is required by the conservation of energy in any electrostatic field.* (If two paths could be found between two points in the field, along which the work done by the forces of the field had two different values, then it would be possible to move a charge around a closed path and continuously extract energy from the field without making permanent changes in the position or the magnitude of the charges responsible for the forces on the moving charge.) Fields which meet this condition are frequently classified as *conservative fields.*

It is an easy step now to show that the potential difference between two points in any electrostatic field is independent of the path, and further that the potential difference involves a purely scalar summation in contrast to the vector summations which are required to evaluate the field intensity of a charge configuration.

Since the field intensity at every point in any electrostatic field is the vector summation of the fields due to all the equivalent point charges, we may write Eq. (4) for the general case as

$$(V_a - V_b) = \int_{R_a}^{R_b} (\mathbf{E}_1 + \mathbf{E}_2 + \mathbf{E}_3 + \cdots + \mathbf{E}_n) \cdot d\mathbf{S} \qquad (8)$$

Distributing the scalar product and indicating separate integrations,

$$(V_a - V_b) = \int_{R_{a1}}^{R_{b1}} \mathbf{E}_1 \cdot d\mathbf{S} + \int_{R_{a2}}^{R_{b2}} \mathbf{E}_2 \cdot d\mathbf{S} + \cdots + \int_{R_{an}}^{R_{bn}} \mathbf{E}_n \cdot d\mathbf{S} \qquad (9)$$

Using Eq. (5) and evaluating the scalar products with the help of

$$\mathbf{r} \cdot d\mathbf{S} = dR,$$

$$(V_a - V_b) = \int_{R_{a1}}^{R_{b1}} \frac{Q_1 \, dR_1}{4\pi\epsilon_0 R_1{}^2} + \int_{R_{a2}}^{R_{b2}} \frac{Q_2 \, dR_2}{4\pi\epsilon_0 R_2{}^2} + \cdots + \int_{R_{an}}^{R_{bn}} \frac{Q_n \, dR_n}{4\pi\epsilon_0 R_n{}^2} \qquad (10)$$

Integrating, substituting limits, and writing the positive terms first

$$V_a - V_b = \frac{Q_1}{4\pi\epsilon_0} \left(\frac{1}{R_{a1}} - \frac{1}{R_{b1}} \right) + \frac{Q_2}{4\pi\epsilon_0} \left(\frac{1}{R_{a2}} - \frac{1}{R_{b2}} \right)$$
$$+ \cdots + \frac{Q_n}{4\pi\epsilon_0} \left(\frac{1}{R_{an}} - \frac{1}{R_{bn}} \right) \qquad (11)$$

When this result is compared with Eq. (7), we see that it can be written as

$$(V_a - V_b) = (V_a - V_b)_1 + (V_a - V_b)_2 + \cdots + (V_a - V_b)_n \qquad (12)$$

This equation tells us that the potential difference between the two points is the *scalar* sum of all the contributions of the individual point charges and is independent of the path between the two points. Thus we have satisfied one of the requirements of the scalar concept which we set out to find. We shall later use Eq. (12) to show how to evaluate the potential without first knowing the field intensity.

Since the line integral of the field-intensity vector in the electrostatic field is independent of the path, the line integral around all closed paths is zero. Mathematically this statement is symbolized by the equation

$$\oint \mathbf{E} \cdot d\mathbf{S} = 0 \qquad (13)$$

There is nothing profound about this statement, or about the mathematics involved. What we are saying here is that the electrostatic field is a very simple kind of field and is very much like the gravitational field. We know already that if we want to move something around a closed path in the gravitational field, any energy dissipated in the process must come from forces other than gravitational forces. Similarly, any energy dissipated in moving a charge around a closed path, such as an electric circuit, must be supplied by forces other than electrostatic forces. From a circuit viewpoint, Eq. (13) is a special case of Kirchhoff's law of *electromotive force*. Solving a circuit problem requires the evaluation of the work done by *all* the forces, electrostatic and nonelectrostatic, around the closed path of the circuit.

We are going to use Eq. (13) many times in our study of electrostatics. While we shall not use it to make numerical calculations, the equation will form a shorthand notation symbolizing all the arguments of this section. Later on in our study, the facts expressed by this shorthand will be useful in helping us to select the one correct answer from a number of plausible, but wrong, answers.

Now a word about the units. As defined in Eq. (3), potential and potential difference have the units of energy per unit of charge—joules per coulomb, in the MKS system. The common name of this set of units is *volts*. In discussing the units of the field-intensity vector, which are those of force per unit of charge, it was suggested that the name newtons per coulomb would be the most appropriate one from the Coulomb's-law viewpoint of the previous chapter. However, since the potential difference is related to the field intensity by scalar multiplication by a distance, an alternative name for the units of the field-intensity vector is *volts per meter*. This is not only the name which is commonly applied to the units of **E**, but one which will seem even more appropriate when we have learned how to evaluate the field intensity from the potential.

3.3   The Potential at a Point, as Related to Energy.   A scalar field is a description of the magnitude of some scalar quantity which can be associated with every point in a region of interest.   In the first chapter, we used as an example the scalar field of temperature found in the various parts of a motor.   It is easy to forget the fact that temperatures are described in terms of a reference temperature which has been assigned the value of zero.   Frequently this is an arbitrary assignment made as a matter of convenience.

The potential energy of a charge configuration, as well as the potential associated with a point in an electric field, is a relative matter with respect to an arbitrarily assigned zero level.   There are two ways of discussing the choice of the reference level.   We shall examine both of them and then use the one which is the most convenient with respect to any problem under study.

We have examined the potential difference between two points in terms of the line integral along a path between the two points.   Let us now think of the final (ending) point on the path, called *b* in the previous section, as being a fixed *reference point* in space.   We shall call the initial (starting) point *a* a *movable point*, which means that it can be located anywhere.   In this way, we are describing the potential difference between the movable point and the reference point when we write the line integral

$$V_a - V_b = \int_a^b \mathbf{E} \cdot d\mathbf{S} \tag{1}$$

Now when the reference point is *arbitrarily* located at infinity, and we write the potential difference as the sum of the scalar contributions of each point charge responsible for the field, as in Eq. (11) of the previous section,

$$V_a - V_\infty = \frac{Q_1}{4\pi\epsilon_0}\left(\frac{1}{R_{a1}} - \frac{1}{\infty}\right) + \frac{Q_2}{4\pi\epsilon_0}\left(\frac{1}{R_{a2}} - \frac{1}{\infty}\right)$$
$$+ \cdots + \frac{Q_n}{4\pi\epsilon_0}\left(\frac{1}{R_{an}} - \frac{1}{\infty}\right) \quad (2)$$

The potential associated with the point at infinity V_∞ is conveniently, but also arbitrarily, assigned the value of zero. When this has been done, Eq. (1) becomes

$$V_a = \int_a^\infty \mathbf{E} \cdot d\mathbf{S} \quad (3)$$

This relationship with the field intensity is known as *the potential at a point* and is occasionally embellished with the term absolute. Since the point a can be any point in space, the subscript can be dropped from V.

Because the line integral is independent of the path, the integral of Eq. (3) is exact, and the potential at a point is a single-valued scalar function of position. This means that there is one and only one value of potential which can be thus associated with every point in an electrostatic field. This potential is numerically equal to the work done per unit of test charge by the forces of the field when a vanishingly small test charge is moved from the point to infinity, or to any other point in the field which has the same potential as a point at infinity.

There is an inconvenience which sometimes arises when Eq. (3) is used to relate the potential at a point to the field intensity. This arises when substitution of the infinite upper limit gives an infinite potential at all points in the field. Such a result occurs in the field of an infinitely long line charge, in the field of an infinite sheet of charge, and in some other charge configurations which, while not physically realizable, form important mathematical building blocks in the study of fields. The inconvenience is avoided by assigning the zero reference level of potential to some other point in the field instead of a point at infinity. The mathematical viewpoint of the choice of reference level is one of complete freedom to suit one's convenience. To discuss this from another aspect we now investigate the differential equation relating the potential at a point to the field intensity.

The work done by the forces of an electrostatic field is equal to the *decrease* in the potential energy of the charge configuration. We could also say that, in order to increase the potential energy of a charge configuration, work must be done by an external agency against the forces of the field. The external agency must provide a force equal and opposite to the forces of the field. Since the quantity dV represents the differential increase in potential, either viewpoint is expressed by the differential equation

$$dV = -\mathbf{E} \cdot d\mathbf{S} \tag{4}$$

When the right-hand side of this equation is an exact differential, both sides of Eq. (4) may be integrated, employing an arbitrary constant of integration C, to write

$$V = \int - \mathbf{E} \cdot d\mathbf{S} + C \tag{5}$$

Whatever value is assigned to this arbitrary constant cannot affect the potential difference between two points. If the potential is evaluated at two different points by means of Eq. (5), and the results are subtracted, the arbitrary constant disappears. We are free, then, not only to choose any convenient point as a reference point, but to assign to that reference point any arbitrary value of potential which we care to select. *When this reference point has been selected, and its potential assigned, there is one and only one value of potential at every point in an electrostatic field.*

As an illustration of both the occasional inconvenience of Eq. (3) and the freedom permitted by Eq. (5), let us examine the potential field of an infinitely long charged line. We found the field intensity in Sec. 2.4, Eq. (16), as

$$\mathbf{E} = \frac{\lambda}{2\pi\epsilon_0 R} \mathbf{r} \tag{6}$$

In this relation, cylindrical coordinates are implied. To evaluate Eq. (3), we resolve the differential displacement vector, $d\mathbf{S}$, of any direction, into its component vectors

$$d\mathbf{S} = dR\,\mathbf{r} + R\,d\theta\,\boldsymbol{\theta} + dz\,\mathbf{k} \tag{7}$$

The scalar product of the vectors of Eqs. (6) and (7) is

$$\mathbf{E} \cdot d\mathbf{S} = \frac{\lambda\,dR}{2\pi\epsilon_0 R} \tag{8}$$

Using this relation in Eq. (3) and integrating,

$$V = \frac{\lambda}{2\pi\epsilon_0} [\log_e R]_{R_a}^{\infty} \tag{9}$$

When the upper limit is substituted, we find that the potential is infinite at every point in the field.

When Eq. (5) is used, however, the difficulty is avoided.

$$V = \frac{-\lambda}{2\pi\epsilon_0} \log_e R + C \tag{10}$$

If we now assign an arbitrary value of potential, V_0, to a point whose distance from the line charge is R_0, we can solve Eq. (10) for C.

$$C = V_0 + \frac{\lambda}{2\pi\epsilon_0} \log_e R_0 \tag{11}$$

Usually we let $V_0 = 0$, and when this is done, substitution of Eq. (11) into Eq. (10) gives, after combining the logarithmic terms,

$$V = \frac{\lambda}{2\pi\epsilon_0} \log_e \frac{R_0}{R} \tag{12}$$

a result identical to that given by evaluating the potential difference between the point in question and the reference point, using the line integral along any path between the two points, as in the previous section. This relationship will be discussed and graphed in the following section.

3.4 Equipotential Surfaces and Potential Maps. In a conservative field, the locus of all points which have the same potential is a surface. The surface is perpendicular to the forces of the field at every point in space, and along all paths confined to such a surface, $\mathbf{E} \cdot d\mathbf{S} = 0$. These "surfaces of no work" are called *equipotential surfaces*. In a few simple charge configurations, it turns out that we can relate the potential at every point to the coordinates of the point by means of an equation. This equation is that of a family of surfaces, one of which passes through every point in the field. The traces of these surfaces on a plane are lines which are perpendicular to the direction lines on a map of a field.

When it is too difficult mathematically to find the equation which relates the potential at every point to the coordinates of the point, one may compute or measure the potential at a number of sampling points, and by connecting points which have the same potential, one may prepare a map of the field. Preparing a field map in this way is analogous to the preparation of a contour map by connecting points of known elevation with contour lines.

In the field of a point charge, the field intensity is

$$\mathbf{E} = \frac{Q}{4\pi\epsilon_0 R^2} \mathbf{r} \tag{1}$$

The potential at every point in the field may be found from Eq. (3) of Sec. 3.3, which was

$$V = \int_a^\infty \mathbf{E} \cdot d\mathbf{S} \tag{2}$$

Since $\mathbf{r} \cdot d\mathbf{S} = dR$, the evaluated integral gives the potential as

$$V = \frac{Q}{4\pi\epsilon_0 R} \tag{3}$$

The equation of the equipotential surfaces is obtained by setting the potential equal to a constant and solving for R.

$$R = \frac{Q}{4\pi\epsilon_0 V} \tag{4}$$

To each constant value of potential V, there is a corresponding value of R. The equipotential surfaces are concentric spheres, and at every point the spherical surfaces are perpendicular to the direction lines on our previous map of the field of a point charge.

   In mapping the field by the use of the direction lines, we draw only a few direction lines and place them symmetrically, to indicate that the field has spherical symmetry.   For similar reasons, though an equipotential surface passes through every point in the field, we shall have to be satisfied with drawing a few of the traces of these surfaces on our map. To assist us in getting the most information onto our field maps, we need to know how to select the spacing of the equipotential lines.   Our guidance comes from differentiating Eq. (3).

$$\frac{dV}{dR} = \frac{-Q}{4\pi\epsilon_0 R^2} \tag{5}$$

Comparing this with the field intensity given in Eq. (1), we see that

$$\mathbf{E} = -\frac{dV}{dR}\mathbf{r} \tag{6}$$

While this expression applies only to a point charge, it does tell us how to put the most information onto its field map.   If we choose *equal increments of potential*, the magnitude of the field intensity will be indicated by the relative spacing of the equipotential lines, just as the slope is indicated on a contour map by the relative spacing of the contour lines if they are drawn at equal increments of elevation.   The upper part of Fig. 3.3a is the potential map of a positive point charge using equal increments of potential.   While it would be easier to draw a map using equal increments of radius, the map would be less informative if this were done.   The lower part of the figure is a graph of the potential as a function of the radius.   From the viewpoint of contours of elevation, the graph is a cross section of a hill.

   In the previous section we discussed the potential field of an infinitely long charged line and wrote Eq. 3.3 (12)

$$V = \frac{\lambda}{2\pi\epsilon_0}\log_e\frac{R_0}{R} \tag{7}$$

for the potential difference between a point of radius R and a reference point of radius R_0, whose potential was arbitrarily taken as zero.   The

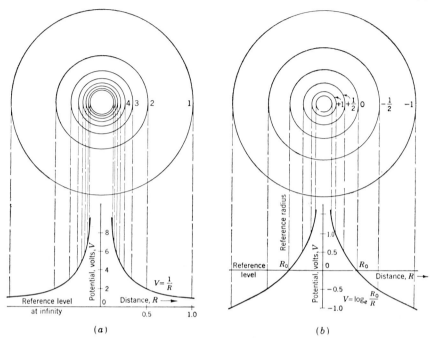

Fig. 3.3   The potential fields of (a) point charge and (b) line charge.   The traces of the equipotential surfaces on a plane are shown at the top.   A graph of the potential as a function of the radius is shown below.   For the point charge, the equipotential surfaces are concentric spheres, while for the line charge, the equipotential surfaces are concentric cylinders.   The surfaces which are drawn are selected at equal increments of potential.   Both the relative spacing of the circles and the slope of the potential curves below are indications of the magnitude of the field intensity.

equation of the equipotential surfaces is found by solving Eq. (7) for R

$$R = R_0 \exp \frac{-2\pi\epsilon_0 V}{\lambda} \tag{8}$$

To every value of potential V, there is a corresponding cylindrical equipotential surface whose radius is given by this equation.   Differentiating Eq. (7),

$$\frac{dV}{dR} = \frac{-\lambda}{2\pi\epsilon_0 R} \tag{9}$$

Comparing this with the expression for the field intensity,

$$\mathbf{E} = \frac{\lambda}{2\pi\epsilon_0 R} \mathbf{r} \tag{10}$$

we observe that

$$\mathbf{E} = -\frac{dV}{dR} \mathbf{r} \tag{11}$$

Here, too, the most information will be placed on the field map if equal increments of potential are used in Eq. (8) in selecting the few cylinders whose circular traces appear on the map of the field. The relative spacing of the equipotential lines is an indication of the magnitude of the field intensity. The potential map of this field has been drawn in the upper part of Fig. 3.3*b*, and a graph of the magnitude of the potential as a function of distance appears directly below the map. In both the fields, the arbitrariness of the selection of the zero potential level may be more clearly indicated by the graphs than by the map itself. The field inten-

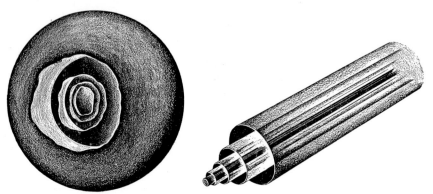

FIG. 3.4   Three-dimensional aspects of the concentric spheres of equipotential in the field of a point charge, and the concentric cylinders of equipotential in the field of a line charge. The two families of surfaces are selected at equal increments of potential.

sity is directly proportional to the slope of the potential curves at every point in the field. The numerical values assigned to the potentials correspond to a convenient magnitude of charge. For any other value of charge, the shape of the curves and the relative spacing of the equipotentials are the same, but different scales would be required.

In Fig. 3.4, a three-dimensional representation of equipotential surfaces is presented as a further aid to visualization.

There is an important exception to the first statement appearing in this section which says that the locus of all points which have the same potential is a surface. In a region in which there are no forces, one can move in any direction without doing work. The whole region, or volume, is then all at the same potential.

3.5   The Potential Field of a Two-wire Line.   In the previous section we prepared a map of the potential field of an infinitely long charged line. The field of two such lines which carry equal and opposite charge densities is important, and the field map is a very interesting one. Figure 3.5 has the same arrangement as Fig. 2.11*a*, which was used to find the equation of the direction lines of the same field configuration in the previous chapter. The potential due to each of the charged lines is given by Eq. (12) of Sec. 3.3, which was

$$V = \frac{\lambda}{2\pi\epsilon_0} \log_e \frac{R_0}{R} \tag{1}$$

Let the reference point, whose distance from the line is R_0, be taken equidistant from both lines. Any point in the yz plane is satisfactory, such as Q in Fig. 3.5. Adapting this expression to the notation of the figure, the potential due to the positively charged line is

$$V_+ = \frac{\lambda}{2\pi\epsilon_0} \log_e \frac{R_0}{R_2} \tag{2}$$

while that due to the negatively charged line is

$$V_- = \frac{-\lambda}{2\pi\epsilon_0} \log_e \frac{R_0}{R_1} \tag{3}$$

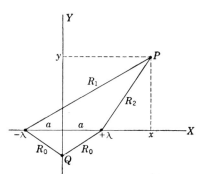

FIG. 3.5   For analysis of the potential field of two line charges, equal, opposite, and infinitely long.

The total potential is the sum of the potentials due to each line. When Eqs. (2) and (3) are added and the logarithmic terms are combined with due regard to the minus sign in Eq. (3),

$$V = \frac{\lambda}{2\pi\epsilon_0} \log_e \frac{R_1}{R_2} \tag{4}$$

In this expression, the zero potential level has been assigned to all points which are at equal distances from the two lines. This is the yz plane in the figure. The potential is also zero at infinite distances from the two lines.

The equation of the equipotential surfaces may be found by setting the potential, as given by Eq. (4), equal to a constant c, and solving for the ratio

$$\frac{R_1}{R_2} = \exp \frac{2\pi\epsilon_0 c}{\lambda} \tag{5}$$

The right-hand side of Eq. (5) is another constant, and to simplify the writing in what follows we shall call this constant k. Then

$$\frac{R_1}{R_2} = k \tag{6}$$

Substituting for R_1 and R_2 in terms of the coordinates of the point,

$$\frac{\sqrt{(x+a)^2 + y^2}}{\sqrt{(x-a)^2 + y^2}} = k \tag{7}$$

By cross-multiplying, collecting terms in x and y, and completing the square in x, this expression may be arranged in the form

$$\left(x - \frac{k^2 + 1}{k^2 - 1}\, a\right)^2 + y^2 = \left(\frac{2ka}{k^2 - 1}\right)^2 \tag{8}$$

This is the equation of a family of circles in the parameter k. The centers are on the x axis at

$$x = \frac{k^2 + 1}{k^2 - 1}\, a \tag{9}$$

and the radii are given by

$$\frac{2ka}{k^2 - 1} \tag{10}$$

From Eq. (5), we observe that the parameter k will be greater than 1 when the potentials are positive, and less than 1 when the potentials are negative. When the potential is zero, the radius of the circle is infinite, as is the location of its center. This condition describes the yz plane. The surfaces of equipotential are two families of cylinders. Each cylinder passes between one of the charged lines and the yz plane. Those cylinders containing the positively charged line are at positive potentials, while those containing the negatively charged line are at negative potentials.

Example. If a line carries a charge numerically equal to $2\pi\epsilon_0$ coulombs per meter of line length, the value of the parameter k in Eq. (5) is e^c, where c is potential in volts. For a line spacing of 2 meters, $a = 1$. The locations of the centers of the circles are given by Eq. (9), and in terms of the potential c, this becomes

$$x = \frac{e^{2c} + 1}{e^{2c} - 1}$$
$$= \coth c$$

The radii of the circles are given by (10)

$$R = \frac{2e^c}{e^{2c} - 1}$$
$$= \operatorname{csch} c$$

Letting the potential take on numerical values differing by 0.25 volt, the radii and centers of the equipotential circles are listed in the accompanying table.

	Potential, volts							
	0	0.25	0.5	0.75	1.0	1.25	1.50	1.75
Center......	∞	4.08	2.16	1.57	1.31	1.18	1.10	1.06
Radius......	∞	3.96	1.92	1.22	0.85	0.63	0.47	0.36

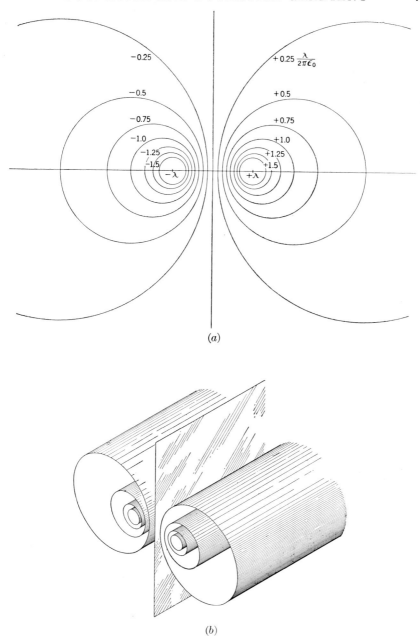

(a)

(b)

FIG. 3.6   Equipotential cylinders in the field of two line charges, equal, opposite, and infinitely long.   In a the circles are traces of the equipotential surfaces on a plane perpendicular to the line charges.   The three-dimensional character of the cylindrical equipotential surfaces is indicated by b.

The field map of Fig. 3.6 was prepared from this table, and the circles are labeled with the value of the potential in volts, for this particular magnitude of charge. For any other value of charge or line spacing, the appearance of the map would be the same, but different values of scale would be required. To remind us that the circles are the traces of cylinders on planes perpendicular to the two charged lines, the three-dimensional sketch, Fig. 3.6b, is included.

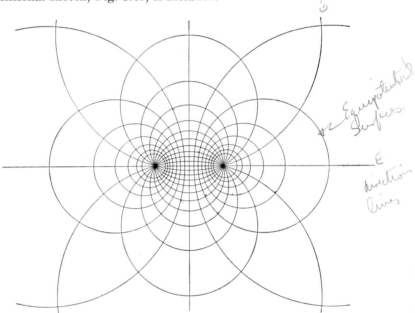

FIG. 3.7   Map of the field of two line charges, equal, opposite, and infinitely long. This map shows both the direction lines and the equipotentials, two families of circles which are orthogonal.

Figure 3.7 is a superposition of the equipotentials onto the previous map of the direction lines from the previous chapter. The two families of cylinders intersect at right angles, and because of this they are said to be *orthogonal*. This is not accidental, because we defined potential in such a way as to require that the equipotential surfaces be perpendicular to the field intensity. This is a very important field map, and we shall have many occasions to use it later in the book.

Figure 3.8 is a transmission-line circle diagram which the reader may have used to compute the magnitude and phase relations of the voltages and currents on a lossless transmission line at high frequencies. This diagram is one-half of the field map of Fig. 3.7. The dashed circles correspond to the direction lines, while the solid circles are equipotentials at a spacing other than that given by equal increments of potential.

The choice of equipotential circles and the labeling of the direction lines is a matter of convenience, determined by the use of the chart. This particular form of the chart was prepared by Dr. A. E. Harrison for use in microwave studies.

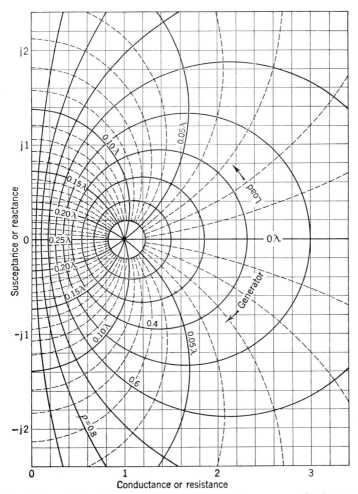

FIG. 3.8   A transmission-line circle diagram. This diagram can be interpreted as one-half of the field map of two line charges. The labels λ on the direction lines here refer to wave length and not to the analogous line charge.

3.6   A Defining Equation for Potential in Terms of an Integral Formulation.

In the preceding sections of this chapter, we have related the concepts of potential difference and potential to the field-intensity vector in terms of potential energy. Though explored only briefly here, these energy considerations are of the utmost importance. In the mathematical sense, however, the methods we have used to compute the potentials are inadequate, since they do not meet all our requirements. We set out to find a scalar concept which could be evaluated by adding up the contributions of each point charge as scalars, and which would yield the field intensity by differentiation. If we are able to compute the potential only from the relations

$$dV = -\mathbf{E} \cdot d\mathbf{S} \tag{1}$$

and

$$V_a = \int_a^\infty \mathbf{E} \cdot d\mathbf{S} \tag{2}$$

we have to know the field intensity before we can begin.

How else, then, can potential be defined? Let us build the definition by considering a number of point charges and write the potential at a point in space as the scalar sum of the contributions of each point charge as we have done before.

$$V = \frac{1}{4\pi\epsilon_0} \left(\frac{Q_1}{R_1} + \frac{Q_2}{R_2} + \frac{Q_3}{R_3} + \cdots + \frac{Q_n}{R_n} \right) \tag{3}$$

Here, the various values of R are the distances from each of the point charges Q to the point at which the potential is being evaluated. Equation (3) is an ample definition of the potential and tells us how to compute it without knowing the field-intensity vector. It is customary and more useful, however, to prepare an integral formulation of Eq. (3). For a continuous distribution of charge with a volume density ρ, we may write Eq. (3) with each of the point charges replaced by its equivalent in the volume-charge distribution, $\rho\, dv$, and indicate the summation by an integral

$$V = \int \frac{\rho\, dv}{4\pi\epsilon_0 R} \tag{4}$$

If we are also required to include charges distributed over a surface and charges distributed along a line, we may treat these, too, as equivalent point charges and write

Implies this when necessary

$$V = \int \frac{\rho\, dv}{4\pi\epsilon_0 R} + \int \frac{\sigma\, dA}{4\pi\epsilon_0 R} + \int \frac{\lambda\, dL}{4\pi\epsilon_0 R} \tag{5}$$

This form is cumbersome to write, so it is customary to use Eq. (4) as an alternative defining equation for potential, and to consider that it implies the longer form of Eq. (5) when necessary. This integral formulation for the potential is similar to the integral formulation for the field-intensity vector presented in Sec. 2.12; however, it is frequently easier to evaluate. *To evaluate Eq. (4), we are instructed to find each equivalent point charge, compute its contribution to the total potential, and find the sum of the resulting scalar quantities.* An example of this type of calculation appears in the following section.

Before passing to the example, however, it is well to point out that the integral formulation of the potential leads to computations which are very similar to those which arise in other fields.   Examples of other concepts which are best defined in terms of an integral are first moments, centroids, and the moments of inertia of plane areas.

3.7   The Potential Field of a Uniformly Charged Line of Finite Length. In the previous section the integral formulation of the potential concept was obtained, so that we could evaluate the potential without going through the steps of finding the field-intensity vector first.   As an

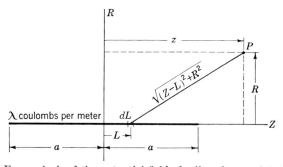

FIG. 3.9   For analysis of the potential field of a line charge of finite length.

example of the application of this method, we shall find the potential due to a uniformly charged line of finite length.

The integral formulation in its shorthand form

$$V = \int \frac{\rho \, dv}{4\pi\epsilon_0 R} \tag{1}$$

implies the longer form

$$V = \int \frac{\lambda \, dL}{4\pi\epsilon_0 R} + \int \frac{\sigma \, dA}{4\pi\epsilon_0 R} + \int \frac{\rho \, dv}{4\pi\epsilon_0 R} \tag{2}$$

instructing us to find the individual scalar contributions to the potential due to each and every equivalent point charge and to add them all up. In the problem at hand only the first of the integrals of Eq. (2) is needed. Referring to Fig. 3.9, the equivalent point charge, $\lambda \, dL$, makes a differential contribution to the potential at the point P in the amount

$$dV = \frac{\lambda \, dL}{4\pi\epsilon_0 \sqrt{(z-L)^2 + R^2}} \tag{3}$$

The variable is L, taken in the same sense as is z, and the limits of integration are from $-a$ to $+a$.   It is easy to find this integral in a table of integrals if the variable is changed by letting $u = z - L$.   The results are

$$V = \left[\frac{-\lambda}{4\pi\epsilon_0} \log_e \{(z-L) + \sqrt{(z-L)^2 + R^2}\} \right]_{L=+a}^{L=-a} \tag{4}$$

When the limits are substituted, the expression for the potential at any point P in terms of its coordinates is

$$V = \frac{\lambda}{4\pi\epsilon_0} \log_e \frac{z + a + \sqrt{(z + a)^2 + R^2}}{z - a + \sqrt{(z - a)^2 + R^2}} \tag{5}$$

With respect to our illustration, or example, of how we can evaluate the potential by means of the integral formulation—that's all there is, there isn't any more. It is not difficult, in general, to set up the differential contributions of each point charge when we know where the charges are and how big they are. IF we can evaluate the integral, as we have done here, the problem is solved. But even so, Eq. (5) is not easily visualized, and we shall have to prepare a map of the field to help us understand what the equation means. This takes more time than did the solution to the main problem.

To map the field, we can obtain the equation of the equipotential surfaces. To do this we replace V in Eq. (5) with the constant C, take the antilogarithm, and after transposing write

$$\frac{z + a + \sqrt{(z + a)^2 + R^2}}{z - a + \sqrt{(z - a)^2 + R^2}} = \exp \frac{4\pi\epsilon_0 C}{\lambda} \tag{6}$$

To simplify the writing, we may denote the entire right-hand side of Eq. (6) by the constant k. After this, we cross-multiply, collect the radicals, and square. We do this twice, as in the algebraic details of problems in analytic geometry. One of the forms into which the results can be placed is

$$\frac{(k - 1)^2}{(k + 1)^2}\left(\frac{z}{a}\right)^2 + \frac{(k - 1)^2}{4k}\left(\frac{R}{a}\right)^2 = 1 \tag{7}$$

This is the equation of a family of ellipses with

$$\text{Semimajor axis} = \frac{(k + 1)}{(k - 1)} a \tag{8}$$

$$\text{Semiminor axis} = \frac{2\sqrt{k}}{(k - 1)} a \tag{9}$$

$$\text{Eccentricity} = \frac{(k - 1)}{(k + 1)} \tag{10}$$

and foci at

$$z = \pm a \tag{11}$$

The ellipses are the traces of the ellipsoidal equipotential surfaces on all the planes $\theta = $ a constant. In the limit, as the parameter k (and the potential) becomes infinitely large, the innermost ellipsoid coincides with the line of charge. At infinite distances from the line of charge, the potential becomes zero, the parameter k becomes unity, and the ellipsoids become spheres.   To a very distant observer, the charge configuration is indistinguishable from a point charge, as was pointed out when we found the equation of the direction lines in Sec. 2.8.   The direction lines are hyperbolas and are perpendicular to the equipotentials.

The traces of the ellipsoidal surfaces on the planes θ = a constant are shown in Fig. 3.10a.   To prepare this field map, the value of λ in Eq. (6) was taken as equal numerically to $4\pi\epsilon_0$, and the half length of the line a was taken as unity.   Numerical values of the major and minor

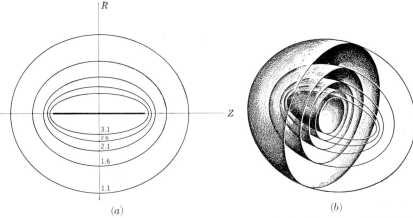

(a)   (b)

FIG. 3.10   In the field of a uniformly charged line of finite length, the equipotentials are confocal ellipsoids with foci at the ends of the charged line.   Their traces on a plane are shown in a, and their three-dimensional character is indicated in b.

axes were computed from Eqs. (8) and (9) for increments in potential of 0.1 volt in tabular form.   From this table, *equal increments of potential* were selected in such a way as to provide the best fit with a set of templates of ellipses such as are found in large drafting offices.   It is, of course, possible to draw the ellipses a little more accurately by laying out individual points on each ellipse.   This is done by utilizing the property that each point on such a curve satisfies the relationship

$$R_1 + R_2 = \text{a constant} \tag{12}$$

and connecting these points with a French curve.   In the figure the numerical value of the potential in volts accompanies each curve.

The purpose of the three-dimensional illustration in Fig. 3.10b is to emphasize the fact that the equipotentials are surfaces and not plane curves.   In studying both figures, it is important to observe the relative spacing of the equipotential surfaces and to recognize that this is an indication of the magnitude and direction of the field-intensity vector. In the next section, we shall pursue this matter in detail.

3.8 Potential Gradient. Now that we have examined some potential functions, let us turn our attention to the problem of finding the field intensity when the potential is known. In discussing the relationships between the potential and the field intensity, we pointed out that the locus of points of constant potential are surfaces which are perpendicular to the field-intensity vector at every point. When we have an equation which relates the potential at every point to the coordinates of the point, that equation represents a family of surfaces. Therefore we can find the direction of the vector we seek by finding the normal (or perpendicular) direction to the equipotential surface which passes through each point. Now that we have stated the direction of the field-intensity vector, we shall find its magnitude by examining the differential equation which relates the potential to the field intensity. This relation was discussed in Sec. 3.6, Eq. (1), which is

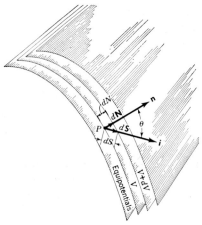

$$dV = -\mathbf{E} \cdot d\mathbf{S} \qquad (1)$$

In this equation the displacement vector, $d\mathbf{S}$, can have any direction whatsoever. Refer now to Fig. 3.11. In order to find the scalar relationship between dV and $\mathbf{E}$, we shall have to restrict the direction of $d\mathbf{S}$ and choose that particular $d\mathbf{S}$ which lies parallel to $-\mathbf{E}$. We shall denote

FIG. 3.11 For analysis of the gradient vector $(dV/dN)\mathbf{n}$.

this particular $d\mathbf{S}$ by $d\mathbf{N}$ to indicate that it is normal to the equipotential surfaces. In this case we can write Eq. (1) as

$$dV = -E\, dN \qquad (2)$$

and

$$\frac{dV}{dN} = -E \qquad (3)$$

We can make a vector equation out of Eq. (3) by using the unit vector $\mathbf{n}$, along $d\mathbf{N}$, in the direction of increasing potential V.

$$\frac{dV}{dN}\, \mathbf{n} = -\mathbf{E} \qquad (4)$$

The vector quantity on the left is known as the *gradient* of the scalar quantity V. In the electrostatic field, the gradient is the negative of the electric field intensity. More generally, the mathematician focuses his attention on the differentiation operations which are involved. Since a derivative measures a rate of *increase*, and the field intensity is in the direction of the maximum rate of *decrease* of potential, the two are opposite in sign.

The gradient vector can be resolved into its components, and these components provide an important description of the gradient vector from another viewpoint. In Fig. 3.11, let **i** be a unit vector in any direction. The component of the gradient vector in this direction is given by its scalar product with **i**

$$\text{Component of } \frac{dV}{dN} \mathbf{n} \text{ along } \mathbf{i} = \frac{dV}{dN} \mathbf{n} \cdot \mathbf{i} \tag{5}$$

The scalar product of the two unit vectors is the cosine of the angle between them. This is the angle θ in the figure, and also the angle between $d\mathbf{N}$ and $d\mathbf{S}$. Therefore

$$\mathbf{n} \cdot \mathbf{i} = \cos \theta = \frac{dN}{dS} \tag{6}$$

$$\text{Component of } \frac{dV}{dN} \mathbf{n} \text{ along } \mathbf{i} = \frac{dV}{dN} \frac{dN}{dS} = \frac{dV}{dS} \tag{7}$$

The gradient vector of a scalar function is that vector whose component in any direction is the derivative of the function in that direction. This statement means that the x component of the gradient is the derivative of the potential in the x direction (holding y and z constant). Since the field intensity is oppositely directed, we may write the equation

$$E_x = - \frac{\partial V}{\partial x} \tag{8}$$

In the following section, we shall examine this in more detail.

Before concluding our general examination of the gradient vector we ought to show that it satisfies the condition, *imposed by the conservation of energy*, that its line integral be independent of the path. This is evident by an extension of the relations of Eqs. (5), (6), and (7). The scalar product

$$\frac{dV}{dN} \mathbf{n} \cdot (d\mathbf{S})$$

may be written in the form

$$\frac{dV}{dN} (\mathbf{n} \cdot d\mathbf{S})$$

But $\mathbf{n} \cdot d\mathbf{S}$ is the component dN of $d\mathbf{S}$ along the normal $\mathbf{n}$. Then

$$\frac{dV}{dN} \mathbf{n} \cdot (d\mathbf{S}) = dV \tag{9}$$

The line integral of the left-hand side of this equation, between the points a and b, is equal to the integral of the exact differential on the right between the limits a and b

$$\int_a^b \frac{dV}{dN} \mathbf{n} \cdot d\mathbf{S} = \int_a^b dV$$
$$= (V_b - V_a) \tag{10}$$

and is therefore independent of the path between the points a and b.

Most of what we have said about the gradient vector is completely independent of any system of coordinates, and this is one of the most important ideas underlying the concept. Since we do not want to confuse the gradient vector itself with the formulas for finding its components in a particular system of coordinates, we leave those details to a separate discussion and retain as the defining equation for the gradient of the scalar function V

$$\text{Gradient of } V = \frac{dV}{dN} \mathbf{n} \tag{11}$$

3.9   The Components of the Gradient Vector in Specific Coordinate Systems. We defined the gradient vector of a scalar potential function as dV/dN $\mathbf{n}$. When it is necessary to evaluate this vector, it is easier to find it in terms of its components than in terms of the defining equation. In the previous section we found that the components in a given direction are the derivatives of the scalar function in that direction. Expressing this fact in an equation,

$$\frac{dV}{dN} \mathbf{n} = \frac{dV}{dS_1} \mathbf{i}_1 + \frac{dV}{dS_2} \mathbf{i}_2 + \frac{dV}{dS_3} \mathbf{i}_3 \tag{1}$$

In this equation the unit vectors $\mathbf{i}_1$, $\mathbf{i}_2$, and $\mathbf{i}_3$ represent any set of mutually perpendicular unit vectors which form a right-hand system, and the differential displacements dS_1, dS_2, dS_3 lie in the corresponding directions. The scalar function V is expressed as a function of the measure numbers or coordinates of a point, u_1, u_2, and u_3. That is,

$$V = f(u_1, u_2, u_3)$$

To evaluate the derivatives of V in a given direction, we hold the other two coordinates constant, which is another way of saying that we perform partial differentiation. The first derivative in Eq. (1) is

$$\frac{dV}{dS_1} = \left(\frac{\partial V}{\partial u_1}\right) \frac{du_1}{dS_1} \tag{3}$$

Repeating for the other two derivatives, Eq. (1) becomes

$$\frac{dV}{dN} \mathbf{n} = \left(\frac{\partial V}{\partial u_1}\right)\left(\frac{du_1}{dS_1}\right) \mathbf{i}_1 + \left(\frac{\partial V}{\partial u_2}\right)\left(\frac{du_2}{dS_2}\right) \mathbf{i}_2 + \left(\frac{\partial V}{\partial u_3}\right)\left(\frac{du_3}{dS_3}\right) \mathbf{i}_3 \tag{4}$$

The quantities du/dS are easily evaluated in terms of the more familiar reciprocal quantity dS/du. For example, in cylindrical and spherical coordinates, an increase in the coordinate θ in the amount $d\theta$ displaces a point a distance of

$$dS = R \, d\theta \tag{5}$$

and

$$\frac{dS}{d\theta} = R \tag{6}$$

In spherical coordinates, Fig. 1.10, an increase in the coordinate ϕ, in the amount $d\phi$, displaces a point a distance of

$$dS = R \sin \theta \, d\phi \tag{7}$$

and

$$\frac{dS}{d\phi} = R \sin \theta \tag{8}$$

In all other cases we have studied, the displacement of the point is the same as the change of the coordinate and

$$\frac{dS}{du} = 1 \qquad \text{(unity)} \tag{9}$$

It is customary to denote the relations of Eqs. (6), (8), and (9) in general terms

$$\frac{dS_1}{du_1} = h_1 \qquad \frac{dS_2}{du_2} = h_2 \qquad \frac{dS_3}{du_3} = h_3 \tag{10}$$

and to use this notation in the gradient expression.

$$\frac{dV}{dN} \mathbf{n} = \frac{1}{h_1} \frac{\partial V}{\partial u_1} \mathbf{i}_1 + \frac{1}{h_2} \frac{\partial V}{\partial u_2} \mathbf{i}_2 + \frac{1}{h_3} \frac{\partial V}{\partial u_3} \mathbf{i}_3 \tag{11}$$

Equation (11) is exactly equivalent to Eq. (4), and the only reason for using the form of Eq. (11) is that the operations of Eq. (10) are simple enough to be remembered instead of evaluating them anew in each problem. The quantities h_i are called *metric coefficients*.

Expressions such as Eqs. (11) and (1), in which the unit vectors, the coordinates, and the displacements can represent any right-hand orthogonal system, are said to be written in *general orthogonal coordinates*. This is an imposing term, but for our present purpose this means that it is a relation which holds equally well for cartesian, cylindrical, and spherical coordinates. It has a very worth-while immediate advantage which justifies the trouble required to become familiar with the notation. This advantage is illustrated by the ease with which we moved from Eq. (3) to Eq. (4). We can make an analysis of a single component, and then simply change the subscripts when we come to the other com-

ponents.   This is called "permuting the subscripts," and this is to be done in cyclic order: 1, 2, 3.   Further, it is now a simple step to convert Eq. (11), which expresses the gradient in terms of its components, to the particular coordinate system we happen to be using at the moment.
    In cartesian coordinates,

$$
\left.
\begin{array}{llll}
u_1 = x & u_2 = y & u_3 = z \\
i_1 = i & i_2 = j & i_3 = k \\
h_1 = 1 & h_2 = 1 & h_3 = 1 & \text{(unity)}
\end{array}
\right\}
\tag{12}
$$

These relations reduce the general case of Eq. (1) to the specific case for cartesian coordinates only

$$
\frac{dV}{dN}\, n = \frac{\partial V}{\partial x}\, i + \frac{\partial V}{\partial y}\, j + \frac{\partial V}{\partial z}\, k
\tag{13}
$$

In spherical coordinates,

$$
\left.
\begin{array}{lll}
u_1 = R & u_2 = \theta & u_3 = \phi \\
i_1 = r & i_2 = \theta & i_3 = \phi \\
h_1 = 1 & h_2 = R & h_3 = R \sin \theta
\end{array}
\right\}
\tag{14}
$$

These relations reduce the general relation of Eq. (1) to the specific case for spherical coordinates

$$
\frac{dV}{dN}\, n = \frac{\partial V}{\partial R}\, r + \frac{1}{R}\frac{\partial V}{\partial \theta}\, \theta + \frac{1}{R \sin \theta}\frac{\partial V}{\partial \phi}\, \phi
\tag{15}
$$

    Throughout our discussion of the gradient we have used a symbolism which clearly denotes the fact that it is a vector and gives its magnitude and direction.

$$
\text{Gradient of } V = \frac{dV}{dN}\, n
$$

Unfortunately this is not the usual symbol for the gradient, and we reluctantly follow custom to adopt a shorthand notation which does not so clearly indicate that the gradient is a vector.   The customary notation for the gradient of the scalar function V is ∇V, where the symbol ∇, del or nabla, indicates that there is a vector operation to be performed on V.   This notation arises from the following viewpoint.   In cartesian coordinates,

$$
\nabla V = \frac{dV}{dN}\, n = \frac{\partial V}{\partial x}\, i + \frac{\partial V}{\partial y}\, j + \frac{\partial V}{\partial z}\, k
$$

may be thought of as a vector operator ∇, operating on the scalar V to produce a vector, ∇V

$$
\nabla V = \nabla \text{ operating on } V
$$

where ∇ is something like a vector

$$\nabla = \mathbf{i}\,\frac{\partial}{\partial x} + \mathbf{j}\,\frac{\partial}{\partial y} + \mathbf{k}\,\frac{\partial}{\partial z} \tag{16}$$

This viewpoint is extended to other operations on vectors which involve partial differentiation of their components. In cartesian coordinates alone, the symbolism of Eq. (16) may be carried over to other operations on vectors without special and careful interpretation. As a word of caution, one must not extrapolate the relation of Eq. (16) into spherical coordinates because

$$\nabla V \underset{\text{(is not equal to)}}{\neq} \frac{\partial V}{\partial R}\,\mathbf{r} + \frac{\partial V}{\partial \theta}\,\mathbf{\theta} + \frac{\partial V}{\partial \phi}\,\mathbf{\phi}$$

The correct expression is Eq. (15).

James Clerk Maxwell gave a word recipe for the gradient operation which some students find appealing. Adapted to our notation, his recipe is: "The symbol of operation of ∇V may be interpreted as directing us to measure, in each of three rectangular directions, the rate of increase of V, and then, considering the quantities thus found as vectors, to compound them into one. This is what we are directed to do by expression (4). But we may also consider it as directing us first to find out in what direction V increases fastest, and then to lay off in that direction a vector representing this rate of increase." The alternative recipe of the last sentence is symbolized in our notation by our defining equation of the previous section.

$$\nabla V = \frac{dV}{dN}\,\mathbf{n}$$

3.10   A Comparison of Gradient and Slope, and a Physical Model.
In common everyday usage, the terms gradient, grade, and slope are practically synonymous. Further, most of us think of the derivative of a function in terms of the slope of a plane curve. It is well, therefore, to compare the concepts of gradient and slope. To do this, let us make a further examination of the field of a uniformly charged line, infinitely long. In Fig. 3.12, parts a and c are repeated from Fig. 3.3b. The equipotential surfaces are concentric cylinders, infinitely long, and are shown in part b. The circles in part a are the traces of the equipotential cylinders on planes perpendicular to the axis. As was previously pointed out, when circles and cylinders with equal increments of potential are selected, the magnitude of the field intensity is indicated by the relative spacing. The field intensity is directed away from the line, as shown by the three direction lines in part a. The magnitude of the potential is plotted as a graph in part c of the figure. The magnitude of the field intensity is proportional to the slope of this curve. Now if we revolve

the potential curve about its axis of symmetry, we obtain the *potential hill* illustrated in part *d* of the figure as an oblique view. On the potential hill, elevation represents the magnitude of the potential and the slope of the surface of the hill represents the magnitude of the gradient and the field intensity.

What we have done here is to interpret the family of circles in part *a* of the figure as the plan view, or contour map, of the hill. The curve of

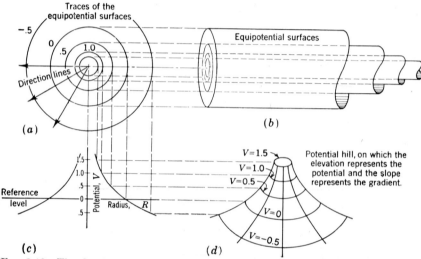

Fig. 3.12   The development of a potential hill (shown in part *d*) in the field of a positive line charge, infinitely long. The traces of the equipotential surfaces (part *a*) are interpreted as the plan view of the hill, as on a contour map. The potential curve (part *c*) is interpreted as a cross section of the potential hill. As a reminder, the true nature of the equipotential surfaces is shown in part *b* as concentric cylinders.

part *c* is interpreted as the elevation view of a cross section of the hill. Though this physical model is neat and physically satisfying, there is a possibility of confusion. The contour lines on the hill are the intersections of the surface of the hill and equally spaced horizontal planes. The horizontal planes are not the equipotential surfaces, and the field intensity is not downward as would be suggested by associating this model with the gravitational field of the earth. With the *understanding* that plan views of potential hills represent the traces of equipotential surfaces on a plane, and that cross sections represent a graph of the potential, we may successfully use the physical model as an aid to visualization.

Figure 3.13 is a photograph of a potential hill representing a part of the field of a positively charged line. A thin sheet of rubber has been stretched over the rim of a cylinder and held there with a clamping ring. The center of the rubber sheet is held above the rim of the outer cylinder by a vertical rod which is hidden by the rubber sheet. The shadows which are suggestive of contour lines were achieved by a lighting technique. The illumination comes from a distant projector containing a slide which is a ruling of fine lines, closely spaced. The slides used in this photograph, and in several others in the book, are scraps of rulings obtained from a photoengraving shop.

Fig. 3.13   A rubber-sheet model of the potential field of a positive line charge infinitely long.   A rubber sheet has been stretched over a cylindrical ring and clamped in position like the head of a drum.   At the center, a vertical rod holds a small part of the sheet in an elevated position.   The unsupported part of the sheet conforms to the potential distribution sketched in Fig. 3.12d.   A distant slide projector, in which the slide is a finely ruled grating, illuminates the foreground.   The edges of the light and dark areas are at the same elevation, and form the contours on the potential hill.   Elevation represents potential.

In this illustration, observe that the contour lines are sharp and close together near the inner cylinder, where the slope of the sheet is greatest, tapering off to widely spaced and quite diffuse shadows where the sheet is almost horizontal.   Viewed from directly above, the shadows would be circular, within an accuracy determined by the time and care used in setting up the model physically.   A rubber sheet gives a correct picture of the potential distribution for small displacements only.   These photographs are not intended to be scaled and are presented more as a qualitative picture than as a quantitative analysis.

In Fig. 3.14, the rubber sheet has been deformed by two rods, one pushing the sheet upward and the other downward.   The resulting displacement suggests the field of two line charges, of equal and opposite polarity. Near the rods, the displacement of the sheet is determined primarily by the rods and not the finite, outer boundaries. Near these outer boundaries, the field does not even approximately represent that of two isolated line charges. Here, the position of the sheet is determined by the frame, and not by the rods.

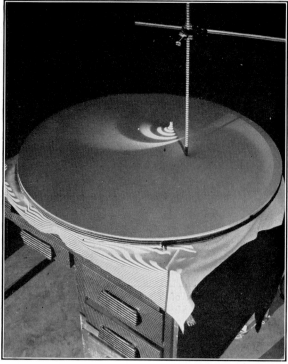

Fig. 3.14 A rubber-sheet model of the potential field of equal and opposite line charges, infinitely long. The contours are cast by a distant slide projector. Compare the circular equipotentials with Fig. 3.6.

Figure 3.15 is a photograph of a more elaborate rubber-sheet model, useful in studying the potential distributions in a cylindrical vacuum tube. The six outer peaks of the hill represent the control grid wires, and the central peak represents the cathode. Cathode and grid are maintained at the same potential level with respect to the outer cylinder which represents the plate. For ease in modeling, the rubber sheet has been pushed upward rather than downward. Either upward or downward, the slope of the hill still represents the gradient of the field, and the contour lines still represent equal increments in potential. Compare this figure with the fluid-flow map of Fig. 2.18, which shows the direction lines in a similar study in which the grid wires are much closer to the plate.

The graphic development of Fig. 3.12 can be repeated, with profit, for the field of a point charge. However, a rubber sheet, or any elastic membrane such as the head of a drum, can only be used to represent two-dimensional fields. When the boundaries of the sheet are concentric cylinders, the sheet conforms ideally to a part of the field of a line charge, and not to that of a point charge. For a further discussion of this matter, see Appendix 1.

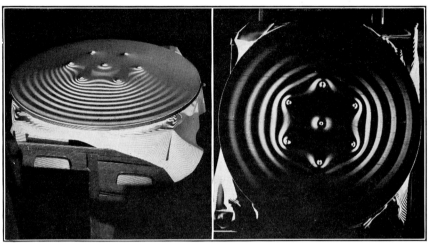

FIG. 3.15.   Rubber-sheet model of the potential distribution in a triode vacuum tube without space charge. At the left is an oblique view with contour lighting in the foreground, and normal background lighting to show the shape of the sheet. The photograph at the right was taken from directly above the sheet. Two slide projectors were used to light both sides of the sheet simultaneously. The wavy edges of the contour lines are imperfections in the ruled gratings. The variable width of the contours on the two halves of the model is due to the fact that the lenses in the two projectors were not of equal quality.

3.11   The Field of a Dipole.   In addition to the point charge, line charge, and sheet of charge, there is another very important and fundamental building block in the study of fields. The charge configuration formed by equal and opposite point charges is called a *dipole*. When the distance between the charges is very much smaller than all other distances under consideration, the formulas for the field quantities are relatively simple. This charge configuration occurs physically in molecules, and the mathematical expressions keep turning up in radiation problems. A good example of the type of field which is readily analyzed by first finding its potential, this illustration should help to tie together the essentials of this chapter.

To begin the analysis, we shall use a mixture of cartesian and spherical coordinates as shown in Fig. 3.16a. At the end we shall express the results in a form independent of the coordinate systems. At the point N, the potential due to the negative charge is

$$V_- = \frac{-Q}{4\pi\epsilon_0 R} \tag{1}$$

while the potential due to the positive charge is

$$V_+ = \frac{Q}{4\pi\epsilon_0 R_1} \tag{2}$$

The total potential at N due to both charges is the sum of Eqs. (1) and

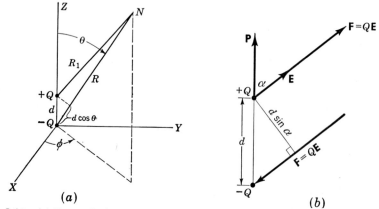

(a)   **(b)**

FIG. 3.16   (a) For analysis of the potential field of a dipole; (b) analysis of the torque on a dipole in a uniform field.

(2) which, after collecting the common terms, can be written as

$$V = \frac{Q}{4\pi\epsilon_0}\left(\frac{1}{R_1} - \frac{1}{R}\right) \tag{3}$$

$$= \frac{Q}{4\pi\epsilon_0}\left(\frac{R - R_1}{RR_1}\right) \tag{4}$$

We see from the figure that to a first approximation

$$R_1 = R - d\cos\theta \tag{5}$$

Substituting Eq. (5) into Eq. (4)

$$V = \frac{Q}{4\pi\epsilon_0}\frac{R - R + d\cos\theta}{R^2 - Rd\cos\theta} \tag{6}$$

The terms in R cancel in the numerator, and in the limit as R becomes essentially infinite in comparison with d, the denominator becomes R^2.

$$V = \frac{Qd\cos\theta}{4\pi\epsilon_0 R^2} \tag{7}$$

Now we define the vector quantity called the dipole moment **P**, which has the magnitude Qd, and is directed along a line from the negative toward the positive charge. The numerator of Eq. (7) is the component of the dipole moment **P**, along the unit vector **r**, drawn from the dipole to the point N, at which the field is evaluated. Hence Eq. (7) may be written as

$$V = \frac{\mathbf{P} \cdot \mathbf{r}}{4\pi\epsilon_0 R^2} \tag{8}$$

The form of Eq. (8) is somewhat neater than that of Eq. (6), and in addition it is easier to handle problems involving dipoles in terms of the vector quantity **P**. An example follows.

When placed in a uniform electric field, each of the charges forming the dipole experiences a force which has the magnitude $Q\mathbf{E}$, but since the two forces are oppositely directed, the net force is zero. These forces form a couple whose torque is the vector

$$\mathbf{T} = \mathbf{P} \times \mathbf{E} \tag{9}$$

and in the limit, as the separation of the charges becomes vanishingly small, this relation is true whether **E** is uniform or not. Equation (9) follows from the definition of the vector product, because the moment arm of the couple is $d \sin \alpha$, as can be seen from Fig. 3.16b.

To obtain the field intensity from the potential as given in Eq. (7), we evaluate the gradient in spherical coordinates, according to Eq. 3.9 (15), which is

$$\boldsymbol{\nabla} V = \frac{\partial V}{\partial R} \mathbf{r} + \frac{1}{R} \frac{\partial V}{\partial \theta} \boldsymbol{\theta} + \frac{1}{R \sin \theta} \frac{\partial V}{\partial \phi} \boldsymbol{\phi} \tag{10}$$

Performing the required partial differentiations on Eq. (7) and writing P for Qd,

$$\frac{\partial V}{\partial R} = \frac{-2P \cos \theta}{4\pi\epsilon_0 R^3}$$

$$\frac{\partial V}{\partial \theta} = \frac{-P \sin \theta}{4\pi\epsilon_0 R^2}$$

$$\frac{\partial V}{\partial \phi} = 0$$

Substituting into Eq. (10) and setting $\mathbf{E} = -\boldsymbol{\nabla} V$ gives

$$\mathbf{E} = \frac{P}{4\pi\epsilon_0 R^3} (2 \cos \theta \, \mathbf{r} + \sin \theta \, \boldsymbol{\theta}) \tag{11}$$

It is interesting to observe that for a dipole the potential and the field intensity drop off with increasing distance at the next higher rate than for a point charge. The field intensity follows the inverse cube, and the potential the inverse-square relationship with distance, in addition to the terms which account for the orientation of the dipole.

To map the field, we observe that the equation of the equipotential surfaces is given by setting Eq. (7) equal to a constant C_1, and solving for R as a function of θ and C_1.

$$R^2 = \frac{\cos \theta}{C_1} \tag{12}$$

The direction lines are the orthogonal trajectories of Eq. (12). Obtaining their equation amounts to solving the differential equation which relates the direction lines to the components of the field-intensity vector. In spherical coordinates, this relation is given by Eq. 2.10 (12), which is

$$\frac{dR}{E_R} = \frac{R\,d\theta}{E_\theta} = \frac{R \sin \theta\, d\phi}{E_\phi}$$

Taking the first equality, substituting the components of **E** from Eq. (11), and rearranging to separate the variables, we have

$$\frac{dR}{R} = 2 \cot \theta\, d\theta \tag{13}$$

Integrating both sides,

$$\log_e R = 2 \log_e \sin \theta + \log_e C_2 \tag{14}$$

The antilogarithmic form

$$R = C_2 \sin^2 \theta \tag{15}$$

is the equation of the direction lines, orthogonal to the equipotentials. The map is beautifully symmetrical and can be plotted quickly when polar coordinate paper is used. The drawing of the map from Eqs. (12) and (15) is left as a problem.

3.12 A Summary and a Criticism. In introducing the concept of potential, we sought a scalar function which could be obtained by summing the contributions of scalars instead of vectors, and we found that this was available from energy considerations in conservative fields. We introduced the concept of gradient as a method of finding the field-intensity vector by differentiating the scalar potential function. This now gives us two methods of approach to the problem of describing a field resulting from a given charge distribution.

Method I

1. We add up *vectorially* the individual contributions of all the little point charges to the field intensity. This is symbolized by the integral formulation

$$\mathbf{E} = \int \frac{\rho\, dv}{4\pi\epsilon_0 R^2} \mathbf{r}$$

2. We obtain the potential from a line integral of the field-intensity vector. This is symbolized by either

$$V_a = \int_a^\infty \mathbf{E} \cdot d\mathbf{S} \qquad \text{or} \qquad V = \int -\mathbf{E} \cdot d\mathbf{S} + C$$

and we use the latter formula if the first does not approach a finite limit.
Method II

1. We add up algebraically the individual contributions of every one of the equivalent point charges to the scalar potential. This is symbolized by the integral formulation

$$V = \int \frac{\rho \, dv}{4\pi\epsilon_0 R}$$

2. We obtain the field-intensity vector from the potential by evaluating the gradient. This is symbolized by

$$\mathbf{E} = -\boldsymbol{\nabla}V = -\frac{dV}{dN}\mathbf{n}$$

in which we are instructed to compute the partial derivatives with respect to distance according to

$$\boldsymbol{\nabla}V = \frac{1}{h_1}\frac{\partial V}{\partial u_1}\mathbf{i}_1 + \frac{1}{h_2}\frac{\partial V}{\partial u_2}\mathbf{i}_2 + \frac{1}{h_3}\frac{\partial V}{\partial u_3}\mathbf{i}_3$$

Both steps are easier in principle in Method II than in Method I. The integration of the first step has to be performed only once in Method II, while it may require three integrations in Method I. There is no argument about step 2; differentiation is easier to sell than integration.

On the other hand, the integral formulation of the potential is something practically impossible to evaluate except in fields with simple geometries and a high degree of symmetry. In addition to this, we still have no way of proceeding unless we know where the charges are located. Not only do we have to find a way to find the charges when the potentials are established in a practical way, but we think it almost imperative to find other ways of evaluating the potential besides this integral formulation. The surprising thing about it is that we shall be able to keep the differentiation process symbolized by $\mathbf{E} = -\boldsymbol{\nabla}V$ and still find other ways of evaluating V without knowing $\mathbf{E}$ first.

Before we can do this, however, it is necessary that we find another scalar method of evaluating the field intensity and gain some experience in handling $\mathbf{E}$ and V as teammates in describing and mapping fields.

REFERENCES

1. Sears, F. W.: "Principles of Physics," Vol. II, "Electricity and Magnetism," Chaps. 2 and 3, Addison-Wesley Press, Inc., Cambridge, Mass., 1947. Recommended collateral reading.
2. Skilling, H. H.: "Fundamentals of Electric Waves," 2d ed., John Wiley & Sons, Inc., New York, 1948. Chapter II contains a comparison of gradient and slope, with two examples worked out in detail. Reference to p. 34 will afford the reader a comparison of two methods of obtaining the gradient formulas.

3. Maxwell, James Clerk: "Treatise on Electricity," 3d ed., Vol. I, Oxford University Press, New York, 1904.   The quotation in Sec. 3.9 was taken from p. 16 of this reference.

4. Phillips, H. B.: "Vector Analysis," John Wiley & Sons, Inc., New York, 1933 Recommended for a further discussion of line integrals and potential, found on pp. 49–54, and for a thorough treatment of general coordinates, pp. 80–90.

PROBLEMS

The nine problems whose numbers are accompanied by an asterisk form a suggested minimum of experience in applying the subject matter of this chapter.

3.1   Evaluate the line integral of the force vector $\mathbf{F} = y\,\mathbf{i} - x\,\mathbf{j}$ around the closed path defined by the circle $x^2 + y^2 = 1$.

*3.2   Transform Prob. 3.1 to plane polar coordinates and repeat.

3.3   For the force vector of Sec. 3.1, which was $\mathbf{F} = y\,\mathbf{i}$, show that the line integral around any closed path is numerically equal to the area enclosed by the path.   Check this against the closed path *aboa* in Fig. 3.1.

3.4   Discuss the acceleration of an electron which finds itself initially at rest in the field of

(*a*) A sheet of charge, infinite in extent

(*b*) A line charge, infinitely long

(*c*) A point charge

In which of these can you obtain an expression for its velocity as a function of its position?

*3.5   For the fields of force of the previous problem, obtain the velocity of an electron as a function of its position, from energy considerations.   Take the initial velocity as zero, and ignore relativistic corrections.

*3.6   Using the differential equation 3.3(4), $dV = -\mathbf{E} \cdot d\mathbf{S}$, find the equation of the equipotential surfaces in the field between parallel, oppositely charged, infinite sheets.   Choose a suitable coordinate system, and discuss your choice of reference potential level.   Map the field.

3.7   Reviewing the discussion of Sec. 2.10, point out the geometrical significance of the differential equation

$$\mathbf{F} \cdot d\mathbf{S} = 0$$

(*a*) For a conservative field

(*b*) For the field $\mathbf{F} = y\,\mathbf{i} - x\,\mathbf{j}$

*3.8   Find the potential on the axis of a charged ring by using the integral formulation, $V = \int \dfrac{\lambda\,dL}{4\pi\epsilon_0 R}$.   Then find the field intensity from the gradient. Check against Prob. 2.4.

*3.9   Find the potential on the axis of a uniformly charged circular disk by using the integral formulation $V = \int \dfrac{\sigma\,dA}{4\pi\epsilon_0 R}$.   Then find the field intensity from the gradient.   Check against Prob. 2.5.

*3.10   In the field of unequal, unlike point charges, Q and $-kQ$, find the equation of the surface which is at zero potential.   For uniformity of results in the classroom, take Q at the origin of cartesian coordinates, place $-kQ$ at $a, 0, 0$, and let k be a number smaller than one. Describe the shape of the zero potential surface and its location with respect to the origin.

3.11 Discuss the results of Prob. 3.10 in the limit as k approaches one and the charges become equal in magnitude.

3.12 The potential due to a particular dipole and a point charge is

$$V = \frac{z}{(x^2 + y^2 + z^2)^{3/2}} + \frac{1}{(x^2 + y^2 + z^2)^{1/2}}$$

Find the field intensity by evaluating the gradient.

*3.13 When a conducting cylinder of unit radius is placed in a uniform field, the potential outside the cylinder is given, in cylindrical coordinates, by

$$V = -R \cos \theta + \frac{\cos \theta}{R}$$

Find the field intensity by evaluating the gradient. What is its direction at the surface of the cylinder?

*3.14 When an uncharged conducting sphere of unit radius is placed in a uniform field, the potential outside the sphere is given in spherical coordinates by

$$V = -R \cos \theta + \frac{\cos \theta}{R^2}$$

Find the field intensity by evaluating the gradient. Compare the results with the field of a dipole as given in Sec. 3.11.

3.15 Write the vector equation for a uniform field-intensity vector along the x axis, and transform to cylindrical coordinates. Is there such a term in the answer to Prob. 3.13?

3.16 Using the methods of Sec. 3.11, find the potential at remote distances from two closely spaced parallel line charges, carrying equal and opposite, uniform, linear-charge densities. Find the field intensity and compare the results with those of Prob. 3.13.

3.17 Using polar-coordinate paper, prepare a reasonably accurate map of the field of a dipole. In one quadrant plot only the equipotentials, in a second only the direction lines, superimposing both in a third. Choose equal increments of potential.

*3.18 On the extended axis of a finite line charge, find the potential from the integral formulation, and the field intensity by evaluating the gradient. Check against your results for Prob. 2.8.

*3.19 Find the equation of the equipotential surfaces when the potentials are given as those of (a) Prob. 3.13 and (b) Prob. 3.14. In each case, show that a part of the zero potential surface is a plane and that the potential is zero on the surface of the conductors.

CHAPTER 4

THE ELECTRIC FIELD IN
CURRENT-CARRYING CONDUCTORS

Some of the most important methods of analyzing electrostatic fields can be said to have been borrowed from the study of the flow of steady currents in conductors. We shall therefore digress from the study of the fields of fixed charges to explore briefly the relationships between the potential distribution and the field intensity in conductors which are carrying steady currents. Here the problems are greatly simplified because we need not concern ourselves ordinarily with the utterly feeble currents in the surrounding regions. For most readers, both the viewpoint and the language of these problems are familiar, and physical visualization of the results is not difficult.

4.1 Current Density. The rate at which charge passes through a surface is the *current* through that surface.

$$I = \frac{dQ}{dt} \tag{1}$$

The units of the current I are coulombs per second, called *amperes*. Current is a scalar quantity, but not the kind of scalar quantity that can be described uniquely at a *point* in space, because a finite value of current implies a surface of finite area. To describe the field in a conductor completely, we must use those scalar and vector quantities which can be defined in terms of their values at a point in space.

In describing the motion of charge it is convenient to use the charge density ρ, a scalar point function, and the average drift velocity $\mathbf{U}$, a vector point function. We will first consider the case in which only one kind of charge is present in the region of interest. In Fig. 4.1, charges move from left to right through a region of space. A differential element of volume dv is shown with its right-hand face normal to the direction of the velocity vector $\mathbf{U}$. At this point the magnitude of the velocity is

$$U = \frac{dL}{dt} \tag{2}$$

The charges which will cross the right face of the boxlike element of volume in the next time interval dt are those now within the box. This

102

represents a total quantity of charge $\rho\,dv$. The differential current through dA is written, from Eq. (1),

[handwritten: $dQ = \rho\,dv$]

$$dI = \frac{\rho\,dv}{dt} \tag{3}$$

We now write dv as the product of its area and its length

$$dv = dA\,dL \tag{4}$$

and substitute this form into Eq. (3). After transposing dA, Eq. (3) becomes

[handwritten: $U = \dfrac{dL}{dt}$]

$$\frac{dI}{dA} = \rho\,\frac{dL}{dt} = \rho U \tag{5}$$

Two of the scalars in Eq. (5) are the magnitudes of vector quantities.

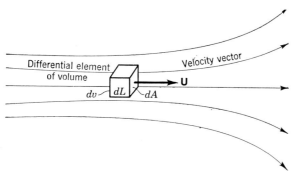

FIG. 4.1 Distributed charges of charge density ρ move through a region with a velocity **U**. In the analysis of this section, we obtain the current density as a vector given by $\mathbf{J} = \rho\mathbf{U}$.

[handwritten: Current Density]

[handwritten: Define $J = \dfrac{dI}{dA}$]

The right-hand side is $\rho\mathbf{U}$. The left-hand side is the *current density*, denoted by the symbol **J**, and

$$\boxed{\mathbf{J} = \rho\mathbf{U}} \qquad \text{[handwritten: } or\ \ \frac{dI}{dA} = \rho\frac{dL}{dt}\text{]} \tag{6}$$

The current-density concept is more useful than that of current, for our purposes, because it can be described by a vector point function. In contrast, a description of a current also requires a description of the surface through which the charge passes.

The units of current density are amperes per square meter in the MKS system. Engineers like to use mixed units of current density such as amperes per million circular mils. A current density of 500 amperes per million circular mils is a conservative practice in copper wires, and this corresponds roughly to 10^6 amperes per square meter.

When several kinds of charge carriers are present, the total current density is the vector sum of the contributions from each kind. If we denote the various kinds of charge carriers and their average drift velocities by numbered subscripts, we may write

$$\mathbf{J} = \rho_1\mathbf{U}_1 + \rho_2\mathbf{U}_2 + \rho_3\mathbf{U}_3 + \cdots + \rho_n\mathbf{U}_n \tag{7}$$

or, in summation form,

$$\mathbf{J} = \sum_n \rho_n\mathbf{U}_n \tag{8}$$

More than two kinds of charge carriers can be present in a chemical solution or in a gas containing several kinds of ions of both polarities and various volume densities. Each contributes to the total current density according to its own charge density and drift velocity. It is conceivable that the various velocity vectors would not be parallel under some conditions, but even then, $\mathbf{J}$ is uniquely defined at every point by the vector sum indicated in Eq. (7). The current-density vector is more useful than the terms involving the individual velocity vectors because of its relative simplicity.

More frequently, charges of opposite polarity move in opposite directions though not with the same magnitudes of velocity. When this occurs, the quantities $\rho_+\mathbf{U}_+$ and $\rho_-\mathbf{U}_-$ have the same direction. *This is the direction of the velocity vector of those charges which have been taken arbitrarily as positive*.

Any of the scalar or vector quantities in Eq. (7) may be zero. In vacuum tubes only the electrons contribute appreciable charge densities. In metals the density of the positive charges is equal to that of the negative charges but the drift velocity of the positive charges is zero. The *net* charge density

$$\rho = \rho_1 + \rho_2 + \rho_3 + \cdots + \rho_n \tag{9}$$

may have any value including zero without affecting the description of the current density.

It is also well to point out that there are occasions when the current density vector can be constant in magnitude and direction throughout a region of space in which the velocities vary widely. This requires that the charge density be inversely proportional to the velocity, like the flow of traffic on a busy highway. The cars are widely spaced between towns where they can travel fast, and all jammed together within the towns where the progress must be slow. In Chap. 8 we shall study an example of this.

4.2 Current, Surface Integrals, and Flux. In the previous section the differential element of area was placed normal to the velocity vector, in order to derive most easily the relationship between the velocity vectors and the current density vector. Any other orientation of the differential element of area produces a smaller current. The general relationship between the differential current and the position of the differential element of area is easily seen by resolving the current-density vector into two perpendicular components, one of which lies along the normal $\mathbf{n}$ to the element of area dA. The other component will lie tangent to the surface and therefore cannot contribute to the current through the surface. The component of $\mathbf{J}$ along the normal gives a differential current

$$dI = \mathbf{J} \cdot \mathbf{n}\, dA \tag{1}$$

The total current through a finite surface will be found by summing the scalar contributions of each element of area. Indicating this summation as an integration over the surface, we write

$$I = \int \mathbf{J} \cdot \mathbf{n}\, dA \tag{2}$$

The importance of the vector-analysis shorthand indicated by Eq. (2) is great enough to warrant a little further discussion.   We are instructed to multiply each element of area by the normal component of the vector quantity $\mathbf{J}$ at that point, and then to integrate over the entire surface. This operation can be visualized by a study of Fig. 4.2 in which the curved surface is bounded by the curves C_1, C_2, and C_3. However, following these instructions would be extremely difficult for a surface like that of the figure, because even the simpler problem of determining the area of such a surface

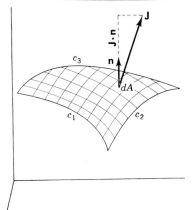

FIG. 4.2 The current through a curved surface is found by adding the differential currents through all the differential areas, by means of the surface integral $I = \int \mathbf{J} \cdot \mathbf{n}\, dA$.

$$A = \int dA \tag{3}$$

is an involved procedure.   Fortunately there are easier cases.   When we can choose a surface which is everywhere perpendicular to the current-density vector, and it happens that $\mathbf{J} \cdot \mathbf{n}$ is a constant J at all points in this surface, the problem of finding the current from the current density is reduced to

$$\int \mathbf{J} \cdot \mathbf{n}\, dA = J \int dA$$

and we have simply

$$I = JA$$

These last two equations have been left unnumbered to remind us that they are a simple special case of the general problem.

The integral of the normal component of *any* vector over a surface is called the *flux* of the vector. When the surface is an open surface, we speak of the flux *through* the surface, and since there is an ambiguity as to the direction of the normal vector on an open surface, we have to specify in some way the sense of that normal vector when speaking of the flux (or current) through it. When the surface is a closed surface, we speak of the flux *over* the surface. In this latter case the outward normal is taken as the positive direction and the result of the integration is unique. We are not used to calling a current a flux, and there is no par-

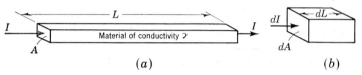

(a)   (b)

Fig. 4.3 Notation used in discussing Ohm's law (a) for a long straight conductor and (b) for a conductor of differential dimensions.

ticular reason for doing so, except to introduce the concept of surface integrals and fluxes in familiar terms.

There are two classes of vector quantities. We met examples of the first in the previous two chapters. These are defined with respect to a line of direction, and as a class they are called *intensities*. Forces and the electric-field vector **E** are intensities. Vectors which can be said to be defined with respect to an area are classed as *flux densities*. The current-density vector is a flux density.

4.3 Ohm's Law. In our present study, it is mathematically convenient to divide all materials into two separate classes, conductors and nonconductors. Conductors are those materials in which charges are free to move with a continuous drift velocity in response to the forces of an electric field. Of the conductors, the simplest are those which obey Ohm's law, an experimental observation in which the relations are

$$R = \frac{V}{I} \tag{1}$$

and the dependence of the resistance R of a conductor on its dimensions,

$$R = \frac{L}{\gamma A} \tag{2}$$

where L = length
A = cross-sectional area
γ = conductivity of the material, mhos per meter
(See Fig. 4.3a.) When the two expressions for the resistance are equated, the result is

$$\frac{V}{I} = \frac{L}{\gamma A} \tag{3}$$

Rearranging,

$$\frac{I}{A} = \frac{\gamma V}{L} \tag{4}$$

Writing this expression for a conductor of differential dimensions, as in Fig. 4.3b, we obtain

$$J = \frac{dI}{dA} = \gamma \frac{dV}{dL} = \gamma E \tag{5}$$

$$\frac{dV}{dL} = E$$

Ohm's law in the form of Eq. (1) is obtained experimentally under conditions in which two surfaces on the conductor are maintained as equipotential surfaces and the total current I through each of these surfaces is the same. Equation (2) is valid for homogeneous conductors when the current has the same direction as the length L and the cross-sectional area A coincides with the equipotential surfaces. Under these conditions, the left-hand side of Eq. (5) is the current density and the right-hand side is the negative gradient of the potential, both of which are vector quantities. We then write Eq. (5) as

$$\mathbf{J} = \gamma \mathbf{E} \tag{6}$$

This is Ohm's law in terms of scalar and vector quantities which can be defined at a point in space. It changes the viewpoint of Ohm's law from one which sees only the over-all dimensions of the conductor, and the potential difference maintained between its "ends," to one which is useful in describing what happens inside the conductor. It is useful in accounting for irregularities in the conductor such as those which arise when holes are drilled in a bus bar to support it as a structure. In examples which follow, we shall use it to investigate the current and potential distributions in conductors which do not have the same cross-sectional area throughout their lengths, and in cases in which the length of the conductor cannot be specified exactly. In such cases, we cannot apply Eq. (2) because we do not know just what L or A is.

4.4 The Field Configuration in a Hollow Conducting Cylinder. Before continuing our examination of the general features of currents, we shall apply the vector formulation of Ohm's law and the scalar concept of current to the problem of finding field configurations in which there is a high degree of symmetry. As our example we shall consider a right circular cylinder of material of conductivity γ, with a concentric hole as shown in Fig. 4.4. We maintain the inner and outer cylindrical surfaces as equipotential surfaces by suitable connection to a source of electrical energy, with the inner surface at the higher potential level.

Though we do not yet know its magnitude, a current will flow from the inner to the outer surface and the direction lines of the current-density vector will be radial because of the symmetry of the problem. The same total current will flow through every surface which is a concentric cylinder of radius R, one of which is shown in the figure. The total current is related to the current density by

$$I = \int \mathbf{J} \cdot \mathbf{n} \, dA \tag{1}$$

Over each of these cylindrical surfaces, $\mathbf{J}$ and $\mathbf{n}$ are parallel and their scalar product is constant in magnitude. By our choice, then, we have

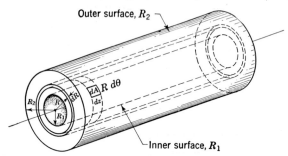

Outer surface, R_2

Inner surface, R_1

FIG. 4.4   A hollow cylindrical conductor in which the current flows from the inner cylindrical surface to the outer cylindrical surface.

simplified the evaluation of Eq. (1) to

$$I = JA \tag{2}$$

Now the area of each of these surfaces can be found from the product of the perimeter and the length of the cylinder, $2\pi RL$. Inserting this value into Eq. (2) and solving for J,

$$J = \frac{I}{2\pi RL} \tag{3}$$

We have pointed out that $\mathbf{J}$ is directed along a radial line at all points, and the vector form of Eq. (3) is thus

$$\mathbf{J} = \frac{I}{2\pi RL} \mathbf{r} \tag{4}$$

The field intensity $\mathbf{E}$ is related to $\mathbf{J}$ by Ohm's law.

$$\mathbf{J} = \gamma \mathbf{E} \tag{5}$$

Using Eq. (5) in Eq. (4) to find the field intensity,

$$\mathbf{E} = \frac{I}{2\pi \gamma RL} \mathbf{r} \tag{6}$$

Both the current density and the field intensity are inversely proportional to the R coordinate at every point. The magnitude of both is directly proportional to that of the total current, as yet undetermined. This will be directly proportional to the applied potential difference, but before finding that relationship, let us pause to compare our results with an earlier analysis.

Using Coulomb's law, we found that in the field of an infinitely long, uniformly charged line, the field intensity is, from Eq. 2.4 (16),

$$\mathbf{E} = \frac{\lambda}{2\pi\epsilon_0 R} \mathbf{r} \tag{7}$$

This result was obtained with rather great difficulty compared to the methods of this section. Comparing Eq. (7) with Eq. (6), we see that in the current-carrying case, the current per unit length, I/L corresponds to the charge per unit length λ; and with the conductivity γ replacing the permittivity ϵ_0, the field is the same as for a section of length L of an infinitely long charged line. This is an example of a general nature rather than a coincidence. The similarities of the two different types of fields is a direct consequence of the similarity of the geometries.

For the charged line, we have computed the potential relationships and mapped them in Sec. 3.4. Because the quantities are expressed in slightly different terms, and because our reference level of potential is also different, we shall repeat the analysis here. When this has been done, the reader should refer to the map of the potential field of the charged line to compare the reference levels.

For the potential relationships we may compute the potential difference between the two surfaces of radii R_1 and R_2 most easily from Eq. 3.2. (4)

$$V_{R_1} - V_{R_2} = \int_{R_1}^{R_2} \mathbf{E} \cdot d\mathbf{S} \tag{8}$$

Since $\mathbf{E}$ is along $\mathbf{r}$,

$$\mathbf{E} \cdot d\mathbf{S} = E \, dR \tag{9}$$

and using E as given in Eq. (6),

$$V_{R_1} - V_{R_2} = \int_{R_1}^{R_2} \frac{I}{2\pi\gamma L} \frac{dR}{R} \tag{10}$$

Integrating and substituting limits,

$$V_{R_1} - V_{R_2} = \frac{I}{2\pi\gamma L} \log_e \frac{R_2}{R_1} \tag{11}$$

Let us denote the potential difference on the left by the single symbol V_m, and solve for the ratio of the current to the potential difference, which is the conductance G. The results are

$$G = \frac{2\pi\gamma L}{\log_e (R_2/R_1)} \tag{12}$$

The resistance is, of course, the reciprocal of the conductance. We prefer to compute conductance rather than resistance because we shall find that expressions for capacitance and conductance in fields of like geometries are mathematically identical.   In addition to this we avoid piling up too many meanings for the same symbols.

To proceed, we can compound this problem, by adding layer after layer of materials with different conductivities in each layer.   Since the total current I is constant, the relation

$$\mathbf{J} = \frac{I}{2\pi RL}\,\mathbf{r}$$

holds in every layer.   But since the conductivity differs from layer to layer, the field intensities must be expressed in terms of $\mathbf{J}$ and the appropriate conductivity for each layer.   This in turn will affect the magnitude of the voltage drop, which is the line integral of $\mathbf{E} \cdot d\mathbf{S}$ in each layer.

We have learned to draw field maps in which the direction lines represent the $\mathbf{E}$ vector.   Since the direction lines show only the direction of the $\mathbf{E}$ vector, we have associated its magnitude with the relative spacing of the equipotentials.   Continuing to draw such field maps, we now associate the direction lines with the $\mathbf{J}$ vector because it is continuous at the boundary between materials.

Figure 4.5a and b show, in approximate fashion, a field map for a two-layer problem, in which the conductivity of the outer layer is considerably smaller than that of the inner layer.   In the first quadrant the equipotential surfaces are shown by their traces on a plane, and the relative values of the potential have been indicated on an arbitrary scale.   The $\mathbf{J}$ vector is shown in the third quadrant.   We notice that, while the relative spacing of the equipotentials is logarithmic in each layer, there is a sharp discontinuity in their spacing at the boundary between the two layers.   At this boundary, observe that the $\mathbf{J}$ vector is continuous but that there is a sharp discontinuity in the $\mathbf{E}$ vector as the conductivity changes from γ_1 to γ_2.

In the fourth quadrant, an attempt has been made to indicate the magnitude of the $\mathbf{E}$ vector by the width of the line segment, a procedure which highlights the discontinuity at the boundary.   In Fig. 4.5b the magnitude of the $\mathbf{E}$ vector is plotted vertically on a graph, as a function of the radius.   The area under the curve is proportional to the difference in potential between the extreme inner and outer boundaries.   Since the total current is a constant, the area under each of the two parts of the curves is proportional to the resistance of the layer, and inversely proportional to its conductance.   We verify this in our thinking by recalling that, from the over-all viewpoint, the two "resistors" are in series.   If the position of the two materials were reversed, practically all of the total potential difference would appear between the boundaries of the inner layer. In Fig. 4.5b, the magnitude of the **E** vector would decrease sharply at R_2.

From our observations of this figure, we have another interpretation of the utility of the current-density vector, **J**. Through its use, we can

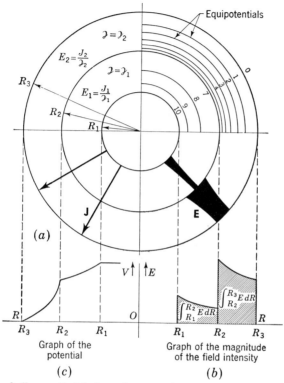

FIG. 4.5 Two hollow cylindrical conductors of different conductivities. In a the notation used in the analysis is illustrated in the second quadrant, the equipotential surfaces are shown in the first quadrant, the continuous current density is shown in the third quadrant, while the discontinuity in the magnitude of the field intensity is shown in the fourth quadrant by letting the width of the line segment represent the magnitude of the vector. In b, the magnitude of **E** is plotted as a function of the radius, while the potential is plotted in c.

say that we are using the conductivity concept to account for the discontinuity in the **E** vector at the boundary.

4.5 Currents in Toroidal Conductors. In this section we shall examine the evaluation of the surface integral of the current density vector in a case which requires more than the evaluation of the area of the surface. A *toroid* is a surface of revolution formed by a closed plane curve, of any shape, rotated about an axis in its plane. A perfectly formed doughnut is a toroid, which could have been cut out by rotating a circle about an axis in its plane. The circular symmetry is indicated in the axial view, Fig. 4-6a. Several types of cross section are shown at the right. To establish circular current flow, two cross sections are maintained as equipotential surfaces by a source of electrical energy. These planes are denoted as $\theta = 0$ and $\theta = \theta_m$ for convenience. It will also be convenient to speak of the potential of the plane $\theta = 0$ as V_m and let the reference potential level be that of the plane $\theta = \theta_m$.

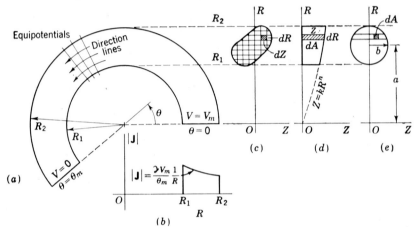

FIG. 4.6 Analysis of the current field in a conductor with circular symmetry and a uniform cross section of any shape. The curve of b shows the magnitude of the current density as a function of the radius, while the cross sections considered are shown in c, d, and e.

The symmetry of the problem suggests that since two planes in which $\theta = $ a constant are maintained as equipotentials, all such planes will remain as equipotentials. This condition will be met by a linear decrease of potential with the coordinate θ,

$$V = C_1\theta + C_2 \tag{1}$$

where C_1 and C_2 are constants. These constants can be evaluated from the boundary conditions established by the source of energy, $V = V_m$ when $\theta = 0$, and $V = 0$ when $\theta = \theta_m$. The results convert Eq. (1) to

$$V = \frac{V_m}{\theta_m}(\theta_m - \theta) \tag{2}$$

The field intensity can be found from the negative gradient of the potential

$$\mathbf{E} = -\nabla V \tag{3}$$

In cylindrical coordinates the gradient expression is

$$\nabla V = \frac{\partial V}{\partial R}\mathbf{r} + \frac{1}{R}\frac{\partial V}{\partial \theta}\boldsymbol{\theta} + \frac{\partial V}{\partial z}\mathbf{k} \tag{4}$$

Performing the indicated differentiation and substituting into Eq. (3),

$$\mathbf{E} = \frac{1}{R} \frac{V_m}{\theta_m} \mathbf{\theta} \tag{5}$$

Since $\mathbf{J} = \gamma \mathbf{E}$, we may write Eq. (5) in terms of the current density

$$\mathbf{J} = \frac{\gamma V_m}{R \theta_m} \mathbf{\theta} \tag{6}$$

The relative magnitude of this expression for the current density is shown graphically in part b of Fig. 4.6, plotted against R.

This field configuration which is suggested by the circular symmetry is also the only configuration which will fulfill the requirement that

$$\oint \mathbf{E} \cdot d\mathbf{S} = 0 \tag{7}$$

be satisfied everywhere within the conductor. A formal proof and discussion will be presented in Chap. 8. Fortunately the configuration suggested by the symmetry satisfies the requirements in two-dimensional problems.

In order to evaluate the conductance we shall need the total current

$$I = \int \mathbf{J} \cdot \mathbf{n} \, dA \tag{8}$$

and this result will depend on the shape of the cross section. However, $\mathbf{J}$ and $\mathbf{n}$ are parallel, so that $\mathbf{J} \cdot \mathbf{n} = J$, and we are faced only with the evaluation of

$$I = \int J \, dA \tag{9}$$

Substituting for J from Eq. (6),

$$I = \frac{\gamma V_m}{\theta_m} \int \frac{dA}{R} \tag{10}$$

The conductance is $G = I/V_m$ which, from Eq. (10), is

$$G = \frac{\gamma}{\theta_m} \int \frac{dA}{R} \tag{11}$$

The evaluation of the integral in Eq. (11) is similar in character to evaluating centroids and moments of inertia of an area with respect to an axis. The weighting function is R^{-1}, however, in contrast to the weighting functions R and R^2 in such problems.

A double integration will be required in the general case of part c in the figure,

$$\int \frac{dA}{R} = \iint \frac{dz \, dR}{R} \tag{12}$$

This will be easy to evaluate when the area is bounded by curves on which

z is a polynomial in powers of R. This includes rectangles, triangles, trapezoids, and parabolas as special cases.

A simple example is shown in part d of the figure in which $dA = z\,dR$ and the boundaries are $R = R_1$, $R = R_2$, $z = 0$, and

$$z = kR^n \tag{13}$$

For this case, Eq. (12) becomes

$$\int \frac{dA}{R} = \frac{k}{n}\,(R_2{}^n - R_1{}^n) \tag{14}$$

From Eq. (11), the conductance which results from this type of cross section is

$$G = \frac{\gamma k}{n\theta_m}\,(R_2{}^n - R_1{}^n) \tag{15}$$

The constant of proportionality k must have units which make our results dimensionally consistent. These units are given by Eq. (13).

For the circular cross section shown in part e of the figure,

$$z = \sqrt{b^2 - (R - a)^2} \tag{16}$$

Integrating Eq. (12) first with respect to z, between the limits

$$-\sqrt{b^2 - (R - a)^2} \quad \text{and} \quad +\sqrt{b^2 - (R - a)^2}$$

leaves for the second integration

$$\int \frac{dA}{R} = 2\int_{R=a-b}^{R=a+b} \frac{\sqrt{b^2 - (R - a)^2}}{R}\,dR \tag{17}$$

This integral can be put into the form of number 187 of B. O. Pierce's "Short Table of Integrals,"[1] a reduction formula whose integrals are found as numbers 161 and 182. After substitution of limits, the results simplify surprisingly to

$$\int \frac{dA}{R} = 2\pi\,(a - \sqrt{a^2 - b^2}) \tag{18}$$

For this case of circular cross section the conductance is

$$G = \frac{2\pi\gamma}{\theta_m}\,(a - \sqrt{a^2 - b^2}) \tag{19}$$

While the primary purpose of this section has been to illustrate the integration of the normal component of a vector over a surface, the results are useful for analyzing the requirements of certain types of bus structures.

4.6 Conditions at a Boundary Between Materials. In circuits, two resistors in parallel share the current according to their relative conduct-

---

[1] Ginn & Company, Boston, 1929.

ances.   Two resistors in series carry the same current and the potential differences across them are proportional to their resistances.   We shall investigate the comparable problems from the field viewpoint, and then examine the intriguing general case in which one cannot say that the configuration is either series or parallel.

In Fig. 4.7a, the direction of the current-density vector is tangent to a boundary between two conductors of different conductivities.   This would occur if a copper bus bar were strapped to an aluminum bus bar. The tangential components of the field intensities are the same in each

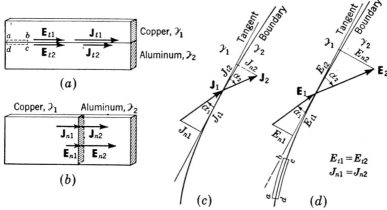

(a)

(b)

(c)   (d)

$E_{t1} = E_{t2}$
$J_{n1} = J_{n2}$

Fig. 4.7   Analysis of the conditions at a boundary between materials of different conductivities.   The results of the general case, c and d, are given also by the two special cases of series and parallel conductors as shown in a and b.   The normal components of the current density are continuous, and the tangential components of the field intensity are continuous at a boundary between materials.

material, but since the conductivities differ, the current densities do not have the same magnitude.   In Fig. 4.7b, the boundary between the two materials is perpendicular to the field vectors.   Since the current is the same on both sides of the boundary, the current density is the same in each material.   With the same current density, the field intensities differ. For the same current density, the voltage drop per unit length is greater in aluminum than in copper.

The general case is illustrated in Fig. 4.7c and d.   Since the current entering every part of the boundary is the same as that leaving it, we may write

$$\mathbf{J}_1 \cdot \mathbf{n} \, dA = \mathbf{J}_2 \cdot \mathbf{n} \, dA \tag{1}$$

This requires that

$$\mathbf{J}_1 \cdot \mathbf{n} = \mathbf{J}_2 \cdot \mathbf{n} \tag{2}$$

In order to satisfy the conservation-of-energy principle, in the absence of any source of energy, we must have

$$\oint \mathbf{E} \cdot d\mathbf{S} = 0 \tag{3}$$

everywhere within the conductors, and in particular around the critical closed paths at the boundary such as *abcda* in the figure. First let the lengths of the parts *bc* and *da* of the path become vanishingly small so that they make a negligible contribution to the total value of the line integral. Then the contribution on the part *ab* must be equal and oppo-site to that on *cd*. The two paths are taken in opposite directions and are equal in length. The magnitude of the contributions will be numer-ically equal to the average of the tangential components multiplied by the path lengths. In equation form

$$\int E_{t1}\, dS + \int E_{t2}(-dS) = 0 \tag{4}$$
$$(E_{t1})_{av}(S) - (E_{t2})_{av}(S) = 0 \tag{5}$$

In the limit, as the components are compared at neighboring points at the boundary, the approximation is removed and the tangential com-ponents are continuous.

$$E_{t1} = E_{t2} \tag{6}$$

In terms of the angles between the direction lines and the tangent to the boundaries, the first boundary condition, Eq. (2), may be written

$$J_1 \sin \alpha_1 = J_2 \sin \alpha_2 \tag{7}$$

Since $\mathbf{J} = \gamma \mathbf{E}$

$$\gamma_1 E_1 \sin \alpha_1 = \gamma_2 E_2 \sin \alpha_2 \tag{8}$$

The continuous tangential components of $\mathbf{E}$ are

$$E_1 \cos \alpha_1 = E_2 \cos \alpha_2 \tag{9}$$

Dividing Eq. (8) by Eq. (9) and rearranging,

$$\frac{\tan \alpha_2}{\tan \alpha_1} = \frac{\gamma_1}{\gamma_2} \tag{10}$$

It is important to observe that when current leaves a very good con-ductor to enter a very poor one, its direction is nearly perpendicular to the boundary in the latter material. This applies very appropriately to the leakage of current from a conductor into imperfect insulation.

4.7 A Graphical Method. Throughout the discussion of the examples of this chapter, reference is made to the conditions which are imposed by the *boundaries* of the current-carrying regions. In each of our problems we have imposed the condition that two of the boundary faces be held as equipotential surfaces. Current enters and leaves at these equipotential surfaces—and it neither enters nor leaves at any of the other boundaries.

One of the most effective ways of seeing how the boundaries of the conductor affect the current distribution within the conductor is to study a graphical method of solving a two-dimensional problem—such as determining the resistance and sketching the field in a rectangular conductor with a circular hole.

In Fig. 4.8a, the conductor is a bus bar with a large hole at its center. The diameter of the hole is half the width of the conductor, so that the effective area of the conductor is reduced by a factor of 2.   Let us maintain the two ends of the conductor, at the left and the right, as equipotential surfaces.

Whether or not the hole is present, the other four boundary faces must correspond to direction lines.   Since current cannot flow in or out

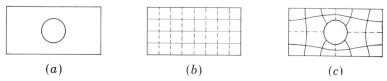

(a)   (b)   (c)

Fig. 4.8   Preliminary steps in preparing a graphical evaluation of the resistance of a conductor with a circular hole.

through these boundaries, it can only flow parallel to these four faces. The equipotentials are normal to the stream lines and, as a consequence, are normal to the boundary faces.   Current cannot enter or leave by the hole either, and it cannot flow across the hole.   All the equipotential surfaces are perpendicular to the new boundary surface which appears when the hole is drilled through the bus bar.

Figure 4.8b shows the conductor without a hole.   The left and right ends are maintained as equipotentials.   Three stream lines representing the direction of current flow have been drawn, and together with the other two stream lines coinciding with the top and bottom edges, the stream lines divide the bus bar into four parallel strips, each carrying the same amount of current.   Nine equipotentials are also shown, two of which coincide with the left and right ends.   The equipotential lines are drawn at equal voltage intervals dividing the field into squares.   This procedure is not essential but will prove helpful in mapping irregular fields; it is easier to sketch squares than rectangles of fixed proportions.

In two-dimensional problems, where the depth is constant, each square represents the same resistance, regardless of size.   The proof of this statement can take either one of two forms:

1. Since each square carries the same amount of current and has the same potential difference across it, the resistances are the same by Ohm's law.

2. The resistance of a rectangular conductor is, as in Eq. 4.3(2),

$$R = \frac{1}{\gamma}\frac{L}{A}$$
$$= \frac{1}{\gamma}\frac{L}{Wd}$$

where d = depth

W = width

The depth and conductivity are assumed constant throughout. Since $L/W = 1$ for a square, each square has the same resistance.

In irregular fields, the squares become "curvilinear squares," or figures with curved sides, roughly equal length and width, and perpendicular edges at the corners. For such cases, proof 1 is more to the point; the resistance of a square may be determined from proof 2 in some portion of the field where the formula is applicable.

Taking the resistance of one square as a convenient unit, the total resistance may be found as a series-parallel combination of unit resistances. For example, in Fig. 4.8b, the total resistance is a series connection of eight resistors, each consisting of four squares in parallel. The equivalent resistance is thus 8/4 or 2 units.

A field map for the conductor after the hole is drilled will look roughly as shown in the freehand sketch of Fig. 4.8c. The horizontal dashed line is a stream line which is correctly drawn to divide the current into two equal portions and is located from the symmetry of the conductor. The vertical dashed line is an equipotential line which represents a potential midway between the end potentials and is again located (correctly) by symmetry properties of the conductor. The other lines are rough attempts at further subdivision of the map and indicate approximately the stream and equipotential lines.

In making a good field map, it is well to start with a relatively large-scale drawing of the conductor, as shown in Fig. 4.9. In starting the map, lines 1-2, 3-4, 5-6, and 7-8 can be drawn from considerations of symmetry; because of symmetry, it will be sufficient to consider only one quadrant, say the first. The next step is stream line 9-11, choosing 9 near the middle of 1-10 and 11 near the middle of 5-6. Line 9-11 should be drawn perpendicular to 5-6 and 1-10 and should roughly bisect the flow space between 5-10 and 2-1. The equipotential lines are then roughed in, perpendicular to all stream lines and boundaries, and spaced so as to divide the field into rough curvilinear squares. At this point, it is well to stand back and inspect the work, indicating any required adjustments by arrows. In this map, it appears that line 15-16-17 should be moved to the right a small amount, necessitating a small downward movement of 13-16-19.

A second attempt will now be carried out in the second quadrant, preserving all the good features of the first try and incorporating any necessary modifications. Two more stream lines are drawn (locating points 26, 27, 28 so as to divide 4-25 equally) and additional equipotential lines inserted. Line 24-3 is drawn to bisect the angle at 3 formed by the line 4-3 and the arc 3-6; 3 is a "singular point," and it is not expected

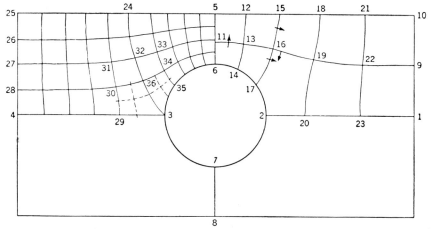

Fig. 4.9 Development of the field map for a conductor with a circular hole. Traced from a freehand sketch.

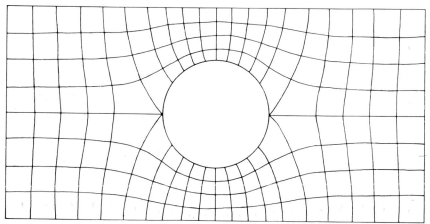

Fig. 4.10 Completed field map of stream lines and equipotentials in a conductor with a circular hole. Traced from a freehand sketch.

that the equipotential line 24-3 be perpendicular to the stream line or boundary at this point. A second inspection indicates a need for only minor adjustments; the map is about as good as can be expected. The complete field is indicated in Fig. 4.10. This figure, too, has been left as sketched freehand.

The resistance is now 10 series combinations of four squares in parallel, for an equivalent resistance of 20/8 or $2\frac{1}{2}$ units. The hole is therefore responsible for a 25 per cent increase in resistance. Further subdivision would probably not change this conclusion, so that the map is good enough as shown. In fact, the rough map in the first quadrant gives the same answer, but few people would be satisfied without one further subdivision!

The portion 2-20-19-16-17-2 of the rough sketch in the first quadrant does not look like a "square." Whether or not this part of the field is correctly mapped may be determined by further subdivision. Inspecting the second attempt, in the second quadrant, it will be observed that this part subdivides into two fairly good squares, 30-31-32-36-30 and 32-33-34-36-32, and two kite-shaped figures. The cor-

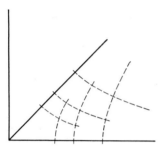

FIG. 4.11   Stream lines and equipotentials at a right-angle corner.

rectness of these figures is again checked by further subdivision, as indicated by the dotted lines. If subdivision of a "kite" results in three good squares and another kite, smaller but similar in shape, the map is correct.

The justification for the statement concerning subdivision of kites is found in analytical studies of simpler cases, such as the right-angle corner shown in Fig. 4.11. Here the stream and potential lines are simple hyperbolas, and the exact field is easily plotted.

Near the corner, kites are observed, and it is noted that each one can be subdivided indefinitely into three squares and a smaller kite. In the limit, the entire field is divided into squares except an arbitrarily small kite in the corner which will be too tiny to matter.

At the point numbers 2 and 3 in Fig. 4.9, there is an intersection of a stream line and an equipotential in which the angle of intersection is not 90°. However, this does not violate the requirement that the field-intensity and current-density vector quantities be perpendicular to the equipotential surface, because the magnitude of these vector quantities is zero at the point of the intersection, and we really cannot specify the direction of a vector quantity whose magnitude is zero. When this situation arises at a point in a field map, the point is called a *singular* point. The corner in Fig. 4.11 is also a singular point.

There is an additional interpretation available in our field map which we shall point out briefly. If we were to cut the conductor up into strips with a very fine band saw, making the saw cuts coincide with the stream lines, we should be able to define a number of individual parallel conductors, each of which carries the same portion of the total current. The current enters each of the strips at one end and leaves at the other, and none either enters or leaves along the sides. Such strips are called *current tubes*. More generally, a volume bounded by stream lines or direction lines is called a *tube of flux*.

The fluid-flow map of Fig. 4.12a may be compared with the results obtained graphically to show how really effective this graphical method is. More important than the results of this rather simple example, however, is the extension of the method to more complicated field problems as a thought process. To this end the illustrations of flow around obstacles of more interesting shape are presented in parts *b* and *c* of the figure. Guided by the fluid-flow maps, the student will find it very instructive to sketch the equipotentials as well as the stream lines on a tracing of the illustrations.

It is perhaps easier to see the significance of the singular points, discussed above, by studying these fluid-flow maps. In hydrodynamics, the singular points are given the much more descriptive name *stagnation points*. There are two of these stagnation points clearly visible at each of the obstacles in Fig. 4.12.

4.8 Kirchhoff's Current Law, and Solenoidal Vectors. In circuit theory, Kirchhoff's current law is frequently stated in form equivalent to the following: *The algebraic sum of the currents entering and leaving a junction is zero.* We should like to examine some of the vector-analysis viewpoints, and it will also be interesting to define the term *junction*. The experimental evidence is now rather conclusive that charge can neither be created nor destroyed, but only separated. If this is true, any net charge brought into a region of space must cross its boundaries. *When the net quantity of charge inside any region of space is not changing with time, then the rate at which charge enters must be equal to the rate at which it leaves.* The term *junction* in the first statement of Kirchhoff's law must then be any region of space. We shall now formulate this simple idea in mathematical terms.

Referring to Fig. 4.13, we consider a region of space of almost any shape or size or location. We think of the surface which bounds the region and divide the surface into two parts bounded by a common curve. The current leaving through each of the two parts of the bounding surface A_1 and A_2 is found from the component of the current density $\mathbf{J}$ along the outward normal $\mathbf{n}$. The sum of the currents leaving is zero. In equation form,

$$\int_{A_1} \mathbf{J} \cdot \mathbf{n} \, dA + \int_{A_2} \mathbf{J} \cdot \mathbf{n} \, dA = 0 \tag{1}$$

Mathematically, to evaluate the integral of the same quantity over the two surfaces A_1 and A_2 is to evaluate it over the entire *closed surface* A. Therefore

$$\oint \mathbf{J} \cdot \mathbf{n} \, dA = 0 \tag{2}$$

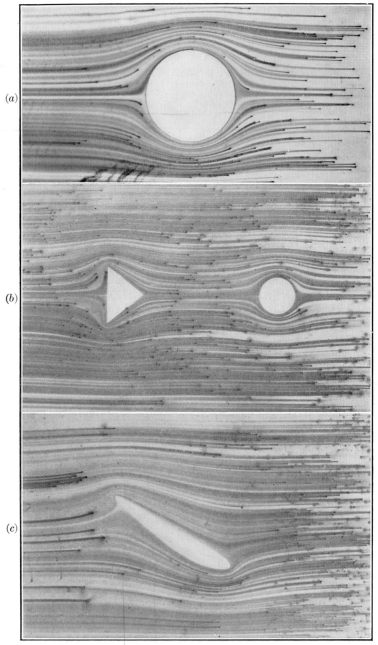

Fig. 4.12   Fluid flow around obstacles.   The round obstacle in a is analogous to the conductor with a circular hole, and has the same dimensions.   Flow around obstacles of more interesting, if more difficult, character is modeled in b and c.   Compare a with the map of Fig. 4.11 obtained graphically.   Observe the stagnation points on each side of each obstacle.

The circle through the integral sign indicates that the integration is to be performed over a closed surface. The result is true for all closed surfaces within which the total amount of charge is not changing with time. It is a very remarkable and useful result. It is a characteristic of a class of vectors whose direction lines or whose stream lines can be drawn with curves having no beginnings and no endings. Such vectors are called *solenoidal*. We are going to see somewhat later that the simple statement that one of the vectors associated with a magnetic field is always a sole-

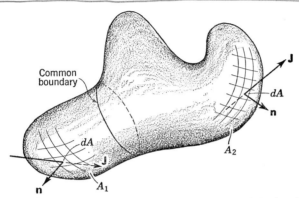

FIG. 4.13   Figure for a mathematical formulation of the principle that if no charge is accumulating within a region, the net rate at which charge crosses the closed boundary surface must be zero. $\oint \mathbf{J} \cdot \mathbf{n} \, dA = 0$.

noidal vector will become one of four basic equations known as Maxwell's equations.

On the other hand, the flux of the $\mathbf{E}$ vector is not zero over all closed surfaces, and we shall evaluate it in the next chapter.

4.9   Some Energy Considerations.   When a conductor carries a current, the work done by the forces of the field is dissipated as heat. The work done by these forces on a differential quantity of charge dQ is related to the potential difference by

$$dW = V \, dQ \qquad (1)$$

The power P is the rate of doing work

$$P = \frac{dW}{dt} \qquad (2)$$

which, from Eq. (1), is

$$P = V \frac{dQ}{dt} = VI \qquad (3)$$

Using Ohm's law, we can also write Eq. (3) as Joule's law:

$$P = I^2 R \qquad (4)$$

This power is a scalar quantity, which, like potential difference and current, cannot be associated directly with a point. The power per unit volume, on the other hand, can be defined at a point, and as might be expected, it bears a simple relationship to the current density and the field intensity at the point. In Fig. 4.3b we have chosen a differential volume of a conductor of conductivity γ. The two faces of area dA lie in equipotential surfaces. The other four faces lie parallel to the direction lines. Under these conditions, the resistance of the differential conductor is written as in Sec. 4.3, Eq. (2),

$$R = \frac{dL}{\gamma \, dA} \tag{5}$$

The current is

$$dI = J \, dA \tag{6}$$

Using Eqs. (5) and (6) in Eq. (4), the power dissipated is

$$P = \frac{dA \, dL}{\gamma} J^2 \tag{7}$$

Since the volume of the differential conductor is $dA \, dL$, the power dissipated per unit volume p is

$$p = \frac{1}{\gamma} J^2 \tag{8}$$

Since $\mathbf{J} = \gamma \mathbf{E}$, an alternative form for Eq. (8) is

$$p = JE \tag{9}$$

Instead of writing Eq. (9) as a scalar equation, it can also be written in terms of the scalar product of the two vector quantities:

$$p = \mathbf{J} \cdot \mathbf{E} \tag{10}$$

The scalar product form, Eq. (10), is customarily used in the literature and is preferable to Eq. (9) because it is valid in conductors which are not *isotropic*. This means that they do not have the same properties in all directions. In this case, then, the conductivity γ is not a simple scalar, and $\mathbf{J}$ and $\mathbf{E}$ are not necessarily parallel. If it were not for this possibility, there would be no distinction between the two formulations. Involving tensors or dyadics, this matter is beyond the scope of this book.

Extending this line of development a little further, we observe that since the total power dissipated in a volume is the volume integral of the power per unit volume

$$P = \int p \, dv \tag{11}$$

then, from Eq. (10), it is customary to write the formula

$$P = \int \mathbf{J} \cdot \mathbf{E} \, dv \tag{12}$$

For a given conductor whose resistance and current are known, there is no more information in the volume integral than in the old friend, $P = I^2R$. On reconsideration, however, we see that we might compute the power dissipated in any interesting part of the conductor more directly and perhaps more easily by using Eq. (12) than by going to the trouble of computing its current and resistance. Further, an analysis of the temperature within a conductor would begin with Eq. (10) rather than with I^2R.

4.10 A Summary and a Criticism. The current-density vector is related to the volume density of the moving charges and their average drift velocity by the relation

$$\mathbf{J} = \rho\mathbf{U} \qquad\qquad 4.1(6)$$

when a single kind of charge carrier is present. When more than one kind of charge carrier is present, each contributes similarly, and the total current density is the vector summation

$$\mathbf{J} = \Sigma\rho_n\mathbf{U}_n \qquad\qquad 4.1(8)$$

The current through a differential element of area is related to the current-density vector by the equation

$$dI = \mathbf{J}\cdot\mathbf{n}\,dA \qquad\qquad 4.2(1)$$

because only that component of the current which is normal to the differential area dA contributes to the charge which passes through its surface. The total current through a finite surface is given by the surface integral of the normal component of the current density

$$I = \int\mathbf{J}\cdot\mathbf{n}\,dA \qquad\qquad 4.2(2)$$

More generally, the surface integral of the normal component of a vector over a surface is called the flux of the vector.

Ohm's law may be formulated as a vector relationship

$$\mathbf{J} = \gamma\mathbf{E} \qquad\qquad 4.3(6)$$

At a boundary between materials of different conductivities, the conservation of electric charge requires that the normal components of the current-density vector be continuous. From 4.6(2),

$$J_{n1} = J_{n2}$$

The conservation of energy requires that the tangential components of the field-intensity vector be continuous

$$E_{t1} = E_{t2} \qquad\qquad 4.6(6)$$

In conductors with a high degree of symmetry, such as those whose boundaries are concentric cylinders (Sec. 4.4) or concentric spheres (Prob. 4.1), it is possible to find the field configuration from the scalar concept of current accompanied by Ohm's law.   Briefly, we assume a total current I, of unknown magnitude, and relate it to the current density through

$$I = \int \mathbf{J} \cdot \mathbf{n} \, dA$$

By a study of the symmetry, we find a surface on which $\mathbf{J}$ and $\mathbf{n}$ are parallel and the magnitude of $\mathbf{J} \cdot \mathbf{n}$ is a constant.   This arranges matters in such a simple way that

$$J = \frac{I}{A}$$

Then Ohm's law is used to relate the $\mathbf{E}$ vector to the total current I:

$$E = \frac{I}{\gamma A}$$

Finally, the potential difference established between two boundaries of the conductor is related to the total current through the line integral

$$V_a - V_b = \int_a^b \mathbf{E} \cdot d\mathbf{S}$$

Maintaining a steady electric field within a conductor, and hence a steady current, requires a source of energy capable of supplying power continuously.   The total power

$$P = I^2 R \qquad\qquad 4.9(4)$$

is a scalar quantity, but not that kind of scalar which can be defined uniquely at a point within the conductor.   The power per unit volume,

$$p = \mathbf{J} \cdot \mathbf{E} \qquad\qquad 4.9(10)$$

is unique at a point, and when the current density is not uniform throughout a conductor, the total power may be obtained by the volume integral

$$P = \int p \, dv$$

which is also

$$P = \int \mathbf{J} \cdot \mathbf{E} \, dv \qquad\qquad 4.9(12)$$

The vector-analysis statement of Kirchhoff's current law is that the steady current leaving all closed surfaces is zero:

$$\oint \mathbf{J} \cdot \mathbf{n} \, dA = 0 \qquad\qquad 4.8(2)$$

The proof is based on the logic that, if no charge accumulates inside a region, whatever enters the region must also leave, and at the same rate. (What goes in, comes out just as fast.)   As a class, vectors whose flux over all closed surfaces is zero are said to be solenoidal.

There are other ways of working the simple examples of this chapter, and most of them are worked out in introductory textbooks on circuit theory without the use of vector analysis. In adopting the vector approach, it has not been the purpose of the material presented here to make a hard problem out of an easy one, but rather to introduce some concepts which are indispensable to our further progress in those terms with which the reader is assumed to be the most familiar. It is not easy to do this, because of the rather restricted nature of the fields in conductors. The currents in the surrounding regions are so utterly feeble as to be practically nonexistent, and potential differences are at low levels. The boundaries of the conductors confine the field effectively to a small region of space, that occupied by the conductor itself.

On the other hand, there are several incidental benefits in a study of this kind. One of these has been the opportunity to view a new aspect of the role of the equipotentials and stream lines in mapping fields. As a mode of thought, the role played by the boundaries of conductors in determining the field configuration is perhaps the most important of our gains. In more advanced problems, satisfying these boundary conditions will occupy a great deal of our attention. In the study of electrical machinery, there is an old and useful adage, "Look to the saturation curve." In fields, "Look at the boundaries" is more than an adage.

REFERENCES

1. Weber, Ernst: "Electromagnetic Fields," Vol. I, Chap. III, John Wiley & Sons, Inc., New York, 1950. A brief, formal treatment of the electric-current field.
2. Attwood, Stephen S.: "Electric and Magnetic Fields," 3d ed., Chaps. 3 and 15, John Wiley & Sons, Inc., New York, 1949.
3. Boast, Warren B.: "Principles of Electric and Magnetic Fields," Chap. 14, Harper & Brothers, New York, 1948.
4. Bewley, L. V.: "Two-dimensional Fields in Electrical Engineering," The Macmillan Company, New York, 1948.
5. Moore, A. D.: Mapping Techniques Applied to Fluid Mapper Patterns, *Trans. AIEE*, Vol. 71, 1952. Excellent discussion of methods of mapping fields with the aid of fluid-flow maps.

References 2 to 5 contain extensive discussions of graphical methods of studying two-dimensional fields.

PROBLEMS

*4.1 Compute the resistance between concentric spherical surfaces, when a material of conductivity γ fills the spherical shell. What happens to the resistance in the limit, as the inner radius approaches zero and the shell becomes a solid sphere? For a fixed inner radius, what happens to the resistance and the conductance in the limit as the outer radius approaches infinity? Interpret these extreme results physically.

$$\frac{1}{4\pi\gamma}\left(\frac{1}{R_1} - \frac{1}{R_2}\right)$$

4.2 For a toroidal conductor of rectangular cross section, compute the conductance and then find the length of a straight conductor which has the same cross section and an equal conductance.   Compare with the average length of the current path in the toroidal conductor.

*4.3   From an inspection of Fig. 4.5, find the ratio of the conductivities, approximately.   Sketch Fig. 4.5*b* and *c* for the case in which the position of the two materials is interchanged.   Sketch the potential hill in oblique view, for both cases.

*4.4   Current enters a boundary between copper and nichrome at an angle of 30°.   At what angle does it leave the boundary?   (The per cent conductivity of nichrome is 5.8.)   Prepare a sketch of the **J** and **E** vectors at the boundary, letting the length of the line segment represent the magnitude of the vector.

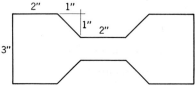

Fɪɢ. 4.14   For Prob. 4.5.

*4.5   Prepare a full-scale field map for the flat fuse link in Fig. 4.14, comparing the resistance with that of a conductor without a restriction in its cross section.

4.6   Map the field of Fig. 4.12*c*, using curvilinear squares.

CHAPTER 5

ELECTROSTATIC FIELDS FROM THE VIEWPOINT OF GAUSS'S LAW

In Chap. 2, using Coulomb's law, we studied the field intensities of the point charge, line charge, and sheet of charge. In Chap. 3, we associated equipotential surfaces with the fields. Our approach in Chap. 4 was quite different, in that the problems involving current flow were essentially problems in geometry. These different approaches gave us the same answers as to the nature of fields which have the same geometries.

When current flows between two concentric spheres, the current density obeys an inverse-square law, as does the associated field intensity. Why is this field so much like that of a point charge isolated in space where no currents flow? Between concentric cylinders, the current density is inversely proportional to the radius. Is it a coincidence that the field intensity associated with this current flow is identical to that of a line charge? Why is the field due to two sheets of charge so much like the flow of current in a long straight conductor? These similarities arise because surface areas and inverse-square-law fields have reciprocal properties. Gauss's law is a generalization of these reciprocal properties, and for one thing, it shows us how to work problems in the electrostatic field like problems in the current field. But more than this, understanding Gauss's law and gaining a little experience in its application are essential steps toward the feeling that one understands Maxwell's equations.

5.1 The Displacement Vector. In the previous chapter the flow of charge was described in terms of the current-density vector $\mathbf{J}$, which has the units of amperes per square meter. In symmetric cases, it was found possible to evaluate the $\mathbf{J}$ vector by performing a surface integration

$$\int \mathbf{J} \cdot \mathbf{n} \, dA = I$$

and to find the field intensity $\mathbf{E}$ in terms of the $\mathbf{J}$ vector from Ohm's law.

One can analyze electrostatic fields by a similar approach after defining a flux vector $\mathbf{D}$ with respect to an area. We have said that the field-intensity vector $\mathbf{E}$ is defined with respect to a line and has the units of volts per meter. We now invent a helper vector $\mathbf{D}$, defined in a vacuum by

$$\mathbf{D} = \epsilon_0 \mathbf{E} \qquad \qquad (1)$$

129

This new helper vector **D** is called the *displacement*, and since it has the units of coulombs per square meter, it may also be called *electrostatic flux density*. Frequently, the direction lines of the **D** vector are called *flux lines*. The **D** vector does not have the physically real significance that can be assigned to the **J** vector, but this does not prevent us from treating it just as though it had such a physical significance.

Like the **E** vector, the **D** vector begins on positive charges and ends on negative charges, and in all the electrostatic field maps we have so far prepared, the direction lines can represent the **D** vector as well as the **E** vector. But we think of the **D** vector as analogous to current density, representing the flux or flow of direction lines between positive charges and negative charges.

5.2 Gauss's Law. As a final step in discussing the current-density vector **J**, we computed its flux through a closed surface and found that for steady currents

$$\oint \mathbf{J} \cdot \mathbf{n} \, dA = 0$$

For the case of the **D** vector, considerable time will be saved by computing this closed-surface integral at the outset of our study. We shall not expect the same results as were found for the **J** vector, because the **D** vector has beginnings and endings and the **J** vector has none.

We intend to compute the net outward flux of the **D** vector through every closed surface, and we can begin by a graphical inspection of several closed surfaces in an electrostatic field. In the rough field map in Fig. 5.1, the magnitude of the point charges is indicated by the number of plus and minus signs. Each plus or minus sign represents a charge of 1 coulomb. One flux line has been shown emanating from each positive charge, and one flux line terminates on each negative charge. Five closed surfaces are shown in the figure. The surfaces numbered 1 and 2 are spheres concentric with a point charge and suggest that, since the number of outward flux lines through these two surfaces is the same, the area of the surface is not the primary factor controlling the total outward flux. Two flux lines flow into and out of cigarlike surface number 3 so that the net outward flux is zero; this surface also encloses no charge. Through surface number 4, three flux lines pass out and one passes in. One flux line crosses surface number 5 three times, twice inward and once outward, leaving a net contribution of once inward to the total. Through each of the closed surfaces, the net outward flux is equal to the net charge contained within the volume enclosed by that surface.

Gauss's law states that the net outward flux through any closed surface is equal to the net positive charge within the volume enclosed by that surface. In vector-analysis shorthand, this is

$$\oint \mathbf{D} \cdot \mathbf{n} \, dA = \int \rho \, dv \qquad (1)$$

We shall begin a more formal proof by considering a single positive point charge within a volume of any arbitrary shape.   For the point charge

$$\mathbf{D} = \frac{Q}{4\pi R^2}\, \mathbf{r} \tag{2}$$

which we shall write as $\mathbf{D} = D\,\mathbf{r}$.   The left-hand side of Eq. (1) becomes

$$\oint D\,\mathbf{r}\cdot\mathbf{n}\,dA$$

To evaluate this integral over a closed surface of unrestricted shape, it is convenient to change the variables to another form.   Solid angle is fre-

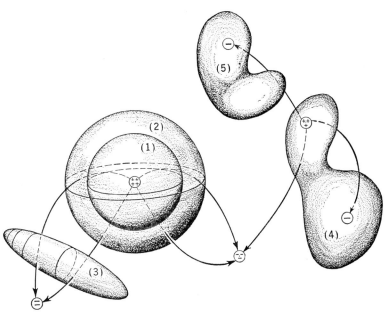

Fig. 5.1   Gaussian surfaces in the field of several point charges.   The net outward flux over each of the surfaces is equal to the charge enclosed.

quently defined in terms similar to this: "The area of a sphere of unit radius with center at a point Q, which is cut out by a conical surface with vertex at Q and having the perimeter of the surface A for its base, is numerically equal to the solid angle subtended by the surface A at the point Q." Welcome will be the vector-analysis shorthand for this definition.

The irregular surface in Fig. 5.2a is shaped somewhat like a potato shell. An ice-cream cone has been forced into the shell until its point (vertex) coincides with the location of the point charge Q. The cone has been trimmed neatly at the surface of the shell so that its perimeter marks out the area dA. The projection of the area dA on the sphere of radius R is

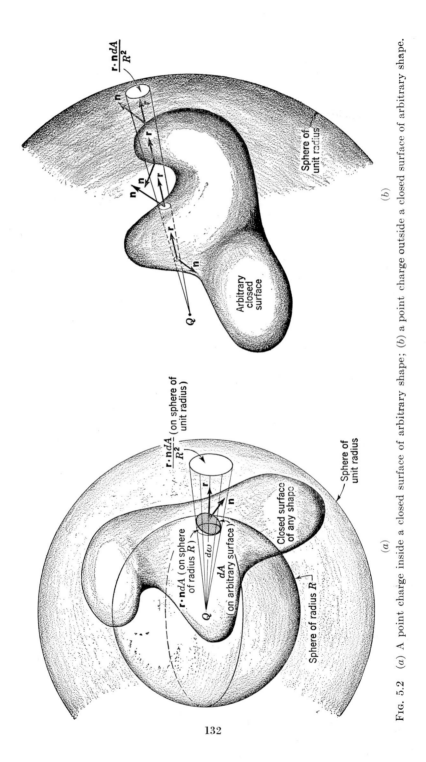

132

Fig. 5.2 (a) A point charge inside a closed surface of arbitrary shape; (b) a point charge outside a closed surface of arbitrary shape.

$\mathbf{r} \cdot \mathbf{n} \, dA$. The projection of $\mathbf{r} \cdot \mathbf{n} \, dA$ onto the sphere of unit radius is

$$\frac{\mathbf{r} \cdot \mathbf{n} \, dA}{R^2}$$

and this coincides with the definition of a differential solid angle.

$$d\omega = \frac{\mathbf{r} \cdot \mathbf{n} \, dA}{R^2} \tag{3}$$

When the entire closed surface has been projected onto the sphere of unit radius, *all* the area of the unit sphere has been cut out by the cones. The unit sphere subtends 4π *sterradians* of solid angle.

Since, from Eq. (2),

$$D = \frac{Q}{4\pi R^2}$$

therefore,

$$\oint \mathbf{D} \cdot \mathbf{n} \, dA = \int_0^{4\pi} \frac{Q}{4\pi} \, d\omega = Q \tag{4}$$

When any number of point charges are contained within the volume enclosed by the surface, we may treat each of them in similar fashion, to write

$$\oint \mathbf{D} \cdot \mathbf{n} \, dA = \frac{1}{4\pi} \int_0^{4\pi} (Q_1 \, d\omega_1 + Q_2 \, d\omega_2 + \cdots + Q_n \, d\omega_n)$$
$$= Q_1 + Q_2 + \cdots + Q_n \tag{5}$$

Instead of indicating the summation of the total charge within the volume as an addition of discrete point charges, we may indicate it by a volume integration of a volume-charge density and write

$$\oint \mathbf{D} \cdot \mathbf{n} \, dA = \int \rho \, dv$$

as stated in Eq. (1).

When there are charges contributing to $\mathbf{D}$, but located outside the volume enclosed by the surface of integration, there is an even number of differential areas, all of which have the same projection on the sphere of unit radius, but with alternating signs. The $\mathbf{n}$ vector is the outward normal, and the successive components along $\mathbf{r}$ will alternate in sign so that the total is zero, as in Fig. 5.2b.

For those without previous experience with the concept, a further discussion of solid angle is in order. Let us reexamine Fig. 5.2a from another interpretation. Let the irregular closed surface be thought of as a transparent balloon enclosing a point source of light Q, which radiates equally well in all directions. The shaded ellipse marked dA is an opaque spot on the surface of the balloon. The spot on the surface of the sphere of unit radius marked

$$d\omega = \frac{\mathbf{r} \cdot \mathbf{n} \, dA}{R^2}$$

is then the shadow cast by the opaque spot on the balloon.   Now if the entire surface of the balloon is made opaque by covering it with paint, the whole unit sphere is in shadow.   This is true regardless of the shape of the balloon.

Whenever we evaluate the closed surface integral in Gauss's law, we speak of the surface of integration as a *Gaussian surface*.   Gauss's law is true for all inverse-square-law vectors, such as in the gravitational field of force.   It suggests to us that the inverse-square factor in Coulomb's law may be thought of as a property of space itself, and not a peculiarity of the electrostatic field.

In examples which follow, we shall find that in many symmetric problems the **D** vector can be evaluated by application of Gauss's law.

5.3   Solutions of One-variable Field Problems Using Gauss's Law.
As an illustration of the use of Gauss's law to determine fields with a high

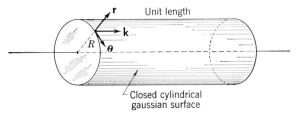

Fɪɢ. 5.3   Analysis of the field of a line charge using Gauss's law.

degree of symmetry, we shall first consider the field of a uniformly charged line, infinitely long as in Fig. 5.3.   Since the line is infinitely long, the field cannot have a component along **k**.   None of the equivalent point charges contributes a component along **θ**, so the field cannot have such a component.   The field must therefore be a function of R alone and be directed along **r**.   For ease in evaluating $\oint \mathbf{D} \cdot \mathbf{n} \, dA$, we choose concentric cylinders of radius R and unit length.   Over the lateral portions of these carefully chosen surfaces

$$\int \mathbf{D} \cdot \mathbf{n} \, dA = \int D\,\mathbf{r} \cdot \mathbf{n} \, dA = \int D \, dA \tag{1}$$

Over the ends, $\mathbf{n} = \pm\mathbf{k}$ and $\mathbf{D} \cdot \mathbf{n} = 0$.   Furthermore D is a constant over the cylindrical portions, allowing us to write, in this case,

$$\oint \mathbf{D} \cdot \mathbf{n} \, dA = DA \tag{2}$$

Since $A = 2\pi R$, and the charge inside the closed surface is λ,

$$\mathbf{D} = \frac{\lambda}{2\pi R}\,\mathbf{r} \qquad \text{and} \qquad \mathbf{E} = \frac{\lambda}{2\pi\epsilon_0 R}\,\mathbf{r} \tag{3, 4}$$

Mathematically, this procedure is somewhat easier than evaluating **E** by a summation of the contributions of equivalent point charges as we did in the study of Coulomb's law.

$$E = \frac{D}{\epsilon_0} = \frac{\lambda}{2\pi\epsilon}\,\hat{r} = $$

As another example, we may determine the nature of the field due to an infinite sheet of uniform charge density by a similarly appropriate choice of a Gaussian surface. The symmetry of the problem requires that the field be normal to the sheet. It is most convenient, then, to enclose an area of the sheet of charge in a Gaussian surface which has the shape of a flat pillbox as in Fig. 5.4. Over the sides of the box which are perpendic-

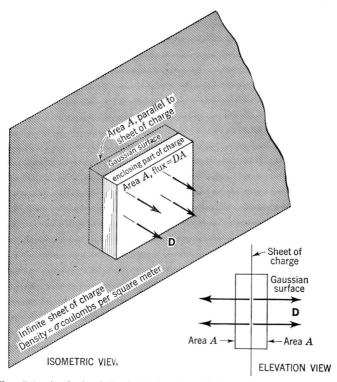

Fig. 5.4   Analysis of the field of a sheet of charge using Gauss's law.

ular to the plane, $\mathbf{D} \cdot \mathbf{n} = 0$. Over the two faces which are parallel to the plane, $\mathbf{D} \cdot \mathbf{n}$ is a constant and

$$\oint \mathbf{D} \cdot \mathbf{n} \, dA = \sigma A \tag{5}$$

becomes simply

$$2DA = \sigma A \tag{6}$$

This gives us

$$D = \frac{\sigma}{2} \quad \text{and} \quad E = \frac{\sigma}{2\epsilon_0}$$

We may write this in the vector form, as in Sec. 2.5,

$$\mathbf{E} = \frac{\sigma}{2\epsilon_0} \mathbf{n} \tag{7}$$

Since the two faces of the box which are parallel to the plane can be separated by any distance we choose without changing the results, we have an additional assurance that the field is independent of the distance from the sheet of charge.

5.4   A Field Involving a Volume-charge Distribution.   Closely related to the field of a line charge is the field due to a cylindrically symmetric

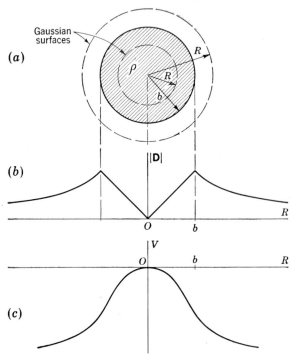

FIG. 5.5   Analysis of the field of a uniform cylindrical volume charge distribution using Gauss's law.   The notation of the analysis is illustrated in a.   The magnitudes of the D vector and the potential are plotted as a function of the radius in b and c.

volume-charge distribution.   Such a field could be caused by the space charge of electrons in a vacuum tube.   We shall also find it convenient to have solved such a problem when we come to investigate the concept of vector potential in connection with the magnetic field.   We shall consider the simplest case, that of a uniform volume-charge distribution confined to a cylinder of radius b.

Refer to Fig. 5.5a.   Over cylindrical Gaussian surfaces concentric with the cylinder of charge and of larger radius, the charge enclosed is the same as in the case of a line charge.   Since the charge enclosed per unit length is $\pi b^2 \rho$, we may use this to replace λ in the result found in the previous

$$D = \frac{\lambda}{2\pi R}\hat{r} = \frac{\pi b^2 \rho}{2\pi R}\hat{r}$$

section

eq (3)

section

$$D = \frac{\pi b^2 \rho}{2\pi R} = \frac{b^2 \rho}{2R} \qquad R \gtrless b \qquad (1)$$

Inside the cylinder, the charge enclosed is $\pi R^2 \rho$, per unit length. The field is radial and constant in magnitude over this surface, so that

$$\oint \mathbf{D} \cdot \mathbf{n} \, dA = \int \rho \, dv \qquad (2)$$

becomes

$$D(2\pi R) = \pi R^2 \rho \qquad (3)$$

and

$$D = \frac{R\rho}{2} \qquad R \lessgtr b \qquad (4)$$

The two expressions match at the boundary where $R = b$.

In Fig. 5.5b the magnitude of the $\mathbf{D}$ vector is plotted as a function of R. The magnitude of the $\mathbf{E}$ vector differs from this by a constant, and as in Chap. 4, the potential of any point relative to the center is proportional to the area under the $|\mathbf{E}|$ curve from the center out to a radius R. Outside the cylinder, the field is identical to that of a line charge. Inside the cylinder the field becomes smaller near the axis instead of increasing without limit as would the field of a line charge.

The equipotential surfaces are concentric cylinders, and since the $\mathbf{E}$ vector has been determined, the potential differences will be found from $\mathbf{E}$. It is convenient here to assign the zero potential level to the center of the cylinder of charge, and to find the potential at other points from the integral

$$V_a - V_b = \int_a^b \mathbf{E} \cdot d\mathbf{S} \qquad (5)$$

By our choice, both V_b and b equal zero, and the subscript can be dropped.

For points which are inside the cylinder of charge, the potential relative to the center is

$$V = \int_R^0 \frac{\rho R \, dR}{2\epsilon_0} \qquad (6)$$

Integrating and substituting limits,

$$V = - \frac{\rho R^2}{4\epsilon_0} \qquad R \lessgtr b \qquad (7)$$

At the surface of the cylinder, where $R = b$,

$$V = - \frac{b^2 \rho}{4\epsilon_0} \qquad R = b \qquad (8)$$

This may be expressed in terms of λ, the charge per unit length of the cylinder, as

$$V = \frac{-\lambda}{4\pi\epsilon_0} \qquad R = b \qquad (9)$$

For points outside the cylinder of charge, the potential is

$$V = -\frac{b^2\rho}{4\epsilon_0} + \int_R^b \frac{\pi b^2 \rho}{2\pi\epsilon_0 R}\, dR \tag{10}$$

Integrating and substituting limits,

$$V = -\frac{b^2\rho}{4\epsilon_0} - \frac{b^2\rho}{2\epsilon_0} \log_e \frac{R}{b} \qquad R \gtrless b \tag{11}$$

and if these are expressed in terms of λ,

$$V = -\frac{\lambda}{2\pi\epsilon_0}\left(\frac{1}{2} + \log_e \frac{R}{b}\right) \qquad R \gtrless b \tag{12}$$

In part c of Fig. 5.5, the potential relative to the center is plotted as a graph. Since the zero potential level has been assigned to the center of

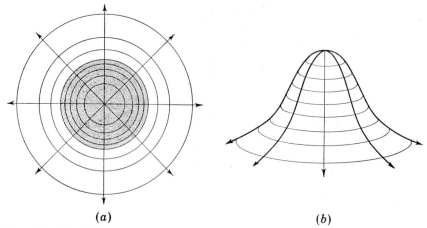

(a)   (b)

FIG. 5.6   (a) Field map of a uniform cylindrical volume-charge distribution; (b) potential-hill interpretation of the same field.

the cylinder, where the potential is the highest, all potentials are negative. Within the cylinder of charge, the curve is a parabola, while outside the cylinder the curve is logarithmic and identical to the curve for a line charge at the center of the cylinder.

The relative spacing of the equipotential surfaces, for equal increments of potential, is shown in Fig. 5.6a. The potential-hill interpretation is shown in part b. This interpretation shows that the potential hill of a line charge has been cut off and replaced with a parabolic cap of finite height, to make a hat or a beehive. Note that there is no discontinuity in the slope of the hill at the boundary between regions.

A fluid-flow map of the field is shown in Fig. 5.7. The distributed charge in the cylinder is represented by a distributed source. The central hole in the slab is filled with sand, and this causes the water to enter the flow space over a distributed region. Correctly representing only the direction of the field, the stream lines appear to begin at the center of the sand bed, as do the direction lines in Fig. 5.6a.

The cylinder of charge is not to be imagined as a metallic cylinder. We shall soon see that in the electrostatic field the charge on a conductor is confined to its surface. On the other hand, cylindrically symmetric

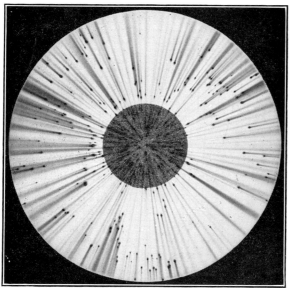

FIG. 5.7   Fluid-flow map of the direction lines in the field of a uniform cylindrical volume-charge distribution. The inner circle is a sand bed which causes the water to enter the flow channel over a distributed region. This region corresponds to the space-charge region.

volume-charge distributions are found in some vacuum tubes. Of perhaps greater importance is the possibility that experience in thinking about volume-charge distributions will assist our understanding of some of the methods which are used in analyzing magnetic fields.

5.5   The Equation of the Direction Lines in a Linear Array of Infinitely Long Line Charges.   In the second chapter we found the equation of the direction lines in the field of two infinitely long line charges, carrying equal and opposite charge densities. There it was necessary to solve a differential equation in which the variables were separated only after considerable manipulation. In fields with a high degree of symmetry, Gauss's law allows us to find the equation of the direction lines by superposition, and compared to the previous method the mathematics is greatly simplified.

As an illustration, we shall consider a linear array of four line charges along the x axis, each carrying a different uniform charge density, as indicated in Fig. 5.8.   The field is symmetrical along the z axis.   The line AB is perpendicular to the x axis and represents a strip which is infinite in extent in the z direction.   When the flux passing through a unit length of the plane strip AB is constant, the point A traces out a direction line as the strip is moved along the x axis.   A slightly different form of the equation is found for the various regions in which the strip is located, as

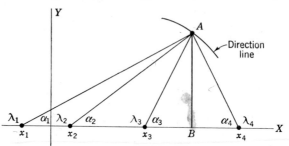

FIG. 5.8   Analysis of the direction lines in the field of a linear array of line charges.

will be evident shortly.   One such region, between x_3 and x_4, will be analyzed.

We have seen that the total current passing through a surface is a scalar quantity.   When several sources contribute to the total current, their individual contributions may be added as scalars.   The total flux through a surface is also a scalar, and when several sources contribute to the total, their individual contributions may be added as scalars.

We can consider the flux due to each line charge separately, add up the results, and equate the total to a constant.   Considering λ_1 alone, the flux through the strip is to the right if λ_1 is positive, and of the total flux from λ_1, the fraction

$$\frac{\alpha_1}{2\pi} \lambda_1$$

will pass through the strip AB.   Treating λ_2 and λ_3 in the same manner, the total passing through the strip AB from left to right is

$$\frac{\alpha_1}{2\pi} \lambda_1 + \frac{\alpha_2}{2\pi} \lambda_2 + \frac{\alpha_3}{2\pi} \lambda_3$$

Considering λ_4 alone, the flux through AB is from right to left, and hence is negative when λ_4 is positive.   Adding this to the total and equating to a constant,

$$\frac{\alpha_1}{2\pi} \lambda_1 + \frac{\alpha_2}{2\pi} \lambda_2 + \frac{\alpha_3}{2\pi} \lambda_3 - \frac{\alpha_4}{2\pi} \lambda_4 = K' \tag{1}$$

or

$$\alpha_1\lambda_1 + \alpha_2\lambda_2 + \alpha_3\lambda_3 - \alpha_4\lambda_4 = K \tag{2}$$

But

$$\alpha_1 = \text{arc tan } \frac{y}{x - x_1} \qquad \text{etc.} \tag{3}$$

Hence

$$\lambda_1 \text{ arc tan } \frac{y}{x - x_1} + \lambda_2 \text{ arc tan } \frac{y}{x - x_2} + \lambda_3 \text{ arc tan } \frac{y}{x - x_3}$$

$$- \lambda_4 \text{ arc tan } \frac{y}{x_4 - x} = K \tag{4}$$

is the equation of the direction lines. When the sign of some of the charges is negative, this can be accounted for by substituting negative

FIG. 5.9   Rubber-sheet model of the potential field of a linear array of line charges. The four line charges have the same polarity and are approximately equal in magnitude, but the relative spacing is random.

values for the appropriate λ. When two of the line charges are absent and the other two are equal and opposite, the expression reduces to that found in Sec. 2.9, Eq. (14).

The potentials may be superimposed in a similar manner, treating each line charge separately. The influence of each line charge can be visualized in terms of a rubber-sheet model, Fig. 5.9, more readily than in terms of the mathematical equation.

5.6   Conductors in Electrostatic Fields, and Corollaries of Gauss's Law. Materials which act as good conductors contain loosely held electrons which are free to move throughout the volume of the conductor but are restrained by atomic forces from leaving the surface of the conductor. When a conductor is placed in an electric field, free charges move under the influence of the forces of the field, until they reach the surface of the conductor, where further motion is prevented by the atomic forces. While charges appear on the surfaces of the conductor, below the surface only an interchange of electrons has occurred, and in this region there is no net charge. Electrostatics deals with fields due to charges at rest, and hence with the equilibrium conditions existing after all motion of charge has ceased. The motion of charge cannot cease until the charges which move have, through their own fields, reduced the forces to zero. Each moving charge has a field of its own and, in moving, changes the nature of the field until the field intensity throughout the volume of the conductor is reduced to zero.

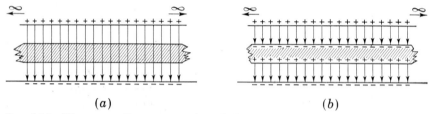

(a)   (b)

FIG. 5.10   Diagrammatic representation of the influence of a conducting slab on a uniform field. When the field is established, as in a, the free charges within the conductor move under the forces of the field, until the field within the conductor is reduced to zero as shown in b.

To examine this idea in the simplest possible example, imagine that we insert a thick plane sheet of copper into the uniform field between oppositely charged sheets.

In Fig. 5.10 the field is sketched before the charges in the conductor have moved, and again, at the right, after equilibrium has been established by reducing the field within the conductor to zero. If this is to occur, the surfaces of the conductor must act as sheets of charge whose field is equal and opposite to that set up by the original sheets of charge. This means that there is an *induced* charge on the surface of the conductor, sufficient to set up a field within the conductor which is equal and opposite to that which would be present if the conductor was absent.

The same sort of charge distribution occurs whenever a conductor is placed in an electrostatic field. Charges appear on the surface to provide a boundary for the electrostatic field. The resulting field at the surface of the conductor must be normal to the surface, because a tangential component would require a corresponding tangential component within the conductor, and this would result in a further motion of charge.

Figure 5.11 shows the resulting field when a conducting rod, infinitely long, is placed in a uniform field. The field within the conductor is reduced to zero, and the field is perpendicular to the surface of the conductor. The surface of the conductor is an equipotential surface. The direction lines of the field map terminate on the charges on the surface of the conductor. It is interesting to observe the similarities between this field and that in Fig. 4.10 for the conductor with a hole in it. The

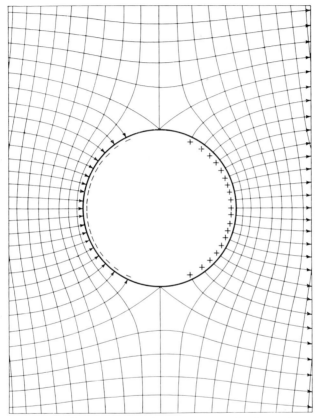

Fig. 5.11   A conducting cylinder in a uniform field.   (*After Maxwell*.)

two maps are very much alike if the stream lines and equipotentials are interchanged.

The two examples of the influence of a conductor on an electrostatic field have an underlying principle of surprising generality. To show this, we shall list several important deductions as corollaries of Gauss's law, proving some and outlining the proof of others.

(1) *Every region occupied by conducting material is an equipotential region.*

If the field intensity is not zero, charges are still in motion. The potential difference between any two points in the conductor is

$$V_a - V_b = \int_a^b \mathbf{E} \cdot d\mathbf{S}$$

Since $\mathbf{E}$ is zero on all paths between the points which lie wholly within the conductor, and the line integral is independent of the path, the potential difference between any two points is zero.

(2) *Unless the point is on its surface, there is no net charge at any point occupied by conducting material. In other words, the charge carried by a conductor resides on its surface.*

Since $\mathbf{E}$ and $\mathbf{D}$ are zero, the total flux of $\mathbf{D}$ over every Gaussian surface taken wholly within the material is zero.

$$\oint \mathbf{D} \cdot \mathbf{n} \, dA = 0$$

Therefore the net charge within every such Gaussian surface is zero, by Gauss's law.

(3) *At a point on the surface of a conductor, the field intensity is normal to the surface and is related to the charge density at that point by the equation*

$$\boxed{\mathbf{E} = \frac{\sigma}{\epsilon_0} \mathbf{n}} \qquad (1)$$

The direction of the field-intensity vector must be normal to the surface, because at a boundary between materials the tangential components are continuous. If there were a tangential component below the surface, charges would still be in motion. To obtain the quantitative relationship between the normal component and surface-charge density, refer to Fig. 5.4. Let the region behind the sheet of charge in the figure be occupied by conducting material, and let the flat faces of the Gaussian surface be a differential segment of area dA. The charge within the Gaussian surface is $\sigma \, dA$, but since $\mathbf{D}$ is now zero on one of the flat faces, $D = \sigma$, by Gauss's law.

(4) *When a charge is placed within a cavity in a solid conductor, an equal quantity of charge is induced on its inner and outer surfaces. Counting the induced charge on the inner surface, a solid conductor can enclose no net charge.*

We prove this with the aid of Fig. 5.12a, which diagrams a conductor with a cavity in which discrete charges have been placed. We establish a Gaussian surface wholly within the conductor and just enclosing the cavity. Over such Gaussian surfaces, $\mathbf{E}$ and $\mathbf{D}$ are zero, so that

$$\oint \mathbf{D} \cdot \mathbf{n} \, dA = 0$$

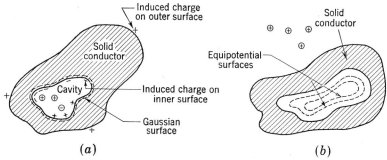

FIG. 5.12 For proof of two corollaries of Gauss's law. (*a*) Charges are placed within a cavity in a solid conductor; (*b*) a configuration of charges wholly outside a cavity in a solid conductor. By treating the assumed equipotential surfaces as Gaussian surfaces, it is readily proved that they cannot exist.

This must mean that there is an induced charge on the inner surface of the cavity, equal and opposite to that within the cavity. As the Gaussian surface is expanded, this relation must hold until the surface lies just outside the conductor, fitting it like a glove. Then

$$\oint \mathbf{D} \cdot \mathbf{n} \, dA = Q$$

where Q = net charge placed within cavity.

This principle is utilized in producing the very high potentials in the Van de Graaff generator.

(5) *No configuration of charge outside a closed hollow conductor can produce a field inside.*

If a field exists inside the cavity, then there are equipotential surfaces which are closed and lie wholly within the cavity, as diagrammed in Fig. 5.12*b*. The field intensity is normal to each of these surfaces and uniformly directed toward a region of lower potential. The flux through such a surface cannot be zero. Thus our assumption of a field inside a cavity due to charges outside leads to a contradiction with Gauss's law. This is the principle of screening or shielding of one region from the influence of the field in another region. It has many important practical applications.

(6) *No point in a field can be at a maximum or at a minimum of potential unless that point is occupied by a charge.*

The proof may be arrived at by reasoning similar to that utilized in proving corollary (5), and is left as a problem for the student.

Comparing corollaries (4) and (5), we see that the shielding provided by a closed hollow conductor is a one-way principle. The closed hollow conductor does not shield the region outside from the influence of the *net* quantity of charge inside the cavity. The principle is not completely one-sided, because the outer region is completely shielded from the details of the charge configuration inside the cavity, as diagrammed in Fig. 5.12a. The two fields exist quite independently.

In Fig. 5.12a, again, let the induced charge on the outer surface be removed and returned to the source of the net charge which was placed within the cavity. Now, outside the cavity there are no separated charges. By corollary (6) no point outside can be at a maximum or minimum of potential. Therefore all points outside must be at the same potential and there is no field outside. The closed hollow conductor can and will shield the region outside from the field inside if the charge is removed from the outer surface. Practically, this is accomplished by connecting the shielding conductor to the earth.

If the shielding conductor is not connected to the earth and carries a charge on its outer surface, the distribution of that charge over the outer surface cannot be influenced by the field inside the cavity, being completely determined by conditions outside the cavity. As an example, consider a point charge placed anywhere within a cavity of any shape inside a conducting sphere. Regardless of the lack of symmetry inside, complete spherical symmetry exists outside. Analysis of the field outside by means of concentric spherical Gaussian surfaces shows that the field outside is identical to that which would be produced by locating the point charge at the center of the sphere.

5.7   The Field between Concentric Cylinders, Infinitely Long.   Now that we have investigated the action of conductors in electrostatic fields, it is appropriate to study some fields whose boundaries are formed by the surfaces of conductors. Instead of an infinitely long line charge of vanishing radius, let us place the same charge per unit length on the surface of a cylindrical wire of finite radius. From the viewpoint of a concentric cylindrical Gaussian surface, the charge enclosed is still λ per unit length. The field outside the wire is the same as it would be for the analogous line charge, but the field intensity inside the wire is zero.

If a second, insulated, concentric cylinder surrounds the inner one, an equal and opposite charge appears on its inner surface, leaving an equal, like charge on its outer surface as in Fig. 5.13a. If no serious attempt is made to isolate or insulate the outer cylinder, the charges which appear on its outer surface would ultimately leak off to the earth. We can hasten the establishment of this equilibrium condition by connecting it to the earth with a conductor as indicated in Fig. 5.13b, and we can conveniently assign the zero reference potential to the earth and the outer conductor. In Fig. 5.13b, the only charges with which we are now concerned are those which appear on the cylinders. The whole field outside the configuration has collapsed, but the field between the cylinders is the same as that due to an isolated charged line.

We found that a Gaussian surface which is a concentric cylinder gives us the field intensity as

$$E = \frac{\lambda}{2\pi\epsilon_0 R} \mathbf{r} \qquad (1)$$

We may evaluate the potential difference between the two cylinders by integrating $\mathbf{E} \cdot d\mathbf{S}$ between the inner and outer cylinders. The results are

$$V_m = V_{R_1} - V_{R_2} = \int_{R_1}^{R_2} \frac{\lambda \, dR}{2\pi\epsilon_0 R} = \frac{\lambda}{2\pi\epsilon_0} \log_e \frac{R_2}{R_1} \qquad (2)$$

as for potential differences in the field of a line charge.

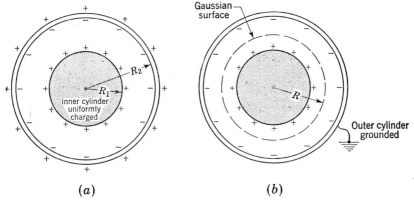

(a)   **(b)**

FIG. 5.13   A configuration of charges on concentric conducting cylinders. (a) Charges placed on the inner cylinder induce charges inside and outside the outer cylinder; (b) when the charges are removed from the outer surface of the outer cylinder, the field outside is zero while the field inside is undisturbed.

In general, the potential difference between two conductors which carry equal and opposite charges is directly proportional to the magnitude of the charge and the ratio of the charge to the potential difference between the conductors depends only on the geometry. This leads us to the subject of capacitance as discussed in the next section.

5.8 Capacitance. In the uniform field between two parallel plane conductors which are infinite in extent and carry equal and opposite surface charge densities $\pm\sigma$ the field is proportional to the charge density

$$\mathbf{D} = \sigma\,\mathbf{n} \qquad \text{and} \qquad \mathbf{E} = \frac{\sigma}{\epsilon_0}\,\mathbf{n}$$

The potential difference between conductors separated a distance L is

$$V_m = \frac{\sigma L}{\epsilon_0} \qquad (1)$$

When Eq. (1) is solved for the surface-charge density in terms of the potential difference

$$\sigma = \frac{\epsilon_0 V_m}{L} \tag{2}$$

Considering a portion of the total area of the infinite planes of area A, the charge carried by each is

$$\sigma A = \frac{\epsilon_0 A V_m}{L} \tag{3}$$

The ratio of the charge to the potential difference is the *capacitance*

$$C = \frac{|Q|}{|V_m|} \tag{4}$$

and for these parallel planes

$$C = \frac{\epsilon_0 A}{L} \tag{5}$$

The capacitance is always taken as a positive parameter; hence the absolute value marks in Eq. (4).

In current-carrying conductors the ratio of the total current to the potential difference is the conductance,

$$G = \frac{I}{V_m} \tag{6}$$

and between parallel planes

$$G = \frac{\gamma A}{L} \tag{7}$$

Comparing Eq. (5) with Eq. (7) gives us an additional viewpoint on permittivity and suggests that it might have been called "capacitivity" to match the term conductivity. The units of conductance are amperes per volt, usually called mhos. The units of capacitance are coulombs per volt, usually called farads. The units of conductivity are mhos per meter, and the units of permittivity are called farads per meter.

A word of caution is required to accompany the comparison of Eqs. (5) and (7). Equation (7) is valid under a great many circumstances in which plane sections of conductors are maintained as equipotentials and the surrounding medium is either free space or extremely poor conducting material (such as air at low field intensities). The conductivities of good conductors are as much as 10^{24} greater than the conductivities of good insulators. Equation (5), on the other hand, is only an approximation when the parallel planes are not infinite in extent, and the edge effects are quite appreciable unless the area of the plates is so large compared to their distance of separation that the field is essentially uniform over a substantial portion of the plates. The analogous situation for Eq. (5) would be the approximation due to ignoring all current flow in the material not immediately between two copper plates immersed in a very large body of water.

As another example, the capacitance per unit length between concentric cylinders, infinitely long, is the ratio of the charge carried per unit length to the potential difference between the conductors. From Eq. 5.7(2), this ratio is

$$\frac{C}{L} = \frac{2\pi\epsilon_0}{\log_e (R_2/R_1)} \tag{8}$$

which has the same form as the conductance per unit length found in Chap. 4.

$$\frac{G}{L} = \frac{2\pi\gamma}{\log_e (R_2/R_1)} \tag{9}$$

The capacitance and conductance of concentric spheres follows as readily and is to be found in the problems, as is the suggested experimental technique for the measurement of capacitance.

In computing capacitance, we must confine ourselves to two conductors which carry equal and opposite charges, and be careful to evaluate the ratio of the charge to the potential difference between the two conductors. While two glass rods might carry equal and opposite charges, we could not evaluate anything as simple as a capacitance because the glass rods would not be equipotential surfaces. If there are more than two conductors in a field, the various charges and potentials are related by *coefficients of capacitance* and *coefficients of induction* rather than by a single capacitance parameter.

5.9 A Summary and Criticism. We have found that Gauss's law has simplified those field problems which have a high degree of symmetry. Like the potential, the flux concept allows us to treat certain vector problems as scalar problems. Some very important phenomena involving the introduction of conductors in electrostatic fields are explained most simply by the use of Gauss's law. These results and the concept of capacitance have enabled us to progress from hypothetical problems to physically real problems. We have seen the concepts and the techniques of the fields in current-carrying conductors carried over into the electrostatic field and have been cautioned that edge effects are often of importance in electrostatics even though they are usually negligible in the corresponding conductance problem.

Gauss's law and the concept of the flux of a vector present some difficulties, too. One of these arises from the pardonable tendency to attribute physical reality to the flux. Our present view is that the **D** vector was introduced purely for convenience. Mathematically it is like the **J** vector in current-carrying conductors, but unlike current, flux does not have physical reality.   In spite of this, it turns out to be a very useful concept.

Since Gauss's law is useful only in problems which have a high degree of symmetry, the next logical question to ask is, "What can be done when the field is not highly symmetrical?"   We shall try to answer this question in Chap. 8 by generalizing Gauss's law to cover other cases.   Before doing so, however, we shall find it helpful to apply Gauss's law to more of the symmetrical problems and to introduce materials other than conductors and vacuum into our studies.

REFERENCES

1. Jeans, J. H.: "The Mathematical Theory of Electricity and Magnetism," 4th ed., Cambridge University Press, New York, 1923.   Probably the best source of further information concerning the use of Gauss's law in electrostatics.   Contains some excellent problems.
2. Harnwell, G. P.: "Principles of Electricity and Electromagnetism," 2d ed., Chap. I, McGraw-Hill Book Company, Inc., 1949.
3. Suydam, V. A.: "Fundamentals of Electricity and Electromagnetism," Chap. I, D. Van Nostrand Company, Inc., New York, 1940.
4. Bennet, E., and H. M. Crothers: "Introductory Electrodynamics for Engineers," McGraw-Hill Book Company, Inc., New York, 1926.   Though now out of print, this book seems to have had an extensive library distribution and should be available to many readers.   Highly recommended as collateral reading at this point is Chap. II, entitled "Fundamental Electrostatic Experiments and Their Interpretation," and the discussion of Gauss's law in Chap. V.

PROBLEMS

*5.1   At the center of a sphere, find the solid angle subtended by a polar cap in terms of the polar angle θ, between the polar axis and the radii drawn to the circumference of the cap.

*5.2   At the center of a cube, find the solid angle subtended by one face. Obtain the results from a study of the symmetry of the problem rather than by attempting to evaluate an integral.

5.3   At one of the lower corners of a cube, find the solid angle subtended by the top face.   Obtain the results as an extension of Prob. 5.2.

(*Answer:* $\pi/6$ sterradians.)

5.4   Find the solid angle subtended by an infinite plane surface, at a point not on the surface.

5.5   Find the portion of the surface of a sphere illuminated by a point source of light external to the sphere.   Find the solid angle subtended by this illuminated surface at the point source of light.

*5.6   Find the capacitance of concentric spheres of radii R_1 and R_2.   Express the field intensity at any point between the spheres in terms of the total charge on the inner sphere.   Express the field intensity at any point between the spheres in terms of the potential difference between the spheres.

*5.7 Find the capacitance of an isolated sphere by considering the results of Prob. 5.6 when the radius of the outer sphere is infinite.

*5.8 Find the field intensity and the potential due to a uniform volume-charge density, within a sphere of radius a. Give the results for points inside and outside the sphere.

5.9 Find the equation of the direction lines in the field of equal and opposite point charges by the methods of Sec. 5.5 and the results of Prob. 5.1.

(*Answer:* $\cos \alpha_1 - \cos \alpha_2 = C$.   Angles as in Fig. 5.8.)

5.10 In a coaxial cable the maximum permissible value of field intensity is E_{max}. The radius of the outer cylinder is fixed at R_2. Find the radius of the inner conductor R_1, which will give the largest possible value of potential difference without exceeding the stated value of E_{max}.

5.11 Describe an experimental technique by which one could determine the capacitance between two conductors by a measurement of conductance.

5.12 Repeat the analysis of Sec. 5.4 when the cylinder of radius b contains a volume-charge density proportional to the square of the radius. Sketch the potential hill.

5.13 Three line charges of the same polarity and equal magnitudes are arranged in a straight line with equal spacing, as a special case of Sec. 5.5. Sketch the appearance of a rubber-sheet model of the potentials, showing the contour lines. Write the equation for the potential.

*5.14 A uniform space charge is confined to the region between two imaginary, infinite parallel planes. Selecting a suitable coordinate system and taking advantage of the symmetry, use Gauss's law to find the field intensity and the potential (*a*) for the region inside the space charge, and (*b*) for the region outside the space charge. Prepare graphs similar to those of Fig. 5.5.

*5.15 Prove the statement listed as corollary (6) of Gauss's law in Sec. 5.6.

5.16 Prepare a more detailed summary of this chapter, similar to that found at the end of Chap. 4.

CHAPTER 6

THE METHOD OF IMAGES

Assigning the zero potential level to a point at infinity may be mathematically convenient, but it is not very realistic. Practically, the earth is very near us. It is not only a rather good conductor but the source of our materials and charges. In physical problems this vast conductor must be taken into account. There is a significant difference between a transmission line erected in our imagination out in space and one built near the surface of the earth. The effect is even more pronounced when the wires of a cable are enclosed in a conducting pipe for physical protection. The radio antenna on an airplane wing lives in a smaller world, but the conducting surface of the airplane wing has its effect on all the characteristics of the antenna, especially its radiation pattern.

Accounting for the influence of a conductor on a field is not difficult when the conductor is an infinite plane, an infinitely long cylinder, or a sphere. The first two will be discussed in this chapter, and the case of the sphere will be left as a problem.

6.1 Images in an Infinite Conducting Plane. We have seen that when a conductor is placed in a field, the free charges in the conductor move under the influence of the forces of the field. In doing so, they change the nature of the field within and without the conductor until

1. The region occupied by the conductor is an equipotential region.
2. The field intensity is normal to the surface of the conductor.

In the field due to equal and opposite point charges, the plane which is the perpendicular bisector of the line between the charges is an equipotential surface. Into this location, an infinite conducting plane can be inserted without changing the nature of the field, as depicted in Fig. 6.1. When this has been done, the negative point charge in the lower part of the figure can be removed without changing the field in the upper part of the figure. This can be thought of as an extreme case of the principle of shielding, developed in the previous chapter as a corollary of Gauss's law. The apparently missing part of the boundary of the closed hollow conductor can be formed by a conducting hemisphere of infinite radius, since the potential is also zero at infinite distance from a point charge.

The induced surface charge on the conducting plane terminates the direction lines of the field, and the total charge induced on the entire plane is equal in magnitude and opposite in sign to the point charge.

On an infinite conducting plane, the induced surface charge produces a field which is identical to that which would be produced by locating an image of each real point charge as a mirror image. The image charge is opposite in sign and equal in magnitude to the real charge, and is located on the extension of the perpendicular dropped from the point charge to the conducting plane and at the same distance.

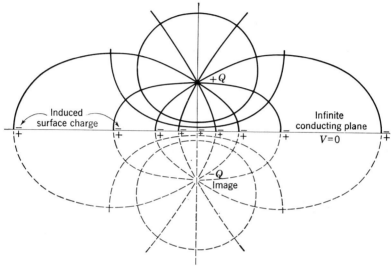

FIG. 6.1 Image of a point charge in an infinite conducting plane. The direction lines have been selected to show the symmetry of the field at the point charge.

The forces of attraction between a point charge and an infinite conducting plane are the same as the forces of attraction between the charge and its image. The field in which the real point charge finds itself is indistinguishable from the field which would be attributed to the presence of its image.

The method of images is used to reduce problems involving conductors to sections or parts of previously solved problems. To find the forces of attraction between a point charge and two infinite planes intersecting at an angle of 60°, for example, as in Fig. 6.2a, we look for a field involving point charges alone which has two plane equipotentials at a 60° angle. Such a field configuration is shown in Fig. 6.2b. Every point in the plane oa is equidistant from the members of three pairs of equal and opposite point charges, paired off by the numbers 1-6, 5-2, 3-4. Similarly, every point in the plane ob is equidistant from equal and opposite charges paired off by the numbers 1-2, 3-6, 5-4. To obtain a numerical answer, we could now compute the force on the real charge which would be caused by the five image charges. In this type of problem, the number of images depends on the angle between the planes. The number is finite only when the angle is a submultiple of 2π.

Since every point charge has an image in an infinite conducting plane, we also find that a line charge has an image, too. The image line has the same magnitude as the actual line and is located as far below the plane as the actual line is above the plane. This is a two-dimensional field and lends itself to striking portrayal in a fluid-flow map. Two versions appear in Figs. 6.3 and 6.4.

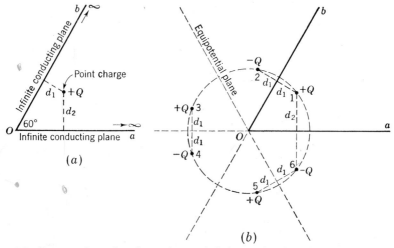

FIG. 6.2   Images of a point charge in two infinite conducting planes intersecting at an angle of 60°.

In physical models, we must be satisfied with finite dimensions. In these models, additional circular boundaries were provided to avoid some of the difficulties. As a result, the maps properly depict the most interesting parts of the field. In Fig. 6.3 the usual random spacing of the potassium permanganate crystals was used, while in Fig. 6.4 the crystals were placed at regular intervals at the boundaries in order to show more clearly the circular nature of the stream lines. The latter figure looks very much like one-half of the map of the two line charges of opposite polarity, in Fig. 2.12.

Figure 6.5 shows a rubber-sheet model of a line charge near a conducting plane. In the model, elevation represents potential, as previously stated. A heavy steel bar holds the sheet in a horizontal position to simulate the conducting plane. This figure should be compared with Fig. 3.14, which is a model of equal and opposite line charges. A better model, arising from the image of a line charge in a cylinder, appears in the following section as Fig. 6.9.

FIG. 6.3   Fluid-flow map of the direction lines in the field of a line charge and an infinite conducting plane, with random placing of the potassium permanganate crystals which dye the stream.

FIG. 6.4   Fluid-flow map of the direction lines in the field of a line charge and an infinite conducting plane, with the crystals of potassium permanganate placed deliberately.

6.2   The Geometric Theorem of Inverse Points.   When cylindrical or spherical conductors are involved in electrostatics problems, it is sometimes possible to find configurations of line charges and point charges which produce equipotential surfaces which can be made to coincide with the conducting surface.   Through this technique one may fit the conductor into a section of the field of a previously solved problem.   Before

FIG. 6.5   Rubber-sheet model of the potential field of a line charge near an infinite conducting plane.   The steel bar at the left prevents the rod, representing the line charge, from lifting the sheet.

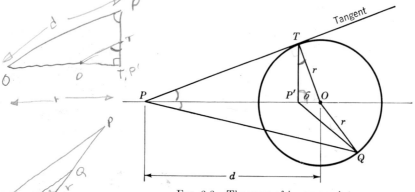

FIG. 6.6   Theorem of inverse points.

illustrating the procedure, a good deal of time will be saved by proving a geometric theorem regarding inverse points.

As in Fig. 6.6, from a point P, external to a circle of radius r, construct the tangent PT and the radius OT.   From T drop a perpendicular to OP, calling the intersection P'.   The two right triangles TPO and $P'TO$ are similar.   Denote the length of the line OP' as δ and that of OP as d. Then

$$\frac{r}{d} = \frac{\delta}{r} = \frac{P'T}{PT} \tag{1}$$

Rearranging the first equality,

$$\delta d = r^2 \tag{2}$$

Because of this relation of distances from the center, points P and P' are known as inverse points.

To any other point Q on the circle, draw PQ, $P'Q$, and OQ. Triangles OPQ and $P'QO$ have a common angle. Since from Eq. (1) the adjacent sides are proportional, these triangles are also similar, permitting us to write

$$\frac{\delta}{r} = \frac{r}{d} = \frac{QP'}{QP} \tag{3}$$

The ratio QP'/QP does not depend on the location of Q on the circle.

6.3   The Image of a Line Charge in a Conducting Cylinder.   We are given a line charge λ inside a conducting cylinder, and our problem is to

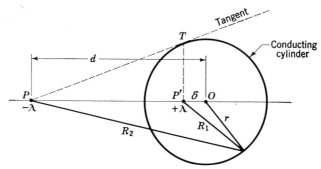

Fig. 6.7   Image of a line charge in a conducting cylinder. The image is equal in magnitude to the actual line charge, and is located at the inverse point.

determine the field.   We are given λ, r, and the distance δ as shown in Fig. 6.7.

In studying the field due to equal and oppositely charged lines in Sec. 3.5, we found that the equipotential surfaces were cylinders and that the equation of these surfaces was

$$V = \frac{\lambda}{2\pi\epsilon_0} \log_e \frac{R_2}{R_1} = \text{a constant}$$

If this is to be true at every point on the conducting cylinder in the present problem, then we must have

$$\frac{R_2}{R_1} = \text{a constant}$$

This is a condition satisfied by R_2 and R_1 if the points P and P' are inverse points as in Sec. 6.2.   Hence, by locating an image of the given line charge at the inverse point, the problem is reduced to one which has been solved previously.   The line charge will raise the cylinder to the potential

$$V = \frac{\lambda}{2\pi\epsilon_0} \log_e \frac{R_2}{R_1} \tag{1}$$

We do not know the numerical value of R_2 and R_1, but from the similarity of the triangles,

$$\frac{R_2}{R_1} = \frac{r}{\delta}$$

Since δ and r are known, we may use the equivalent expression

$$V = \frac{\lambda}{2\pi\epsilon_0} \log_e \frac{r}{\delta} \tag{2}$$

for the potential of the cylinder.

The induced charge on the outer surface of the cylinder is uniformly distributed, giving a symmetrical uniform field which is the same as that

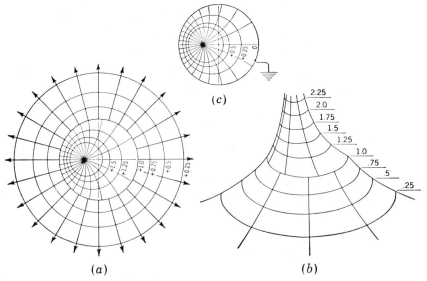

FIG. 6.8   A line charge inside a conducting cylinder induces an equal charge distributed uniformly on the outer surface.   The field outside is like that due to a line charge placed at the center of the cylinder.   The field inside is a part of the field of two line charges.   A potential-hill interpretation is shown in b.   The field inside does not change when the outer charge is removed by grounding the cylinder, but the reference level of potential changes, as shown in c.

which would be produced if the line charge were located at the center of the cylinder.   Figure 6.8a was traced, in part, from the field of two line charges, Fig. 3.7, and the potential levels in the two figures are the same. The potentials outside the conducting cylinder are given with respect to a reference level determined from Eq. (2).   A potential-hill interpretation of this field is shown in Fig. 6.8b.   In this part of the figure, again, elevation represents the potential. A rubber-sheet model of the field would conform to the shape of the hill if conditions were ideal.

When the induced charge is removed from the outer cylinder, as in part *c* of Fig. 6.8, only the reference level changes, and the potential differences between successive equipotentials inside the conducting cylinder remain the same as before. Outside, however, the field has vanished. The potential-hill drawing suggests that removing the induced charge

Fig. 6.9.   Rubber-sheet model of a line charge in a conducting cylinder.

from the outer surface is equivalent to pushing the lower part of the hill down until it becomes a flat plane.

Figure 6.9 is a photograph of a rubber-sheet model of a line charge inside a conducting cylinder. This configuration is much easier to model than is the image of a line charge in a plane, because the model can be constructed accurately with boundaries of finite dimensions. By comparing the Figs. 6.9 and 6.5, one sees that the image of a line charge in a plane is the limiting case of the image of a line charge in a cylinder whose radius is infinite.

When a single line charge λ is located outside a conducting cylinder which is grounded so that it can acquire a charge of $-\lambda$, then it is the field outside the cylinder which can be fitted into the field map of two line charges. To assign the zero potential level to the cylinder requires a shift in reference level as indicated by those shown in Fig. 6.10. If the cylinder is insulated so that it cannot acquire any charge, the field is no longer that due to two line charges, but is the superposition of this field and a third line carrying $+\lambda$ but located at the center of the cylinder as required by Gauss's law. We shall not pursue this particular phase of images any further, however. An analysis can be found in Weber, listed in the references at the end of this chapter.

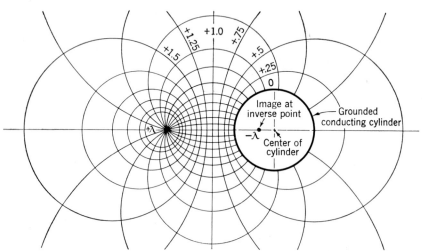

FIG. 6.10   Field due to a line charge and a grounded conducting cylinder. Here the potential of the bisecting plane, as well as the potential at infinity, is arbitrarily assigned a value other than zero.

6.4   The Capacitance of Parallel Cylinders, Infinitely Long. If we know the radii of two parallel conducting cylinders, infinitely long, and the spacing between them, we can determine the nature of the field due to a given potential difference. In order to do this now, we must find two line charges which would produce equipotentials of the proper magnitudes and radii to coincide with the surfaces of the cylinders. While this problem can be solved for cylinders of unequal radii, we shall confine our analysis to the special case in which the cylinders are of the same size. This is the problem of the two-wire transmission line, when the wires have the same size and the effect of the earth is neglected. In a later section we shall consider the effect of the earth.

The given conditions are shown in Fig. 6.11a, and the necessary geometry needed to solve the problem is indicated directly below in part b. We establish a potential difference of V_m between the cylinders, and choose the bisecting plane of symmetry as the zero potential level. This places one cylinder at a potential of $+\frac{1}{2}V_m$ and the other at $-\frac{1}{2}V_m$. The equivalent image line charges would produce an equipotential surface coinciding with the right-hand cylinder, and the potential so produced may be written from our analysis of two line charges as

$$V = \frac{\lambda}{2\pi\epsilon_0} \log_e \frac{R_2}{R_1} \tag{1}$$

For coincidence with our established potential differences the value of the potential given by Eq. (1) must equal $\frac{1}{2}V_m$ on the positive cylinder.

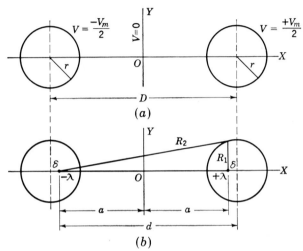

FIG. 6.11 Analysis of the field due to two charged conducting cylinders. The given conditions are shown in a, while the images and the necessary geometry to solve the problem are shown in b.

Writing this as an equation,

$$\frac{V_m}{2} = \frac{\lambda}{2\pi\epsilon_0} \log_e \frac{R_2}{R_1} \tag{2}$$

This relation must hold for all points on the right-hand cylinder, and for this to be true the equivalent line charges must be located at inverse points. Therefore

$$\frac{R_2}{R_1} = \frac{d}{r} \tag{3}$$

When this is substituted into Eq. (2) and the common factors are canceled,

$$V_m = \frac{\lambda}{\pi\epsilon_0} \log_e \frac{d}{r} \tag{4}$$

Unfortunately, we do not yet know d, since we have been given only D and r in the original problem. To express Eq. (4) in terms of D, we have the other equality from the theorem of inverse points

$$\delta d = r^2 \tag{5}$$

and see from the figure that

$$d = D - \delta \tag{6}$$

Solving Eqs. (5) and (6) for the ratio d/r by the quadratic formula, we obtain

$$\frac{d}{r} = \frac{D}{2r} \pm \sqrt{\left(\frac{D}{2r}\right)^2 - 1} \tag{7}$$

The negative radical is extraneous because the value of d here sought is greater than $D/2$. We may now write Eq. (4) in terms of D and r. First, however, we shall include an identity in hyperbolic functions

$$\log_e (x + \sqrt{x^2 - 1}) = \cosh^{-1} x \tag{8}$$

to obtain the shorter and conventional form

$$V_m = \frac{\lambda}{\pi \epsilon_0} \cosh^{-1} \frac{D}{2r} \tag{9}$$

This equation relates λ to the potential difference established between the two cylinders. The capacitance per unit length is the charge per unit length λ divided by the potential difference between the cylinders. From Eq. (9), this is

$$\frac{C}{L} = \frac{\pi \epsilon_0}{\cosh^{-1} (D/2r)} \qquad \text{farads per meter} \tag{10}$$

From Eq. (4),

$$\frac{C}{L} = \frac{\pi \epsilon_0}{\log_e (d/r)} \tag{11}$$

Both Eq. (10) and Eq. (11) are exact, but Eq. (11) has been recorded because, when the separation of the wires is considerably greater than their radii, there is little numerical difference between the exact results of Eq. (11) and the approximate form obtained by using D/r instead of d/r.

$$\frac{C}{L} = \frac{\pi \epsilon_0}{\log_e (D/r)} \qquad \text{(approximately)} \tag{12}$$

6.5   The Field of a Two-wire Transmission Line over a Conducting Earth.   When a two-wire transmission line is erected over a conducting earth, the exact nature of the field is difficult to determine. As in Fig. 6.12, a line charge should be located at point c in cylinder 2 due to the charge on cylinder 1, but at d due to the image of 2 below the surface of the earth. However, when the radius of the wires is small compared to their height and spacing no great numerical error will result from locating the equivalent line charges at the center of the wires, as in Fig. 6.13. Here we consider the case of unequal heights over the earth, to obtain the results for equal heights as a special case.

We shall use the notation of Fig. 6.13.   Taking a as a point on the surface of the positively charged wire, and b as a point on the negatively charged wire, we may determine the approximate potential difference between the wires by finding the potential at each of the wires, using a point on the earth as the reference point.

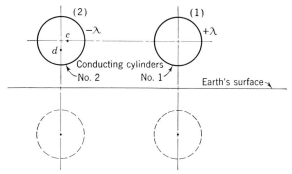

FIG. 6.12   Two charged cylinders over a conducting earth.

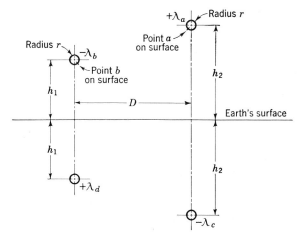

FIG. 6.13   Analysis of capacitance of two long wires over a conducting earth.

The potential at a due to λ_a is

$$\frac{+\lambda}{2\pi\epsilon_0} \log_e \frac{h_2}{r}$$

The potential at a due to λ_b is

$$\frac{-\lambda}{2\pi\epsilon_0} \log_e \frac{\sqrt{D^2 + h_1{}^2}}{\sqrt{D^2 + (h_2 - h_1)^2}}$$

The potential at a due to λ_c is

$$\frac{-\lambda}{2\pi\epsilon_0} \log_e \frac{h_2}{2h_2}$$

FIG. 6.14   Fluid-flow map of the direction lines in the field of two charged cylinders above a conducting plane at unequal heights.

The potential at a due to λ_d is

$$\frac{+\lambda}{2\pi\epsilon_0} \log_e \frac{\sqrt{D^2 + h_1{}^2}}{\sqrt{D^2 + (h_2 + h_1)^2}}$$

Then the approximate total potential at a is the sum of the four contributions:

$$\frac{\lambda}{2\pi\epsilon_0} \log_e \frac{2h_2}{r} \sqrt{\frac{D^2 + (h_2 - h_1)^2}{D^2 + (h_2 + h_1)^2}} \qquad (1)$$

On the surface of the other wire, the potential at b due to λ_b is

$$\frac{-\lambda}{2\pi\epsilon_0} \log_e \frac{\sqrt{D^2 + h_1{}^2}}{r}$$

The potential at b due to λ_a is

$$\frac{+\lambda}{2\pi\epsilon_0} \log_e \frac{h_2}{\sqrt{D^2 + (h_2 - h_1)^2}}$$

The potential at b due to λ_d is

$$\frac{+\lambda}{2\pi\epsilon_0} \log_e \frac{\sqrt{D^2 + h_1{}^2}}{2h_1}$$

The potential at b due to λ_c is

$$\frac{-\lambda}{2\pi\epsilon_0} \log_e \frac{h_2}{\sqrt{D^2 + (h_2 + h_1)^2}}$$

FIG. 6.15 Fluid-flow map of the direction lines in the field of two charged cylinders at equal heights above a conducting plane.

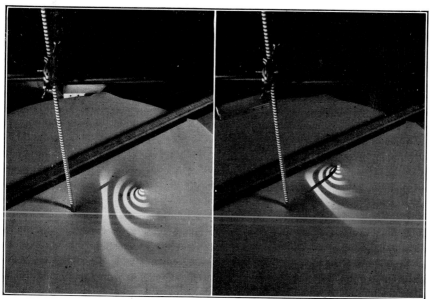

FIG. 6.16 Rubber-sheet models of the potential field of two line charges near a conducting plane. Unequal distances from the plane at the left, and equal distances from the plane at the right.

The total potential at b is

$$\frac{-\lambda}{2\pi\epsilon_0} \log_e \frac{2h_1}{r} \sqrt{\frac{D^2 + (h_2 - h_1)^2}{D^2 + (h_2 + h_1)^2}} \tag{2}$$

Then the potential difference between wires is the potential at a minus the potential at b, which is

$$V_m = \frac{\lambda}{2\pi\epsilon_0} \log_e \frac{4h_1h_2}{r^2} \frac{D^2 + (h_2 - h_1)^2}{D^2 + (h_2 + h_1)^2} \tag{3}$$

For the purposes of comparison with Eqs. 6.4 (4) and (9), we may write this as

$$V_m = \frac{\lambda}{\pi\epsilon_0} \log_e \frac{2\sqrt{h_1h_2}}{r} \sqrt{\frac{D^2 + (h_2 - h_1)^2}{D^2 + (h_2 + h_1)^2}} \tag{4}$$

When the wires are at the same height, $h_2 = h_1 = h$ and

$$V_m = \frac{\lambda}{\pi\epsilon_0} \log_e \frac{D}{r} \frac{2h}{\sqrt{D^2 + (2h)^2}} \tag{5}$$

The equivalent capacitance, for wires at the same height, is obtained from Eq. (5) as

$$\frac{C}{L} = \frac{\pi\epsilon_0}{\log_e \dfrac{D}{r} \dfrac{2h}{\sqrt{D^2 + (2h)^2}}} \tag{6}$$

Comparing the last expression with Eq. 6.4 (12), we see that the effect of the earth is to increase the capacitance[1] by reducing the magnitude of the logarithmic term.

Fluid-flow maps for the cases of unequal and equal heights are shown in Figs. 6.14 and 6.15, respectively. Both figures were made from one model with three holes, one of which is temporarily plugged and shows as a circular shadow in each photograph. Here, again, most effective study of the field can be made by sketching in the equipotentials on a piece of tracing paper laid over the figures.

Photographs of rubber-sheet models for unequal and equal heights are shown as Fig. 6.16 with contour lighting on the upper part of the sheet, where the potentials are positive.

6.6 A Conducting Cylinder in a Uniform Field. In the previous chapter, the map of a conducting cylinder in a uniform field was presented as Fig. 5.11, to accompany a qualitative discussion of what happens when a conductor is placed in an electric field. We are now prepared for a

---

[1] In finding the capacitance between the wires, we have here computed the ratio of the charge to the potential difference between two conductors carrying equal and opposite charges, in the presence of a third conductor, the earth, which is uncharged. This has extended the concept of capacitance beyond our definition, which applied to a field in which only two conductors were involved. Though we shall not investigate the procedure in this book, in a study of fields in which more than two conductors are involved, it is customary to define *capacitance coefficients* and from these to obtain a system of *partial capacitances*. Discussions will be found in both the references listed at the end of this chapter.

quantitative analysis of this problem, which can be made by using the method of images.

We have found a zero potential plane midway between equal and opposite line charges which are infinitely long. When the separation of the line charges is very great, the field approaches a uniform field at the center of this plane. In Fig. 6.17, the region of the uniform field is at the origin.

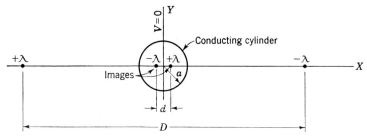

FIG. 6.17 Analysis of the field due to a conducting cylinder in a uniform field by the method of images.

At the origin the field intensity due to the remote line charges may be written from Eq. 2.9 (3) by adapting it to this figure.

$$\mathbf{E} = \frac{2\lambda}{\pi\epsilon_0 D}\,\mathbf{i} \tag{1}$$

In order to produce a uniform field of this magnitude, let the charge λ and the distance D each approach infinity in such a manner that the right-hand side of Eq. (1) is a constant equal to E_u where the subscript denotes the given value of field intensity in the uniform field. That is,

$$\frac{\lambda}{D} = \frac{\pi\epsilon_0}{2}\,E_u \tag{2}$$

Due to the conducting cylinder, the image charges appear on the x axis at the inverse points separated a distance d, in which

$$\left(\frac{d}{2}\right)\left(\frac{D}{2}\right) = a^2$$

and

$$d = \frac{4a^2}{D} \tag{3}$$

The product λd is

$$\lambda d = \frac{4a^2\lambda}{D} \tag{4}$$

which, in terms of (2), is

$$\lambda d = 2a^2\pi\epsilon_0 E_u \tag{5}$$

As λ and D approach infinity, the product λd remains finite and the image lines form a line dipole of moment λd, similar to the point charge dipole of moment $P = qd$, in Sec. 3.11. We shall treat the problem now as a superposition of the uniform field E_u and the field due to the line dipole λd.

For convenience and to parallel the previous dipole analysis, we shall shift the origin by the infinitesimal distance $d/2$ as in Fig. 6.18 and use cylindrical coordinates. The potential at the point P due to the line dipole is

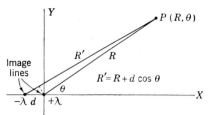

FIG. 6.18   Analysis of the field due to the images of two line charges in a conducting cylinder, as a line dipole.

$$V_{dp} = \frac{\lambda}{2\pi\epsilon_0} \log_e \frac{R'}{R} \tag{6}$$

To a first approximation

$$R' = R + d \cos \theta$$

and

$$\frac{R'}{R} = \left(1 + \frac{d}{R} \cos \theta\right) \tag{7}$$

A Taylor-series expansion of $\log_e (1 + x)$ is

$$\log_e (1 + x) = x - \frac{x^2}{2} + \frac{x^3}{3} \cdots \tag{8}$$

Using the first term and substituting in Eq. (6),

$$V_{dp} = \frac{\lambda d}{2\pi\epsilon_0 R} \cos \theta \tag{9}$$

But λd is known from Eq. (5) *in the limit in which these approximations are removed;* hence

$$V_{dp} = E_u \frac{a^2 \cos \theta}{R} \tag{10}$$

Adding a term expressing the potential at point P due to the uniform field, the total potential at P is

$$V = + \frac{E_u a^2}{R} \cos \theta - E_u R \cos \theta \tag{11}$$

To find the field intensity, we have

$$\mathbf{E} = -\nabla V$$

which in cylindrical coordinates is

$$\mathbf{E} = -\frac{\partial V}{\partial R} \mathbf{r} - \frac{\partial V}{R\partial \theta} \boldsymbol{\theta} - \frac{\partial V}{\partial z} \mathbf{k} \tag{12}$$

Applying the partial differentiation in Eq. (12) to Eq. (11),

$$\frac{\partial V}{\partial R} = -E_u \cos \theta - E_u \frac{a^2 \cos \theta}{R^2}$$

$$\frac{\partial V}{\partial \theta} = E_u R \sin \theta - E_u \frac{a^2 \sin \theta}{R}$$

$$\frac{\partial V}{\partial z} = 0$$

Substituting in Eq. (12),

$$\mathbf{E} = \left(E_u \cos \theta + \frac{E_u a^2 \cos \theta}{R^2} \right) \mathbf{r} + \left(-E_u \sin \theta + E_u \frac{a^2 \sin \theta}{R^2} \right) \mathbf{\theta} \quad (13)$$

On the surface of the cylinder when $R = a$, the θ component is zero, as we expect from the requirement that all electrostatic fields be normal to the surface of conductors.

The expression for $\mathbf{E}$ when $R = a$ is

$$\mathbf{E} = 2E_u \cos \theta \, \mathbf{r} \qquad R = a \qquad (14)$$

which has, as its greatest value, twice the magnitude of the uniform field. The surface-charge density is related to $\mathbf{E}$ by a Gauss's-law corollary,

$$\mathbf{E} = \frac{\sigma}{\epsilon_0} \mathbf{n} \qquad (15)$$

which gives

$$\sigma = 2\epsilon_0 E_u \cos \theta \qquad (16)$$

As was stated in the beginning paragraph of this section, the field was mapped as Fig. 5.11, and reference to this figure should again be made.

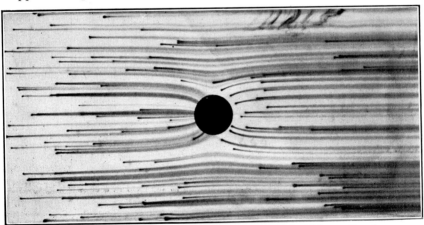

FIG. 6.19   Fluid-flow map of the direction lines in the field which results when a conducting cylinder is placed in a uniform field.

A fluid-flow map of the field appears in Fig. 6.19.   The hole in the center of the figure simulates an equipotential surface in the electric field, because it is an equal-pressure surface in the fluid-flow field.   Neither source nor sink, the circular region is simply a hole in the stream, in which the still waters run deep (to quote an old saw).

A rubber-sheet model of a conducting cylinder in a uniform field is shown as Fig. 6.20.   The frame holding the rubber sheet is tilted to simulate the uniform field.   By means of rods from above and below, a circular region of the sheet is held in a horizontal position. The confi-

guration suggests that someone has created a neat symmetrical level spot
on the side of a steep hill in order, perhaps, to plant a tree.   To do this,
he cut into the bank above and filled in below.   The stream lines follow
the paths of drainage.   As in the other rubber-sheet models in this book,
the contourlike shadows are cast onto the sheet by a projector in which
the slide is a ruled grating of horizontal lines.   The true nature of this

Fig. 6.20   Rubber-sheet model of the potentials in the field of a conducting cylinder
placed in a uniform field.

two-dimensional problem should not be forgotten as the mind pursues the
similarity of the physical model to familiar things.   Indeed, it would be a
good idea now to refer to Sec. 3.10, in which these models were first introduced, and especially to our *understanding* which appears in the second
paragraph of that section.

We shall solve this problem again by a different method as an illustration of a solution of Laplace's equation.   The purpose of the present
illustration is to tie together as many of our previous ideas as possible,
and we have utilized the following:

1. A line charge as a building block
2. Gauss's law
3. The concept of potential

4. The use of the gradient operation
5. The use of the dipole as a building block
6. Superposition of fields and potentials
7. The method of images

6.7 A Summary and a Criticism. The method of images reduces some field problems involving conducting planes, cylinders, and spheres to previously solved problems.

The image of a point charge in an infinite conducting plane is equal in magnitude and opposite in sign and is located at a distance behind the plane equal to the perpendicular distance from the real charge to the plane. The same statement applies to the image of a line charge in a plane. The image of an infinite line charge in an infinite conducting cylinder has the same magnitude and the opposite sign but is located at the inverse point. The image of a point charge in a grounded conducting sphere is opposite in sign and is also located at the inverse point, but the magnitude of the image is smaller than that of the real charge. Numerically, the magnitude of the image Q' is

$$Q' = -Q\frac{a}{d}$$

where a = radius of sphere

d = distance from real charge to center of sphere

(See Prob. 6.2.)

With the finesse which comes from experience, the method of images may be used to solve such relatively advanced problems as the field due to a conducting cylinder in a uniform field and a conducting sphere in a uniform field. Study of this approach helps to tie the various concepts of fields together and to emphasize again the importance of boundary conditions. The method of images may also be used with nonconductors, but we shall not pursue the subject that far in this book. We are still limited by the same requirements of symmetry inherent in the approach of Gauss's law as studied in the previous chapter.

REFERENCES

1. Weber, Ernst: "Electromagnetic Fields," Vol. I, John Wiley & Sons, Inc., New York, 1950.
2. Smythe, William R.: "Static and Dynamic Electricity," McGraw-Hill Book Company, Inc., New York, 1939.

    Both these books contain extensive discussions and examples of the method of images.

PROBLEMS

*6.1 (a) Derive an expression for the work per unit of charge required to remove an electron from a point near an infinite conducting plane, against the force of attraction of its image.   (b) If the work function of the material of the conducting plane is experimentally determined as equal to 3.6 volts, what is the equivalent initial distance between the electron and the plane?   (c) Is there any essential difference in the energy required to remove the electron from the initial point in (b) to infinity, compared to that required to remove it to a point 1 millimeter from the plane?

*6.2   A positive charge q is located at the origin.   A conducting sphere of radius R has its center on the $+x$ axis at d.   The sphere is grounded so that its potential is zero.   Find the magnitude and position of the image charge in terms of d and R.   The answer is stated in the summary.

*6.3   A charged line is erected in a vertical position in the corner of a large room with conducting walls.   The distance to the two walls is a and b.   Describe the field and the force on the line in terms of images.

6.4   By methods similar to those of Sec. 6.5, find an approximate expression for the capacitance of two spheres of equal radii which are separated by a great distance compared to a radius.   Find a similar expression for the conductance of two remote spheres floating half in and half out of a vast extent of sea water of conductivity γ.

6.5   (a) Outline a procedure of obtaining the field due to an uncharged conducting sphere placed in a uniform field using images of point charges.   (b) Solve the problem.

6.6   Show that Eq. 6.6(1) follows from Eq. 2.9(3).

6.7   Compare the numerical magnitudes of the capacitance of a two-wire line as given by Eqs. 6.4(11) and (12) for (a) $D = 4r$, and (b) $D = 10r$.

6.8   For $D = h = 10r$, compare the capacitance of a two-wire line over a conducting earth as given by Eq. 6.5(6) with that given by Eq. 6.4(12) which ignores the effect of the earth.

6.9   Find the charge distribution induced on the surface of an infinite plane by (a) a point charge, (b) a line charge.   Using the methods of Prob. 2.5 or 3.9, show that the point charge and the line charge find themselves in a field identical to that due to their images.

6.10   In Fig. 6.8a, find the radius of the cylinder on which the potential is zero, in terms of the radius of the conducting cylinder.   The charge inside the cylinder has the magnitude of $2\pi\epsilon_0$ coulombs per meter of line length.   Find the radius of the cylinder on which the potential is -0.25 volt with respect to this arbitrary reference level.

CHAPTER 7

DIELECTRICS AND INSULATION

7.1 Dielectric Materials and Their Response to Electric Forces.
Metals act as good conductors because of an abundance of free electrons
which are free to move from one molecule to another. Many liquid solutions act as good conductors because of the mobility of the ions which act
as current carriers. In another class of materials, known as nonconductors, the binding forces on the valence electrons prevent their interchange
and the conduction phenomenon is practically absent. While there is no
sharp dividing line between the two classes of materials, at the extremes
their relative conductivities are vastly different. The conductivity of
copper exceeds that of fused quartz by a factor of 10^{24}. When our attention is focused on the internal rearrangement of charge which results from
the application of electric fields, nonconducting materials are called *dielectrics*. We also refer to these materials as dielectrics when investigating
their relative effects on capacitance. When a dielectric material is used
as a part of a physical structure to confine conduction currents to a limited
region of space, we refer to the dielectric material as an insulator.

When a material substance is placed in an electric field, its action
depends on its molecular structure. A simple classification which permits
us to examine two types of response to electric fields is to group molecules
into categories described as nonpolar and polar. In nonpolar molecules
the centers of the positive and negative charges coincide, while in polar
molecules there is a permanent displacement of the centers of charge
which causes them to act like dipoles. The simplest example of a nonpolar molecule is the hydrogen atom, which can be thought of as a relatively massive positive point charge surrounded by a jellylike volume
charge distribution of negative charge. The jellylike volume charge distribution represents the time-average position of the electron. Under
the action of an external electric field there is no net force on the atom
itself, but the electron will spend a little more of the time on one side of
the nucleus than the other so that the equivalent jelly of negative charge
is no longer centered at the nucleus as indicated in Fig. 7.1*b*. When this
occurs, the molecule acts like a dipole only when it is being influenced by
an electric field, and it is said to be an induced dipole.

173

In polar molecules, on the other hand, we are told that there is a permanent displacement of the centers of charge. The resulting *permanent* charge configuration responds to an electric field as does our dipole consisting of two point charges which are very close together. The electric field produces a torque on such a dipole tending to align it with the electric field. The observable effects of such an alignment will be obscured, of course, by any random movements of the molecules, but the time-average will give us an equivalent picture in which the molecules are fixed in position. An extreme case of polar molecules is that of carnauba wax. If the melted wax is placed in an electric field, the polar molecules align

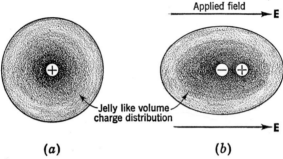

(a)   **(b)**

Fig. 7.1   (*a*) In a nonpolar molecule, in the absence of an electric field, the centers of positive and negative charge coincide; (*b*) when an electric field is applied, the electron spends a little more of its time on one side of the nucleus than on the other, resulting in a displacement of the two centers of charge. In either case, the time-average position of the electron is equivalent to a jellylike volume charge distribution.

themselves with the field. If the material is allowed to solidify in the field, the "polarization" is frozen into the material and it becomes the electric counterpart of a permanent magnet called an *electret*. Electrets have the property of aligning themselves with electric fields when suspended like compass needles, and if they are cut into smaller pieces, each piece has the same property. The two sketches in Fig. 7.2 are an exaggerated pictorial representation of the changes occurring in the formation of an electret.

In this qualitative picture there are two essential ideas; the electric field produces a *stretching* and a *twisting*, and the stretching and twisting forces are opposed by the forces which hold each molecule together and by the intermolecular forces holding the molecules of a solid into a relatively fixed position. The displacements involve a time delay, energy storage, and a dissipation of energy throughout the volume of the material. Though a volume phenomenon is clearly present, in developing a quantitative description of this phenomenon we shall show that it is equivalent to a surface effect. This will prove quite satisfactory for electrostatics and for simple materials which are isotropic (which means that they have uniform properties in all directions). In considering time-varying fields it is necessary to account for the time delays and the dissipation of energy.

In Fig. 7.3, a sheet of dielectric material has been placed in a uniform electric field. Here, only the dipoles near the surface are shown. In the

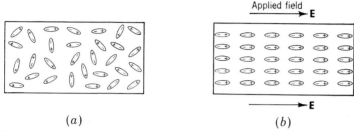

Applied field
$\longrightarrow$ **E**

$\longrightarrow$ **E**

(a) (b)

FIG. 7.2 A diagrammatic representation of polarization, as in the formation of an electret. In the absence of an applied field, the polar molecules are arranged in a random fashion as in part a. Under the influence of the field (part b), the dipoles tend to align themselves with the field.

free-space region outside the dielectric, the field intensity is denoted as E_0. Because of the induced surface charges σ_i, there is a field within the dielectric which opposes the external field and reduces the field inside to

$$E_i = E_0 - \frac{\sigma_i}{\epsilon_0} \qquad (1)$$

In the simplest kinds of materials, the magnitude of the induced surface charge is proportional to the field intensity within the material, E_i.

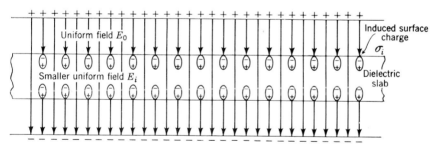

Uniform field E_0

Smaller uniform field E_i

Induced surface charge
σ_i

Dielectric slab

FIG. 7.3 Diagrammatic representation of a dielectric slab in a uniform field. For the case shown, the dielectric constant is equal to 2. The field intensity in the slab is reduced in magnitude to half that outside the slab by the induced surface charge.

Denoting this proportionality constant as k and rewriting Eq. (1), we obtain

$$E_i = E_0 - \frac{kE_i}{\epsilon_0} \qquad (2)$$

Solving now for E_i

$$E_i = \frac{E_0}{1 + (k/\epsilon_0)} \tag{3}$$

The entire denominator of this expression is known as the *dielectric constant* K. The constant k is known as the dielectric susceptibility, obtained experimentally from the dielectric constant.

$$K = 1 + \frac{k}{\epsilon_0} \tag{4}$$

In terms of Eq. (4), Eq. (3) may be written

$$E_i = \frac{E_0}{K} \tag{5}$$

The product of the dielectric constant and the permittivity of free space is called the permittivity of the dielectric material, denoted as ϵ.

$$\epsilon = K\epsilon_0 \tag{6}$$

In Fig. 7.3, it was necessary to indicate the magnitude of the field by the number of direction lines. The field inside is half as strong as that

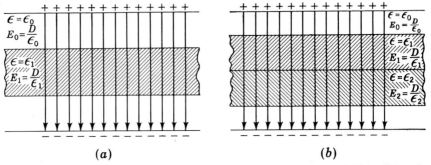

(a)   (b)

Fig. 7.4   Use of the continuous normal **D** vector to represent the field in dielectric materials.   In *a*, a single dielectric slab is bounded by a uniform field in a vacuum. Two different dielectric slabs, also in a uniform field, are shown in *b*.

outside, indicating a dielectric constant of 2.   In our other field maps, especially those in current-carrying conductors, we have been using the direction lines to represent only the direction of the vector quantity and not its magnitude.   In dielectrics it would be convenient to continue the direction lines right through the boundary between materials, ignoring the surface charges entirely, since in this case they do not change the direction of the field but only its magnitude.   Two such field maps appear in Fig. 7.4.   In part *a* a single dielectric material is present, while in part *b* two different dielectric materials are shown.   Here the direction lines are suggestive of the continuous current-density vector **J** in field maps of two current-carrying conductors "in series." In a similar way, we associate the discontinuity in the **E** vector with a property of the material itself, called its permittivity. We write a vector relationship similar to Ohm's law, which relates the **D** vector to the **E** vector through

$$\mathbf{D} = \epsilon\mathbf{E} \tag{7}$$

From this comparative viewpoint, the permittivity of a material plays the same role, mathematically and topographically, as the conductivity. The dielectric constant can be thought of as analogous to a factor of conductivity relative to the standard "material," free space. All other permittivities are greater than that of free space. To make a word most suggestive of conductivity, the term *capacitivity* is sometimes used. Capacitivity is much more suggestive of the analogy to conductivity than is the term permittivity.

So far, we have examined conditions within and without the dielectric only in a uniform field. The polarization which reduces the field intensity within the dielectric does not affect the field outside, but this is true only in this one special case. When a dielectric is placed in a nonuniform field, or the dielectric is not in the form of an infinite slab, the polarization changes the field outside, too. Figure 7.5 shows a dielectric cylinder placed in a field originally uniform. The field outside is the superposition of the uniform field and the field due to the rearrangement of the position of the dipoles within the dielectric. This has the effect of reducing the field along the top and bottom of the cylinder and increasing it along the horizontal axis of symmetry. The net effect is to produce a uniform field of finite magnitude within the dielectric cylinder, and this uniform field is smaller than the original uniform field, as may be seen from the relative spacing of the equipotentials. Observe, too, that the direction lines are not normal to the surface of the cylinder. This surface is not an equipotential surface as it was in the case of a conducting cylinder. A further discussion of these conditions will appear in a following section, in which we shall examine the general boundary conditions at the surface of a dielectric.

7.2 Dielectric Breakdown and Dielectric Strength. The point at which a dielectric material ceases to be essentially a nonconductor, and either permits appreciable conduction currents or is physically disrupted, is one of considerable interest to the engineer. There are so many factors which enter into a prediction of the field intensity at which breakdown occurs that we are forced to treat the problem empirically. One of the most important considerations for a given material is the degree of refinement, or freedom from impurities. The presence of ever so slight amounts of water reduces the dielectric strength of transformer oil to a marked degree. Such surface discontinuities as sharp corners may cause a failure of insulation not because of the field in the insulation, but because of the bombardment of the surface by ionized gas particles as a result of the concentration of the field intensity at the discontinuity.

The mechanism of breakdown in gases is somewhat easier to explain than that in solids. Here, too, the engineer uses empirical information,

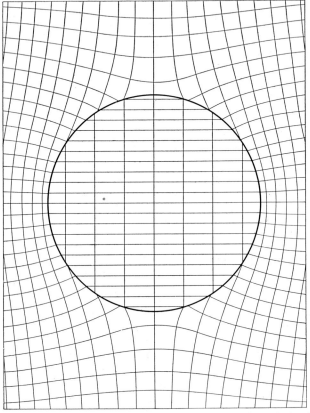

FIG. 7.5   A dielectric cylinder placed in a uniform field. The polarization changes the field both inside and outside the dielectric material. The stream lines run across the page. (*Traced from a drawing by Maxwell.*)

though it is possible to derive certain relationships which explain a part of the phenomena fairly well. We shall examine the breakdown of air under two different conditions, as illustrations of the processes involved. In another section we shall discuss corona, while here we consider an intense uniform field between parallel plane surfaces as suggested in Fig. 7.6a. The two plane surfaces are maintained at a controlled potential difference. Air at atmospheric pressure is the dielectric. The field is uniform away from the edges of the planes, which have been rounded to prevent concentration of the field.

As the applied potential is increased, the field intensity is uniform, and the conduction current very small, until the field intensity is increased to such an extent that stray electrons gain enough energy between molecular collisions to ionize the gas, as indicated in Fig. 7.6b. When the electrons released by ionization are also able to produce further ionization, a chain reaction, or *electron avalanche*, provides a path for a spark. Along the path of the avalanche, the once-neutral gas has become a local channel of charged ions and electrons. Through their own field, these charges completely disrupt the uniformity of the original field, hastening the cumulative processes. Secondary emission at the negative electrode also contributes to the supply of electrons.

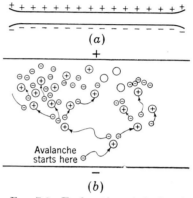

The energy gained by the electrons as a result of the forces of the field depends on the average path length between collisions. This *mean free path* is a function of the density. When the field is established between parallel planes which are extremely close together, the stray free electrons can be collected by the field without sparking, at considerably higher field intensities than for greater separations. The number of collisions made by an electron in crossing the gap is a function of the product of the density

FIG. 7.6 Explanation of the breakdown of the air between parallel-plane electrodes by the mechanism of an electron avalanche.

and gap length. An empirical curve showing this relationship appears in Fig. 7.7. From this curve we observe that at the separations which might be used in a high-voltage variable air capacitor, a very round figure for the field intensity is 3×10^6 volts per meter.

In liquid and solid dielectrics the breakdown process is probably similar to that in air, though much more complex. Breakdown is usually preceded by abnormal conduction currents which may be due in part to the disruption of the bound charges of the molecules. Like air, *most dielectrics have very much greater strengths when arranged in very thin sheets placed in a uniform field* than under other conditions. This fact probably arises because the materials can be made purer and more homogeneous in thin sheets.

7.3 Corona. Both the breakdown strength of a dielectric and the character of the breakdown phenomena depend on the nature of the field configuration. In a uniform field the breakdown of air is heralded by the passage of a spark. In nonuniform fields breakdown is sometimes evident long before the passage of a spark. We shall examine briefly the breakdown of the air surrounding a long cylindrical wire such as a transmission-line conductor.

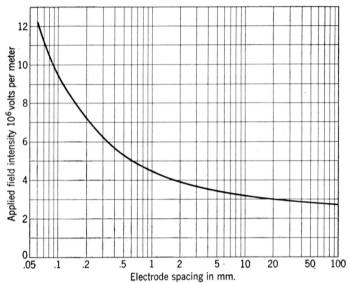

FIG. 7.7 Apparent spark breakdown field intensity for parallel-plane electrodes, in air at 760 mm Hg, 20°C. (*Adapted from J. D. Cobine, "Gaseous Conductors," p. 173, McGraw-Hill Book Company, Inc., New York, 1941.*)

The field intensity due to a long isolated charged cylinder has been found to be

$$\mathbf{E} = \frac{\lambda}{2\pi\epsilon_0 R}\, \mathbf{r} \tag{1}$$

outside the cylinder, and zero inside the cylinder. In Fig. 7.8, the magnitude of $\mathbf{E}$ is plotted against R. The field intensity has its maximum value at the surface of the cylinder. If we denote the radius of the cylinder as R_w, we have for the maximum value of field intensity

$$E_{\text{max}} = \frac{\lambda}{2\pi\epsilon_0 R_w} \tag{2}$$

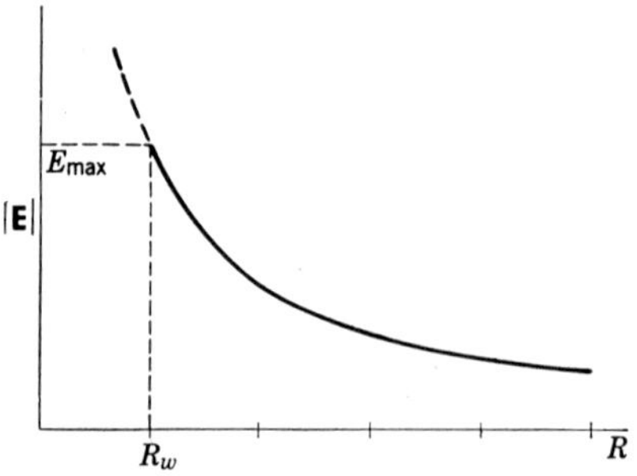

FIG. 7.8 Field intensity near an isolated round wire.

For a two-wire line in which the spacing between wires is very much greater than the radius of the wires, we have Eq. 2.9 (3):

$$\mathbf{E} = \frac{\lambda}{2\pi\epsilon_0}\left(\frac{\mathbf{r}_2}{R_2} - \frac{\mathbf{r}_1}{R_1}\right)$$

At the surface of either wire this reduces to Eq. (2) approximately.

The capacitance is given approximately by Eq. 6.4 (12)

$$\frac{C}{L} = \frac{\pi \epsilon_0}{\log_e (D/R_w)}$$

From this we can express λ in terms of the potential difference between the wires

$$\lambda = \frac{C}{L} V_m = \frac{\pi \epsilon_0}{\log_e (D/R_w)} V_m \tag{3}$$

Using this in Eq. (2),

$$E_{\max} = \frac{V_m}{2R_w} \frac{1}{\log_e (D/R_w)} \tag{4}$$

where D = wire spacing

As the potential difference between the wires is increased until ionization is possible at the surface of the wires, a violet glow known as *corona* surrounds the wires. The air near the wire is ionized, but in the surrounding region the air is still acting as a good insulator. The corona does represent a power loss and a source of radio interference.

The critical field intensity at which corona begins depends on the smoothness of the wire, the atmospheric pressure, the radius of the wire, and the amount of water vapor present. Salt-water fog is particularly susceptible to corona. An empirical relation which holds for low-frequency alternating voltages on parallel wires is due to F. W. Peek, Jr.:

$$E_c = 3(10^6)m\delta \left(1 + \frac{0.301}{\sqrt{\delta R_w}}\right) \tag{5}$$

where E_c = critical field intensity, volts per meter

m = roughness factor (1.0 for smooth cylinders; as small as 0.83 for stranded cables)

δ = relative density of air (unity at standard conditions)

R_w = radius of wire, centimeters

When m and δ are unity, Eq. (5) becomes

$$E_c = 3(10^6) \left(1 + \frac{0.301}{\sqrt{R_w}}\right)$$

and for a radius of 1 centimeter this has the numerical result

$$E_c = 3(10^6)(1.301) = 3.9(10^6) \text{ volts per meter}$$

The factors which can be used to control corona are the voltage, the smoothness factor, and the radius of the wire. The voltage is fixed by economic considerations, and of the other two, the radius of the wire is the more effective. The Boulder–Los Angeles transmission lines use hollow copper conductors to increase the radius for a given cross section. Aluminum conductors with their larger cross sections have a definite advantage in corona prevention when compared to solid copper wires of the same conductance, and about the same cost. "Bundle conductors," formed of two or more paralleled small wires at a spacing of several diameters, are also effective in reducing corona. This latter method has been pioneered in Sweden.

The Geiger counter used to detect radiation of nuclear energy and cosmic rays is, in a sense, a small coaxial cable operated just below the critical value of field intensity. When the radiation strikes the walls of the tube, an electron is released from the wall which triggers an electron avalanche. This forms a pulse of current which is suitably amplified and sent to an indicator such as an oscillograph or headphones.

7.4 Dielectrics in Series in a Uniform Field.   In the construction of capacitors, it is seldom that multiple dielectrics are employed deliberately,

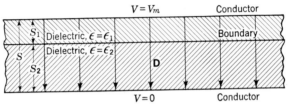

Fɪɢ. 7.9 Two dielectric materials between parallel-plane electrodes, for analysis of the relative field intensities and the potential distribution.

but accidental films of air or voids may present the multiple-dielectric problem anyway. In building insulation, however, different types of materials are employed quite frequently for economic and structural reasons. One of the commonest examples is the insulation surrounding the conductors in the slots of an electric machine. We shall here consider two different dielectric materials in series in a uniformly applied field, and then investigate the interesting case in which one of the dielectrics is an accidental thin film of air.

Applying the notation of Fig. 7.9, we assume a continuous normal component of displacement $\mathbf{D}$ in the two materials, that is,

$$D_1 = D_2 \tag{1}$$

Then

$$\epsilon_1 E_1 = \epsilon_2 E_2 \tag{2}$$

To relate these to the applied potential difference V_m,

$$V_m = \int \mathbf{E} \cdot d\mathbf{S} = E_1 S_1 + E_2 S_2 \tag{3}$$

Solving Eqs. (2) and (3) for E_1 and E_2,

$$E_1 = \frac{V_m}{S_1 + (\epsilon_1/\epsilon_2)\, S_2} \tag{4}$$

and

$$E_2 = \frac{V_m}{S_2 + (\epsilon_2/\epsilon_1)S_1} \tag{5}$$

Denoting that part of the total potential difference in each material as V_1 and V_2,

$$V_1 = E_1 S_1 = \frac{V_m}{1 + (\epsilon_1/\epsilon_2)(S_2/S_1)} \tag{6}$$

and

$$V_2 = E_2 S_2 = \frac{V_m}{1 + (\epsilon_2/\epsilon_1)(S_1/S_2)} \tag{7}$$

Since the D vector is terminated by a uniform charge distribution σ and $D = \sigma$, the capacitance per unit area may be obtained from Eqs. (1) and (3):

$$\frac{C}{A} = \frac{1}{(S_1/\epsilon_1) + (S_2/\epsilon_2)} \tag{8}$$

neglecting edge effects.

When one of the materials is an accidental film of air and the other is a dielectric such as glass, the limiting value of E as S_1 approaches zero and S_2 approaches S is obtained from Eqs. (4) and (5):

$$E_1 = \frac{\epsilon_2}{\epsilon_1}\frac{V_m}{S} \qquad \text{in the air} \tag{9}$$

and

$$E_2 = \frac{V_m}{S} \qquad \text{in the dielectric} \tag{10}$$

Even though the potential drop is almost entirely across the glass, the field intensity in the air film is greater than that in the glass by the ratio of the permittivities, and breakdown of the configuration will begin in the air unless the film is so thin that ionization is highly unlikely. This requires a very thin film indeed, and it explains the precautions taken to fill up such voids in insulation by pressure and by the use of oil or varnish. Equation (9) is sometimes used as a method of defining dielectric constant in terms of the relative field intensity appearing in a thin flat cavity in a dielectric material.

Before drawing final conclusions about the role of permittivity in determining the relative field intensities, the reader is cautioned to consider also the viewpoint of Sec. 7.8 to follow. We shall see there that, when the conductivities are finite, the analysis of this section is incomplete.

7.5 Coaxial Cables. We may begin the study of an important insulation problem by analyzing the field distribution in a two-dielectric coaxial cable. The notation is indicated in Fig. 7.10a, and we proceed in a manner identical to that in Sec. 4.4. Through concentric cylindrical Gaussian surfaces in either dielectric (of unit length),

$$\oint \mathbf{D} \cdot \mathbf{n} \, dA = \lambda \tag{1}$$

For such surfaces, D is normal to the surface and $\mathbf{D} \cdot \mathbf{n} = D$. Then

$$D = \frac{\lambda}{A} = \frac{\lambda}{2\pi R} \tag{2}$$

Though the D vector is continuous in the two materials, the field inten-

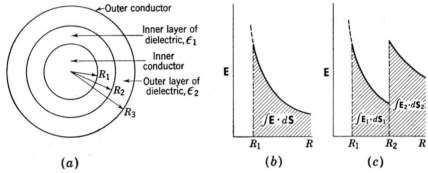

FIG. 7.10   (a) Notation for analysis of the field in a two-dielectric coaxial cable; (b and c) the field intensities plotted for single and dual dielectrics, respectively.

sities require separate expressions

$$E_1 = \frac{\lambda}{2\pi\epsilon_1 R} \qquad R_1 < R < R_2 \tag{3}$$

and

$$E_2 = \frac{\lambda}{2\pi\epsilon_2 R} \qquad R_2 < R < R_3 \tag{4}$$

The maximum field intensities are

$$E_{1m} = \frac{\lambda}{2\pi\epsilon_1 R_1} \tag{5}$$

and

$$E_{2m} = \frac{\lambda}{2\pi\epsilon_2 R_2} \tag{6}$$

The total potential difference between the inner and outer conductors is

$$V_m = \int_{R_1}^{R_3} \mathbf{E} \cdot d\mathbf{S} = \frac{\lambda}{2\pi} \left(\frac{1}{\epsilon_1} \log_e \frac{R_2}{R_1} + \frac{1}{\epsilon_2} \log_e \frac{R_3}{R_2} \right) \tag{7}$$

The capacitance per unit length, neglecting end effects, may be written from Eq. (7).

In a coaxial cable, the engineering problem is that of insulating the inner conductor, whose radius is fixed by the current capacity, for a given potential difference between inner and outer conductors. The maximum field intensity can be controlled by increasing the radius of the inner conductor, but this is seldom economical. The reason for this lies in the fact that the volume of the entire cable is ordinarily the controlling economic factor, particularly if armor is to be added to the outside of the outer conductor.

When a single dielectric material is used, Eq. (7) becomes

$$V_m = \frac{\lambda}{2\pi\epsilon} \log_e \frac{R_2}{R_1} \tag{8}$$

Eliminating λ between Eqs. (5) and (8),

$$E_{1m} = \frac{V_m}{R_1} \frac{1}{\log_e (R_2/R_1)} \tag{9}$$

For a material of a given dielectric strength, Eq. (9) may be solved for the required radius of the outer conductor

$$R_2 = R_1 \exp \frac{V_m}{R_1 E_{1m}} \tag{10}$$

This is independent of the dielectric constant of the material, and it tells us that the smallest volume of the cable, for a single dielectric, results from choosing the material with the highest possible breakdown strength. If the capacitance is important, and it usually is, an economical balance is required between low dielectric constant and high dielectric strength.

In any single-dielectric cable, the dielectric is not uniformly stressed, as is seen vividly by plotting Eq. (3) as in Fig. 7.10b. The potential difference V_m is the area under the curve, and for a given value of R_1, one must use a large enough value of R_2 to provide the required area. Most of the material is understressed, and if the outer radius is as much as twice the inner radius, it is important to find some way of increasing the area under the curve in order to reduce the volume of the cable. The material near the outer conductor is increasing the volume very rapidly and the allowable potential difference very slowly.

The use of two dielectrics of about the same breakdown strengths but of different dielectric constants is one practical way to decrease the volume by stressing the material more uniformly. The discontinuity at the surface between the dielectrics is an increase in $|\mathbf{E}|$ if the outer material has a lower dielectric constant. If the ratio of the dielectric constants is 2, for example, the field intensity will be doubled. The resulting increase in area under the E curve, compared to a single dielectric, is striking. For a given V_m and R_1 substantial economies can result from the use of two or more dielectric materials. As seen in Fig. 7.10c, if the dielectric strength of the second material is not so great as that of the first material, the value of R_2 at which the discontinuity in E may occur must be correspondingly increased. The use of thin sheets of dielectric material also increases its dielectric strength, and this alone may warrant the use of several layers and make the manufacture of the cable somewhat cheaper in the bargain.

To produce a uniform field intensity in a coaxial cable, the dielectric constant should be inversely proportional to the radius, but apparently the economic factors have not yet required the development of such an interesting material. It is economically feasible to provide layers of material of the same dielectric constant in successive degrees of refinement, placing the material with the highest breakdown strength nearest the inner conductor and using the less expensive material on the outside where the field intensity is reduced. This is a simple example of an important branch of engineering called "graded insulation."

7.6 Condenser Bushings. A condenser bushing is the physical structure used to insulate a high-voltage conductor at its point of passage through a support such as the case of a transformer. The method of its construction is an excellent illustration of the economical use of expensive insulating materials through (1) the use of thin sheets of relatively higher dielectric strength than thick sheets, and (2) uniformly stressing the material used.

As suggested by Fig. 7.11, the insulation is built up of thin sheets of dielectric material separated by layers of conducting material such as aluminum foil. In the figure the thickness of the dielectric is greatly exaggerated. The conducting sheets assure that slight imperfections in the dielectric of one layer do not distort the field in the next. By providing equipotential surfaces, the layers of metal each require that the field be radial at these surfaces.

Neglecting edge effects, which are very difficult to analyze here, the total charge appearing on each conducting layer is the same. To a first approximation, each layer is a separate capacitor with equal and opposite charges appearing on the two conducting surfaces. The charge density, and therefore the field intensity, can be held almost constant throughout the whole structure by holding the area constant as the radius increases. For example, the area of the third sheet is

$$2\pi R_3 L_3$$

and that of the fourth sheet is

$$2\pi R_4 L_4$$

Then if $R_3 L_3 = R_4 L_4$, the charge density is the same on each sheet and the field intensity has the same maximum value in each layer. Throughout the bushing

$$R_n L_n = R_{n+1} L_{n+1}$$

By the combination of the use of thin sheets and uniform field intensity the volume of material required is greatly reduced compared to a single layer of dielectric material of uniform length.

The construction method diagrammed in Fig. 7.11 does not have great mechanical strength. When this is not a requirement, as for an indoor installation, it is satisfactory to encase the assembly in a cone-shaped

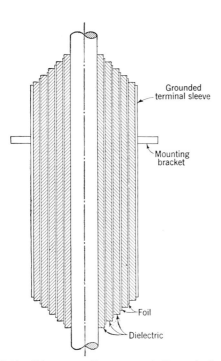

Grounded terminal sleeve

Mounting bracket

Foil

Dielectric

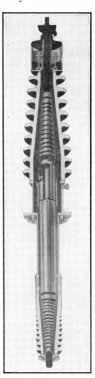

Fig. 7.11 Diagrammatic representation of the construction of a condenser bushing of alternate layers of dielectric and conducting foil.

Fig. 7.12 A cut-away photograph of a condenser bushing for outdoor installation on a transformer. (*Courtesy of Westinghouse.*)

paper tube to keep the structure clean. For an outdoor installation, it would not do to have snow piling up on the ends of the dielectric sleeves. For this reason, and to provide greater mechanical strength, the bushing is housed in and is supported mechanically by an outer sleeve of porcelain, as illustrated in the manufacturer's drawing of Fig. 7.12.

7.7 Some Further Energy Relations in Electrostatic Fields. We may establish the most commonly used energy relations in an electrostatic field most easily by investigating them in a uniform field, such as that in regions remote from the edges of a parallel-plate capacitor in vacuum, as indicated in Fig. 7.13a.   We first wish to evaluate the energy which must be supplied by an external force to move a small positive test charge between the conducting sheets carrying equal and opposite charges Q uniformly distributed.

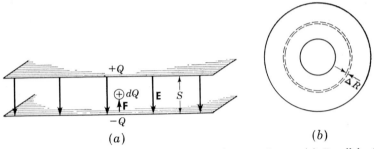

(a)   (b)

FIG. 7.13   For discussion of energy relations in capacitors.   (a) Parallel planes, (b) concentric cylinders.

The field intensity is uniform between the planes and has the value

$$E = \frac{\sigma}{\epsilon_0} \tag{1}$$

where σ = surface-charge density
For the present we shall write this as

$\sigma = \dfrac{Q}{A}$

$$E = \frac{Q}{A\epsilon_0} \tag{2}$$

The force on the charge dQ to be moved is

$$\mathbf{F} = dQ\,\mathbf{E} = \frac{dQ\,Q}{A\epsilon_0} \tag{3}$$

and the energy which must be supplied in moving the test charge against $\mathbf{F}$ along a path length S taken perpendicular to the planes is

$$dW = FS = \frac{dQ\,Q\,S}{A\epsilon_0} \tag{4}$$

Then the total energy which must be supplied by an external force in establishing the total charge Q on each plate can be found by integrating Eq. (4) after substituting from Eq. (3)

$$W = \int_0^Q Q\,dQ\,\frac{S}{A\epsilon_0} \tag{5}$$

giving us the result

$$W = \frac{Q^2}{2}\frac{S}{A\epsilon_0} \tag{6}$$

Since the capacitance, neglecting edge effects, is

$$C = \frac{\epsilon_0 A}{S} \tag{7}$$

an alternative expression for the energy is

$$W = \frac{Q^2}{2C} \tag{8}$$

Since the total charge Q is

$$Q = \sigma A \tag{9}$$

we may write Eq. (6) as

$$W = \frac{\sigma^2}{2\epsilon_0} AS \tag{10}$$

From Eq. (1) and the additional relation

$$D = \epsilon_0 E \tag{11}$$

we may write Eq. (10) in the form

$$W = \frac{DE}{2} (AS) \tag{12}$$

Now since (AS) is the volume occupied by the field, the energy per unit volume w is

$$w = \frac{DE}{2} = \frac{\epsilon_0 E^2}{2} = \frac{D^2}{2\epsilon_0} \tag{13}$$

Though derived for a uniform field, Eq. (13) may be applied at a point in a nonuniform field by considering the limit of the energy divided by the volume as the volume becomes vanishingly small and the field within the vanishing volume becomes uniform. For example, in the nonuniform field between concentric cylinders sketched in Fig. 7.13b, we may treat the field between two concentric equipotential surfaces, separated by the distance ΔR, as a uniform field in the limit as ΔR approaches zero.

This gives us a method of obtaining the energy required to establish a charge configuration by integration of the energy per unit volume in terms of the field quantities instead of working each problem all over again. It also permits us to evaluate the energy in terms of the capacitance and the potential difference through Eq. (8).

It is a great convenience to think of the potential energy of a charge configuration as being distributed throughout the field with a density given by Eq. (13). This is a physical interpretation of a mathematical relationship which, though useful, is not always easy to justify physically. It is equivalent to stating that the potential energy of an elevated object over the surface of the earth is distributed throughout space.

It is also found very convenient to extrapolate the results of the energy distribution in space to regions containing dielectric materials, and an exactly similar analysis can be made without visualization difficulties for a parallel-plate capacitor containing transformer oil or other liquid dielectric. For a solid dielectric one may visualize carrying the test charge through a needle-like cavity in which the field intensity is the same as that in the surrounding dielectric.   When the analysis is completed, Eq. (13) contains the permittivity of the material instead of that of vacuum and is written

$$w = \frac{DE}{2} = \frac{\epsilon E^2}{2} = \frac{D^2}{2\epsilon} \qquad \text{joules per cubic meter} \qquad (14)$$

But in the dielectric case, Eq. (14) *does not include the energy storage due to the stresses and strains of an elastic dielectric material;* it represents only the electrostatic part of the total energy stored.   The pursuit of the elastic energy is a fascinating topic but would be out of place here.

7.8   Boundary Conditions at a Dielectric Surface.   In Chap. 4, we found that when two materials carrying conduction currents were placed "in series," the relative field intensities were determined by the relative conductivities.   In this chapter we have proceeded on the basis that the relative field intensities were determined by the relative permittivities. Now these two approaches could give quite different answers, and we wonder which is correct and under what conditions.

We got into this difficulty from the mathematically convenient, but physically inaccurate, assumption that all materials could be divided rigidly into conductors or nonconductors.   If we resolve the difficulty by experiment, we find that the fields are determined initially by the permittivities *and finally by the conductivities.*   If we use the very best dielectric materials, we find that the steady-state condition may be reached only after an uninterestingly long time interval.   If we use "leaky" dielectrics such as those in electrolytic capacitors, we have to be quick about it if we are to observe the initial distribution.   The following analysis considers the final steady-state distribution.

In Fig. 7.14, the **J**, **D**, and **E** vectors are shown normal to a boundary between materials, and we shall carry along the *n* subscripts to remind us that we are concerned with the normal components in the general case. We have no conflict to resolve with the tangential components, anyway, because the conservation of energy requires that the tangential components of the **E** vector be continuous at the boundary.

If the steady state has been reached, and therefore if charge is not accumulating at the boundary, the conservation of electric charge requires that the current entering the boundary be the same as that leaving it. At each point of the boundary, then,

$$J_{n1} = J_{n2} \qquad (1)$$

Whether or not the conductivity is a constant in the Ohm's-law sense, in each material **J** and **E** will be related by a conductivity factor which will have a single value after the steady-state condition has been reached, and which may be written as

$$\mathbf{J} = \gamma \mathbf{E} \tag{2}$$

for each material.   Writing Eq. (1) in terms of Eq. (2), we obtain

$$\gamma_2 E_{n2} = \gamma_1 E_{n1} \tag{3}$$

Or, because of the conservation of electric charge, the field intensities must be related by

$$E_{n2} = \frac{\gamma_1}{\gamma_2} E_{n1} \tag{4}$$

Now if we are also to be able to define both the displacement vectors whose normal components are related to the field intensity and the permit-

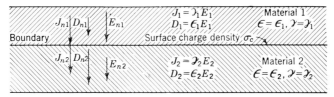

FIG. 7.14   For study of the boundary conditions at a boundary between dielectric materials.   Here the field is normal to the boundary.

tivity by the equations

$$D_{n1} = \epsilon_1 E_{n1} \tag{5}$$

and

$$D_{n2} = \epsilon_2 E_{n2} \tag{6}$$

then we *cannot* also have

$$D_{n1} = D_{n2}$$

without conflicting with Eq. (4), which we got from the conservation of electric charge.   The conflict is resolved by the following line of reasoning.

When the steady-state condition has been reached, the current must have carried a charge of density σ_c to, or away from, the surface.   This surface charge carries the subscript c to indicate that it has reached the surface because of a conduction current and that it is over and above the induced surface charge which we chose to overlook in introducing the **D** vector.   Further, this additional surface charge can account for the necessary discontinuity in the **D** vector at the boundary, through the equation

$$\sigma_c = D_{n1} - D_{n2} \tag{7}$$

from Gauss's law.   We now need to find σ_c in terms of the conductivities. First we substitute Eqs. (5) and (6) into Eq. (7) and obtain

$$\sigma_c = \epsilon_1 E_{n1} - \epsilon_2 E_{n2} \tag{8}$$

Then, using Eq. (4), Eq. (8) becomes

$$\sigma_c = \epsilon_1 E_{n1} - \epsilon_2 \frac{\gamma_1}{\gamma_2} E_{n1} \tag{9}$$

Factoring E_{n1} gives

$$\sigma_c = \left(\epsilon_1 - \epsilon_2 \frac{\gamma_1}{\gamma_2} \right) E_{n1} \tag{10}$$

Going back to Eq. (5), we write Eq. (10) in terms of D_{n1} as

$$\sigma_c = \left(1 - \frac{\epsilon_2 \gamma_1}{\epsilon_1 \gamma_2} \right) D_{n1} \tag{11}$$

Equating the two expressions for σ_c, Eqs. (7) and (11), and solving for D_{n2}, we obtain the ultimate boundary condition

$$D_{n2} = \frac{\epsilon_2 \gamma_1}{\epsilon_1 \gamma_2} D_{n1} \tag{12}$$

Only if

$$\frac{\epsilon_1}{\gamma_1} = \frac{\epsilon_2}{\gamma_2} \tag{13}$$

will the solution to the current-field problem, given by Eq. (12), reduce to that of the electrostatic problem

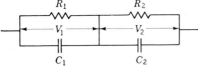

FIG. 7.15   When a steady field is maintained in two capacitors in series, the relative potentials are determined by the conductances and not by the capacitances. To maintain a fixed potential division, the capacitors are paralleled by relatively large conductances.

$$D_{n1} = D_{n2}$$

We cannot achieve Eq. (13) ordinarily, because good dielectrics do not obey Ohm's law. Practically, if one wants to ensure a proper voltage division across capacitors in series, he must connect relatively small resistors across them as in the circuit of Fig. 7.15.

7.9   A Summary and a Criticism.   In this chapter we have investigated some of the possibilities of handling problems which involve dielectric materials from the viewpoint of the dielectric circuit. To do this, we invented a helper vector **D** related to the **E** vector by a relationship similar to Ohm's law, **D** = ϵ**E**. Because of this, we were able to find the resulting field intensities by the same methods which were used in Chap. 4. No new mathematics was introduced and no new problems were solved, though we took quite a different viewpoint of the results, physically.

We have pursued electrostatics about as far as we can without introducing partial differential equations. With our background of experience, understanding the role of the partial differential equations should be somewhat easier than it would have been without such experience.

In analyzing conditions at a boundary between dielectric materials, we found some difficulties with the $\mathbf{D}$ vector. We chose to ignore the induced surface charges, yet found it necessary to include a similar surface charge σ_c, which arrived at the surface because of the conduction current. We are now faced with the necessity of making a clear statement as to which charges to include, and which charges to exclude, in applying Gauss's law when dielectric materials are present. We are to include those charges which arrive by means of a conduction current, or those which involve a transfer of charge from one molecule to another. The induced charges on the surface of conductors are to be included. We are to exclude charges which appear because of polarization, as this does not involve transfer of charge from one molecule to another.

Such explanations as this do leave much to be desired from the standpoint of rigor. This has caused some of the foremost writers to define the electric field in terms of the $\mathbf{E}$ vector alone. When this is done, one accounts for the influence of dielectric materials by considering them as a region of free space containing a field which is the superposition of the applied field and that due to the resulting distribution of dipoles. Gauss's law is developed for the $\mathbf{E}$ vector instead of the $\mathbf{D}$ vector. The concept of dielectric constant is then unnecessary, and the permittivity of free space retains the significance which we originally gave it, that of a constant of proportionality in Coulomb's law. In the end, however, one needs the $\mathbf{D}$ vector as a helper vector and still uses it to account for the discontinuity in the normal component of the $\mathbf{E}$ vector at a boundary between materials, under the same special conditions which we have found necessary. The utility of this approach, as opposed to the one which we have followed, lies in the fact that it is easier to explain the action of materials which do not have the same properties in all directions, and hence are called anisotropic. It would be difficult for us to handle such problems as are posed by these materials in which the $\mathbf{D}$ and $\mathbf{E}$ vectors are not necessarily parallel. The theory is developed in terms of tensors or dyadics, which are more general and more powerful than our vector analysis. In an electret, the counterpart of a permanent magnet, the $\mathbf{D}$ and $\mathbf{E}$ vectors are oppositely directed in general, and their direction lines do not even have the same shape.

The approach which is preferred by the physicist today is to define a polarization vector $\mathbf{P}$ which is the dipole moment per unit volume within the dielectric material. This vector need not be parallel to the $\mathbf{E}$ vector at all. He then defines the displacement vector as $\mathbf{D} = \epsilon_0 \mathbf{E} + \mathbf{P}$.

In spite of the difficulties with the relationship between $\mathbf{D}$ and $\mathbf{E}$, it is still possible to retain the boundary conditions at a surface which does not carry a charge. The normal components of **D** are continuous, and the tangential components of **E** are continuous even at the surface of an electret. In the following chapter we shall focus our attention on the boundary conditions more than anything else, and having done this we shall appreciate the value of the continuity of the boundary conditions as opposed to the value of having **D** and **E** simply related.

REFERENCES

1. Sears, F. W.: "Principles of Physics," Vol. II, "Electricity and Magnetism," Chap. 7, Addison-Wesley Press, Inc., Cambridge, Mass., 1947. Recommended collateral reading.
2. Attwood, Stephen S.: "Electric and Magnetic Fields," 3d ed., Chaps. III and VIII, John Wiley & Sons, Inc., New York, 1949. Recommended collateral reading.
3. Cobine, J. D.: "Gaseous Conductors," McGraw-Hill Book Company, Inc., New York, 1941. Extensive treatment of spark breakdown and corona.
4. Boast, Warren B.: "Principles of Electric and Magnetic Fields," pp. 84–92, Harper & Brothers, New York, 1948. Problems 7.3, 7.4, and 7.5 were suggested by the material in this reference.
5. Gutmann, F.: The Electret, *Revs. Mod. Phys.*, Vol. 20, No. 3, July, 1948. A technical review with an extensive bibliography.
6. Whitehead, S.: "Dielectric Breakdown of Solids," Oxford University Press, New York, 1951.

PROBLEMS

*7.1 Develop the law of refraction at a dielectric boundary, assuming that the conductivities are zero (see Sec. 4.6).

7.2 What is the practical limitation on the outer radius which may be achieved by using, as transmission-line conductors, hollow conductors of a given cross-sectional area of conducting surface?

*7.3 Design a coaxial cable using fused quartz, $K = 5$, and polystyrene, $K = 2.5$, for a potential difference of 100,000 volts. The maximum field intensity in the two materials may be $10(10^6)$ and $12(10^6)$ volts per meter, respectively. The radius of the inner conductor is 0.5 centimeter. (Though fused quartz is not a practical material for this application, its high dielectric constant simplifies the arithmetic.)

*7.4 In Prob. 7.3, compare the volume of the cable with that required if a single dielectric is used (for each of the materials alone). Compare the capacitance per unit length.

7.5 In Prob. 7.3, find the voltage rating of the cable below which there is no point in using two materials.

7.6 Supposing one could construct a coaxial cable with a material whose dielectric constant was inversely proportional to the radius, find the resulting expression for the capacitance per unit length.

7.7 At standard pressure, compute the critical potential difference for corona on a two-wire line whose conductors are stranded cables with a radius of 0.5 centimeter. The wire spacing is 1 meter.

*7.8 Repeat the analysis of Sec. 7.5 for concentric spheres.

7.9 In a single-dielectric coaxial cable, obtain a formula for the distribution of the electrostatic energy per unit volume.   State the results in terms of the radius, the inner and outer radii, the dielectric constant, and the potential difference.

*7.10 A sheet of glass 1 centimeter thick has a dielectric constant of 8 and forms the dielectric of a parallel-plate capacitor.   The applied potential difference is 10^4 volts.   From the curve of Fig. 7.7, estimate the maximum permissible thickness of an accidental film of air at the surface of the glass.   As a first approximation, neglect the potential across the air film.

CHAPTER 8

DIVERGENCE AND THE EQUATIONS OF
POISSON AND LAPLACE

8.1 Divergence. We have been using a scalar equation known as Gauss's law in the form

$$\oint \mathbf{D} \cdot \mathbf{n} \, dA = \int \rho \, dv \tag{1}$$

To use this relation, we have evaluated the surface integral by choosing those surfaces in which $\mathbf{D} \cdot \mathbf{n} = D$, and over which D was a constant. It is not always easy to find such a surface, and *we should like some way of relating the* $\mathbf{D}$ *vector to the charge density without performing a surface integration.* We can do this by evaluating the flux through a Gaussian surface which shrinks to enclose a point.

Consider a small but finite volume Δv and its average charge density $\bar{\rho}$. For this volume we may write Eq. (1) as

$$\oint \mathbf{D} \cdot \mathbf{n} \, dA = \bar{\rho} \, \Delta v \tag{2}$$

Now dividing by the volume Δv, and passing to the limit,

$$\lim_{\Delta v \to 0} \frac{\oint \mathbf{D} \cdot \mathbf{n} \, dA}{\Delta v} = \rho \tag{3}$$

As the volume shrinks to zero, so does the area of the Gaussian surface and the flux through that surface. Yet their ratio approaches a definite limit. This limit is numerically equal to the charge density at the point. The left-hand side of Eq. (3) represents the flux gain per unit volume, in the limit as the volume becomes vanishingly small. This concept appears so frequently in physical science that it has a name and a special shorthand notation in vector analysis. The name is divergence, and its defining equation is

$$\nabla \cdot \mathbf{D} = \lim_{\Delta v \to 0} \frac{\oint \mathbf{D} \cdot \mathbf{n} \, dA}{\Delta v} \tag{4}$$

Divergence is a scalar quantity which expresses the rate of growth of the flux of a vector, per unit volume.

Utilizing the shorthand notation to rewrite Eq. (3), we have

$$\nabla \cdot \mathbf{D} = \rho \tag{5}$$

Maxwell Eq.

196

Equation (5) is Gauss's law in differential form.   It tells us that rate of growth of the flux at a point, per unit volume, is equal to the charge density at that point.   Since the units of the right-hand side must match those of the left, and the units of $\mathbf{D}$ are coulombs per square meter, we expect that the operation symbolized by $\mathbf{\nabla} \cdot \mathbf{D}$ can be transformed into a differentiation with respect to distance.   To make the transformation, it is necessary to evaluate Eq. (4) in a system of coordinates.

It is now interesting to carry the result of Eq. (5) back to Gauss's law, Eq. (1).   When this is done we have

$$\oint \mathbf{D} \cdot \mathbf{n} \, dA = \int \mathbf{\nabla} \cdot \mathbf{D} \, dv \tag{6}$$

Equation (6) is known as the *divergence theorem;* it is sometimes known as Gauss's theorem, but since Gauss was responsible for many theorems, the former name recalls the nature of the theorem more quickly.   The divergence theorem allows us to replace an integration over a closed surface with an integration throughout the enclosed volume, and vice versa. Sometimes one is considerably easier to evaluate than the other.   Though we shall not prove it here, Eq. (6) is valid for all vectors.   The proof retraces the steps leading to Eq. (4) in reverse order.

To aid in visualizing this limiting process which leads to the concept of divergence, it is helpful to get a toy balloon and blow it up quite large. The balloon forms the Gaussian surface.   Imagine that the balloon is placed in a region containing distributed charges.   As the air is let out of the balloon, the charge contained therein becomes smaller and smaller, as does the flux of the $\mathbf{D}$ vector over the surface of the balloon, and the volume enclosed by the balloon.   Of course, a toy balloon will not shrink in size to a point, but one can imagine that it does so as he lets out the air.

8.2   Divergence in Cartesian Coordinates.   Let us follow our instructions and compute $\mathbf{\nabla} \cdot \mathbf{D}$ for a known $\mathbf{D}$ in cartesian coordinates.   In order to make the work as easy as possible, suppose we select a point and there resolve $\mathbf{D}$ into its components.

$$\mathbf{D} = D_x \mathbf{i} + D_y \mathbf{j} + D_z \mathbf{k} \tag{1}$$

Now let us try to find a closed surface where it is easiest to evaluate $\mathbf{D} \cdot \mathbf{n} \, dA$.   This will not be difficult if we select a cubical volume $dx \, dy \, dz$, because each component of $\mathbf{D}$ will be perpendicular to two faces and parallel to the other four faces of the cube.   To find the total flux through the closed surface, all we have to do is to multiply the values of the components of $\mathbf{D}$ by the area of the faces to which they are perpendicular, and carefully add the resulting scalars.   We can do the job in three steps by considering the components of $\mathbf{D}$ one at a time.

The cubical volume and its faces are shown in the two- and three-dimensional sketches, Fig. 8.1, as is the D_x component of D.   Because of the D_x component, the flux *leaving* the cube at $x + dx$ is

$$[D_x \, dy \, dz]_{x=x+dx}$$

The flux *entering* the cube at the opposite face is

$$[D_x \, dy \, dz]_{x=x}$$

The net flux gain within the cube is the excess of that which leaves over

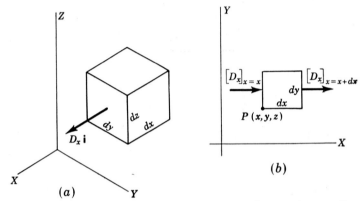

FIG. 8.1   For analysis of the divergence of a vector in cartesian coordinates.

that which enters, or

$$[D_x \, dy \, dz]_{x+dx} - [D_x \, dy \, dz]_x$$

Expressing this as a differential quantity for the flux originating within dv,

$$\text{Differential flux gain} = \left[\frac{\partial}{\partial x}(D_x \, dy \, dz)\right] dx$$

When this has been evaluated by the product rule for differentiation, treating dy and dz as a constant, the total flux gain within the cube, due to the change in the D_x component, is

$$\text{Differential flux gain} = \left(\frac{\partial D_x}{\partial x}\right) dx \, dy \, dz$$

Repeating for the other two components of **D** and the corresponding faces of the cube, or by advancing the subscripts in cyclic order, we find that the total flux originating within the volume dv is

$$\text{Differential flux gain} = \left(\frac{\partial D_x}{\partial x} + \frac{\partial D_y}{\partial y} + \frac{\partial D_z}{\partial z}\right) dx \, dy \, dz$$

The flux gain per unit volume is the divergence, and dividing by the volume of the cube we have

$$\nabla \cdot \mathbf{D} = \frac{\partial D_x}{\partial x} + \frac{\partial D_y}{\partial y} + \frac{\partial D_z}{\partial z} \qquad (2)$$

in cartesian coordinates.

This explains the notation used for the shorthand. If ∇ is thought of as something like a vector

$$\nabla = \mathbf{i}\,\frac{\partial}{\partial x} + \mathbf{j}\,\frac{\partial}{\partial y} + \mathbf{k}\,\frac{\partial}{\partial z} \qquad (3)$$

when it operates on another vector by "scalar multiplication,"

$$\nabla \cdot \mathbf{D} = \left(\mathbf{i}\,\frac{\partial}{\partial x} + \mathbf{j}\,\frac{\partial}{\partial y} + \mathbf{k}\,\frac{\partial}{\partial z}\right) \cdot (\mathbf{i}\,D_x + \mathbf{j}\,D_y + \mathbf{k}\,D_z) \qquad (4)$$

the result is Eq. (2):

$$\nabla \cdot \mathbf{D} = \frac{\partial D_x}{\partial x} + \frac{\partial D_y}{\partial y} + \frac{\partial D_z}{\partial z}$$

Unfortunately the expression for divergence in other coordinate systems is not so simple as this. It is very difficult to use Eq. (2) as a defining equation for divergence and to convert it suitably to other coordinate systems. For this reason, the "flux gain per unit volume" formulation of the previous section, Eq. 8.1 (4),

$$\nabla \cdot \mathbf{D} = \lim_{\Delta v \to 0} \frac{\oint \mathbf{D} \cdot \mathbf{n}\, dA}{\Delta v}$$

is greatly to be preferred.

8.3 Divergence in Orthogonal Curvilinear Coordinates. In discussing gradient we found it possible to write a single expression which was valid in any orthogonal coordinate system. In the case of divergence and some other vector operations, it turns out to be considerably easier to relate the concept to the general coordinate system than to relate it to any one system except cartesian. When the expression for divergence was obtained in cartesian coordinates, it was necessary to obtain the contribution of only one component, and the others could be written down by advancing the subscripts cyclically—called "permuting the subscripts." In general orthogonal coordinates one may again obtain the contribution of one component and write the others by permutation, but in any particular coordinate system this is difficult, and it is necessary to do the work three times, once for each component.

As in the case of gradient, Sec. 3.9, we call any three orthogonal coordinates such as R, θ, and ϕ, by the names u_1, u_2, and u_3. Along each of the coordinate axes or curves, the differential elements of length are ds_1, ds_2, ds_3, related to the coordinates by the metric coefficients

$$ds_1 = h_1\,du_1 \qquad ds_2 = h_2\,du_2 \qquad ds_3 = h_3\,du_3$$

We resolve the **D** vector into three orthogonal components D_1, D_2, D_3, along the three right-handed unit vectors, i_1, i_2, i_3. By doing this, each of the components of the **D** vector will be perpendicular to two faces of the differential element of volume, as in Fig. 8.2.

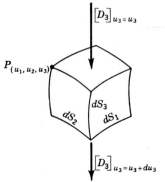

Considering the D_3 component which is normal to the faces formed by $ds_1\, ds_2$, the flux leaving the volume $ds_1\, ds_2\, ds_3$ is

$$\text{Flux leaving} = [D_3\, ds_1\, ds_2]_{u_3+du_3}$$

The flux entering is

$$\text{Flux entering} = [D_3\, ds_1\, ds_2]_{u_3}$$

The net flux gain is the difference between that which leaves and that which enters

FIG. 8.2 For analysis of the divergence of a vector in general orthogonal coordinates.

Differential flux gain
$$= [D_3\, ds_1\, ds_2]_{u_3+du_3} - [D_3\, ds_1\, ds_2]_{u_3}$$

Writing this in differential form,

$$\text{Differential flux gain} = \left[\frac{\partial}{\partial u_3}(D_3\, ds_1\, ds_2)\right] du_3$$

Replacing ds_1 and ds_2 by $h_1\, du_1$ and $h_2\, du_2$

$$\text{Differential flux gain} = \left[\frac{\partial}{\partial u_3}(D_3 h_1\, du_1\, h_2\, du_2)\right] du_3$$

Now while du_1 and du_2 are constants, h_1 and h_2 are variables. Differentiating the product, we obtain the result, for the D_3 component,

$$\text{Differential flux gain in } dv = \left[\frac{\partial}{\partial u_3}(h_1 h_2 D_3)\right] du_1\, du_2\, du_3$$

Repeating for the D_2 and D_1 components and adding the results, the total flux originating within the volume dv is

$$\text{Total differential flux gain in } dv = \left[\frac{\partial}{\partial u_1}(h_2 h_3 D_1) + \frac{\partial}{\partial u_2}(h_1 h_3 D_2) \right.$$
$$\left. + \frac{\partial}{\partial u_3}(h_1 h_2 D_3)\right] du_1\, du_2\, du_3$$

Writing the differential volume as

$$ds_1\, ds_2\, ds_3 = h_1 h_2 h_3\, du_1\, du_2\, du_3$$

and dividing the total flux gain by the volume, we have

$$\mathbf{\nabla \cdot D} = \frac{1}{h_1 h_2 h_3}\left[\frac{\partial}{\partial u_1}(h_2 h_3 D_1) + \frac{\partial}{\partial u_2}(h_1 h_3 D_2) + \frac{\partial}{\partial u_3}(h_1 h_2 D_3)\right] \tag{1}$$

This expression is valid in any orthogonal coordinate system, and may be converted to any particular one by substituting the proper values of h.

If the student finds himself confused by the relatively unfamiliar notation, he should set up the problem in spherical coordinates and repeat the development step by step for each of the three components, writing instead of u_1, u_2, u_3, the more familiar R, θ, ϕ and using $h_1 = 1$, $h_2 = R$, $h_3 = R \sin \theta$. Figures 1.9 and 1.10 show the differential elements of volume.

8.4 The Physical Significance of Divergence. The flow of liquid and gaseous fluids is considerably more complex mathematically than the corresponding electrical problems. James Clerk Maxwell began his

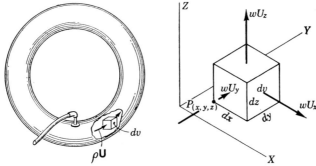

FIG. 8.3 When air enters a vessel, some passes through each little region on its way elsewhere, while some remains to build up the local pressure. The excess of the weight entering over that leaving, per unit volume, is the rate of increase of density at a point.

famous treatise on electricity and magnetism after many years of study of gases. Noting the similarities between electric and magnetic fields and the flow of both incompressible and compressible fluids at very low velocities, he was led to introduce the concept of divergence, though he defined its negative and called it convergence. Over and above relating the divergence of the **D** vector to Gauss's law, a physical interpretation requires a problem with more physical reality than the **D** vector has. One of the ways of getting a feeling of satisfaction with the concept is to pick up a little of the sort of experience which Maxwell had had when he first studied electricity.

When gas flows into or out of a region, its pressure and its density may be changing with time, and further, these quantities may have different values throughout the region. While the air is entering an automobile tire, the pressure, density, and velocity are all greatest at the inlet. Air is accumulating in the region occupied by the tire. It happens that the density and the velocity are most simply related. For our analysis, we shall need the notation of Fig. 8.3 and the following new quantities:

W = the weight of gas within a volume v

$w = dW/dv$ = the density of gas at a point, in any convenient set of units, such as pounds per cubic inch if these are most familiar

$\mathbf{U}$ = the velocity of the gas at any point

As we watch the box dv, we observe that some of the gas is just passing through on its way elsewhere, while some remains inside to build up the pressure there. Gas enters at the three faces of the box dv which meet at the point P, and leaves again at the other three faces. Rather than repeat our previous method exactly, let us account for three faces at a time in this analysis.

Rate at which gas enters $dv = [wU_x\,dy\,dz]_{x=x} + [wU_y\,dz\,dx]_{y=y}$
$$+ [wU_z\,dx\,dy]_{z=z}$$

Rate at which gas leaves $dv = [wU_x\,dy\,dz]_{x=x+dx} + [wU_y\,dz\,dx]_{y=y+dy}$
$$+ [wU_z\,dx\,dy]_{z=z+dz}$$

The rate at which gas is accumulating within dv is the excess of the rate at which it enters over the rate at which it leaves. This quantity is also $\partial/\partial t\,dW$. Subtracting the contributions above, and rearranging,

$$\frac{\partial}{\partial t}\,dW = [wU_x\,dy\,dz]_{x=x} - [wU_x\,dy\,dz]_{x=x+dx} + [wU_y\,dz\,dx]_{y=y}$$
$$- [wU_y\,dz\,dx]_{y=y+dy} + [wU_z\,dx\,dy]_{z=z} - [wU_z\,dx\,dy]_{z=z+dz} \quad (1)$$

The pairs of terms on the right are the differential quantities

$$-\left[\frac{\partial(wU_x\,dy\,dz)}{\partial x}\,dx + \frac{\partial(wU_y\,dz\,dx)}{\partial y}\,dy + \frac{\partial(wU_z\,dx\,dy)}{\partial z}\,dz\right] \quad (2)$$

Differentiating by the product rule and collecting common terms,

$$\frac{\partial}{\partial t}\,dW = -\left[\frac{\partial(wU_x)}{\partial x} + \frac{\partial(wU_y)}{\partial y} + \frac{\partial(wU_z)}{\partial z}\right]dx\,dy\,dz \quad (3)$$

Now on the left-hand side, since $w = dW/dv$ and $dv = dx\,dy\,dz$, we divide both sides by dv:

$$\frac{\partial w}{\partial t} = -\left[\frac{\partial(wU_x)}{\partial x} + \frac{\partial(wU_y)}{\partial y} + \frac{\partial(wU_z)}{\partial z}\right] \quad (4)$$

Now, in terms of the vector-analysis shorthand for divergence,

$$\frac{\partial w}{\partial t} = -\nabla \cdot (w\mathbf{U}) \quad (5)$$

The negative sign of this result is probably what caused Maxwell to define the negative of divergence, and the significance of the result must have led him to the term *convergence*. His convergence is the rate of flow into a volume, and for a conserved entity like a fluid, this is equal to the rate of increase of density. In this sense, the fluid is converging or piling up at a point, because more of it is entering the region than is leaving it. An expanding gas has divergence, while a contracting gas has convergence.

Now all we have used in this analysis is the principle of the conservation of mass, that is, everything which enters a region must pass through its walls, since it cannot be created inside. An incompressible fluid is one whose density cannot be increased or decreased. One cannot pack any more of it into a region which is already full. Unless tremendous pressures are exerted, the compressibility of water and most other liquids is negligible. However, they are just as subject to the principle of the conservation of mass as gases are, and they meet this requirement in a very familiar and a very interesting way.

When water falls over a dam or out of the kitchen faucet, or when molasses is poured out of a pitcher, the stream contracts as the velocity increases, and finally breaks up into drops. Now the gravitational forces act only in the downward direction. If the cross section of the flow stream were to remain constant, fluid would flow out of the bottom of a region faster than it enters at the top, and this can occur only if the fluid expands. Resisting expansion, the molecular forces which hold the fluid together constrict the flow, reducing the cross section as the velocity increases. When the molecular forces can no longer restrict the flow sufficiently, the stream breaks up into individual drops. As the individual drops fall, they become farther and farther apart on the way down, thus achieving the over-all reduction in density required by the conservation of mass. Because of air resistance, small drops soon reach the limiting velocity, and from there on they fall without divergence.

In all the fields we have studied, point charges and surface-charge distributions provide a boundary for the **D** vector, or a discontinuity. Here, mathematically, the volume-charge density is infinite. From the viewpoint of fluid flow, the **D** vector has a sharp discontinuity, and its divergence is infinite. When the field is due to volume-charge distributions, on the other hand, there is no sharp discontinuity in the field. See, for example, the plot of the magnitude of the D vector in the field of a cylindrical volume-charge distribution which we analyzed by Gauss's law in Chap. 5, Sec. 5.4, Fig. 5.5b.

8.5 Poisson's Equation and Laplace's Equation. In spite of the simplicity of the illustration in the previous section, our new differential formulation of Gauss's law is seldom used directly in electrostatics. Instead, it is combined with the concept of potential, to relate the potential to the charge distribution in a differential equation known as Poisson's equation. To derive Poisson's equation in the general case would require reformulating Gauss's law for the **E** vector alone, but for homogeneous linear isotropic materials we may arrive at it as an extension of

$$\mathbf{\nabla} \cdot \mathbf{D} = \rho \tag{1}$$

by substituting the relations

$$\mathbf{D} = \epsilon \mathbf{E} \tag{2}$$

and

$$\mathbf{E} = -\mathbf{\nabla} V \tag{3}$$

to write

$$\mathbf{\nabla} \cdot (\mathbf{\nabla} V) = -\frac{\rho}{\epsilon} \tag{4}$$

Usually the successive applications of the operations of taking the gradient and then the divergence are further shortened to a symbol known as the Laplacian operator $\mathbf{\nabla}^2$.

Poisson's Equation
$$\mathbf{\nabla}^2 V = -\frac{\rho}{\epsilon} \tag{5}$$

Equation (5) is Poisson's equation.   In regions free of charges, the charge density is zero and the special case of Poisson's equation

Laplace's equation
$$\mathbf{\nabla}^2 V = 0 \tag{6}$$

is known as Laplace's equation.

Two distinct scalar concepts have been introduced to assist us in solving vector problems; these were the concept of potential and the concept of the flux of a vector through a surface.   In Poisson's equation and Laplace's equation, *the two concepts have been tied together into partial differential equations, and by using them we can solve problems that would present tremendous difficulties to less powerful methods.*   The solutions to these equations form a whole branch of applied mathematics.   Functions which satisfy Laplace's equation are known as harmonic functions, and they have wide applications in physical science.

These partial differential equations are perhaps too powerful.   Every electrostatic field is described by Poisson's equation, and in a practical application we have to select, out of a wealth of possibilities, the particular solution which fits the problem at hand.   This is almost always selected by focusing attention on the boundaries.   Thorough treatises on electrostatics are frequently organized by selecting particular types of mathematical functions which satisfy Laplace's equation, and then pointing out the many field configurations which can be described by those functions.   Functions known as the Legendre polynomials are readily applied with spherical boundaries, while Bessel functions occur frequently in problems with cylindrical boundaries.   We shall investigate an application of Fourier series to boundary-value problems in a later section.

8.6   The Laplacian Operator in Cartesian Coordinates.   When the successive differentiation operations of gradient and divergence are applied to a scalar function, the result is a second-order partial differential equation. In cartesian coordinates, the differential expression for the gradient of a scalar function is given by

$$\mathbf{\nabla} V = \mathbf{i}\,\frac{\partial V}{\partial x} + \mathbf{j}\,\frac{\partial V}{\partial y} + \mathbf{k}\,\frac{\partial V}{\partial z} \tag{1}$$

which is a vector with components

$$\frac{\partial V}{\partial x} \qquad \frac{\partial V}{\partial y} \qquad \frac{\partial V}{\partial z}$$

For the divergence of the **D** vector, we wrote

$$\mathbf{\nabla} \cdot \mathbf{D} = \frac{\partial D_x}{\partial x} + \frac{\partial D_y}{\partial y} + \frac{\partial D_z}{\partial z} \tag{2}$$

A similar expression with the vector $\mathbf{\nabla} V$ is

$$\mathbf{\nabla}^2 V = \mathbf{\nabla} \cdot (\mathbf{\nabla} V) = \frac{\partial^2 V}{\partial x^2} + \frac{\partial^2 V}{\partial y^2} + \frac{\partial^2 V}{\partial z^2} \tag{3}$$

As long as we are in cartesian coordinates, we may indicate the operator ∇^2 by the simple relation

$$\mathbf{\nabla}^2 = \frac{\partial^2}{\partial x^2} + \frac{\partial^2}{\partial y^2} + \frac{\partial^2}{\partial z^2} \qquad \text{operating on a scalar} \tag{4}$$

8.7   The Laplacian in Orthogonal Curvilinear Coordinates. As in the case of divergence, it is easier to write the expression for the Laplacian in general orthogonal coordinates than in any one system except cartesian coordinates. We are to apply successively the operations of gradient and divergence to the scalar potential function V.

$$\mathbf{\nabla} V = \frac{1}{h_1}\frac{\partial V}{\partial u_1}\mathbf{i}_1 + \frac{1}{h_2}\frac{\partial V}{\partial u_2}\mathbf{i}_2 + \frac{1}{h_3}\frac{\partial V}{\partial u_3}\mathbf{i}_3 \tag{1}$$

$$\mathbf{\nabla} \cdot \mathbf{D} = \frac{1}{h_1 h_2 h_3}\left[\frac{\partial (h_3 h_2 D_1)}{\partial u_1} + \frac{\partial (h_1 h_3 D_2)}{\partial u_2} + \frac{\partial (h_1 h_2 D_3)}{\partial u_3} \right] \tag{2}$$

Treating the components of $\mathbf{\nabla} V$ like the components of **D**,

$$\mathbf{\nabla}^2 V = \frac{1}{h_1 h_2 h_3}\left[\frac{\partial}{\partial u_1}\left(\frac{h_2 h_3}{h_1}\frac{\partial V}{\partial u_1} \right) + \frac{\partial}{\partial u_2}\left(\frac{h_1 h_3}{h_2}\frac{\partial V}{\partial u_2} \right) + \frac{\partial}{\partial u_3}\left(\frac{h_1 h_2}{h_3}\frac{\partial V}{\partial u_3} \right) \right] \tag{3}$$

This expression looks involved, but a beautiful symmetry of the subscripts appears on further study.

In cylindrical coordinates, we have

$$\begin{array}{ccc} u_1 = R & u_2 = \theta & u_3 = z \\ h_1 = 1 & h_2 = R & h_3 = 1 \end{array}$$

and Eq. (3) becomes

$$\nabla^2 V = \frac{1}{R}\left[\frac{\partial}{\partial R}\left(R\frac{\partial V}{\partial R}\right) + \frac{\partial}{\partial \theta}\left(\frac{1}{R}\frac{\partial V}{\partial \theta}\right) + \frac{\partial}{\partial z}\left(R\frac{\partial V}{\partial z}\right)\right] \tag{4}$$

Differentiating the bracketed factors according to the product rule and collecting, we may write Eq. (4) as

$$\nabla^2 V = \frac{\partial^2 V}{\partial R^2} + \frac{1}{R}\frac{\partial V}{\partial R} + \frac{1}{R^2}\frac{\partial^2 V}{\partial \theta^2} + \frac{\partial^2 V}{\partial z^2} \tag{5}$$

In spherical coordinates,

$$u_1 = R \qquad u_2 = \theta \qquad u_3 = \phi$$
$$h_1 = 1 \qquad h_2 = R \qquad h_3 = R\sin\theta$$

Substituting in Eq. (3),

$$\nabla^2 V = \frac{1}{R^2 \sin\theta}\left[\frac{\partial}{\partial R}\left(R^2 \sin\theta \frac{\partial V}{\partial R}\right) + \frac{\partial}{\partial \theta}\left(\sin\theta \frac{\partial V}{\partial \theta}\right)\right.$$
$$\left. + \frac{\partial}{\partial \phi}\left(\frac{1}{\sin\theta}\frac{\partial V}{\partial \phi}\right)\right] \tag{6}$$

Differentiating according to the product rule, and collecting,

$$\nabla^2 V = \frac{\partial^2 V}{\partial R^2} + \frac{2}{R}\frac{\partial V}{\partial R} + \frac{1}{R^2}\frac{\partial^2 V}{\partial \theta^2} + \frac{\cot\theta}{R^2}\frac{\partial V}{\partial \theta} + \frac{1}{R^2 \sin^2\theta}\frac{\partial^2 V}{\partial \phi^2} \tag{7}$$

It is unfortunate that the Laplacian results in such difficult expressions. In cartesian coordinates one soon learns to remember the expression, long

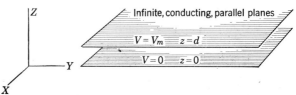

FIG. 8.4   For analysis of the field between infinite conducting parallel planes using Laplace's equation.

familiarity will help some to recall Eq. (3), but one simply looks up Eqs. (5) and (7) in a table. They are listed in many handbooks, the standard tables of integrals, and most books on heat, vibration and sound, fluid mechanics, and differential equations, as well as those on electric and magnetic fields.

8.8   Solutions of Laplace's Equation in a Single Variable.   The fields due to some simple charge configurations have been obtained from Coulomb's law and from Gauss's law. It will be instructive to obtain the fields as solutions to the Laplace equation.

Example 1. The field between infinite parallel conducting planes may be obtained from Laplace's equation in cartesian coordinates

$$\frac{\partial^2 V}{\partial x^2} + \frac{\partial^2 V}{\partial y^2} + \frac{\partial^2 V}{\partial z^2} = 0 \tag{1}$$

As in Fig. 8.4, let the conducting planes lie parallel to the xy plane, and occupy the geometrical planes $z = 0$ and $z = d$, the former maintained at zero potential and the latter at the potential V_m. The potential cannot be a function of x or y, so that Eq. (1) becomes

$$\frac{d^2 V}{dz^2} = 0$$

Two integrations give

$$V = Az + B \tag{2}$$

Since $V = 0$ when $z = 0$, $B = 0$. Since $V = V_m$ when $z = d$, $A = V_m/d$ and the solution is

$$V = \frac{V_m}{d} z \tag{3}$$

The field intensity E is found from $-\nabla V$

$$\mathbf{E} = -\nabla V = (-\mathbf{k}) \frac{V_m}{d} \tag{4}$$

This solution is a special case of a more general solution to be found later.

Example 2. The field between infinitely long concentric cylinders is a one-variable problem in cylindrical coordinates, illustrated in Fig. 8.5. The only variable is R, and Laplace's equation reduces to

$$\frac{d^2 V}{dR^2} + \frac{1}{R} \frac{dV}{dR} = 0 \tag{5}$$

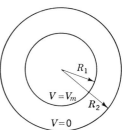

Concentric conducting cylinders, infinitely long

FIG. 8.5   For analysis of the field between concentric conducting cylinders, infinitely long, using Laplace's equation.

This may be written in the form

$$\frac{d}{dR} \left(\frac{dV}{dR} \right) = -\frac{1}{R} \frac{dV}{dR} \tag{6}$$

Separating variables,

$$\frac{d(dV/dR)}{dV/dR} = -\frac{dR}{R} \tag{7}$$

Integrating,

$$\log_e \left(\frac{dV}{dR} \right) = -\log_e R + \log_e C \tag{8}$$

or

$$\frac{dV}{dR} = \frac{C}{R} \tag{9}$$

Separating variables again,

$$dV = C \frac{dR}{R} \tag{10}$$

Integrating,

$$V = C \log_e R + D \tag{11}$$

When the cylinder of radius R_2 is maintained at zero potential, and that of radius R_1 is maintained at V_m, $V = 0$ when $R = R_2$, giving in Eq. (11)

$$C \log_e R_2 + D = 0 \tag{12}$$

and

$$D = -C \log_e R_2 \tag{13}$$

This reduces Eq. (11) to

$$V = C \log_e \frac{R}{R_2} \tag{14}$$

When $R = R_1$, $V = V_m$, giving in Eq. (14)

$$V_m = C \log_e \frac{R_1}{R_2} \tag{15}$$

or

$$C = \frac{V_m}{\log_e (R_1/R_2)} \tag{16}$$

The solution, when the constants are evaluated, is then

$$V = \frac{V_m}{\log_e (R_1/R_2)} \log_e \frac{R}{R_2} \tag{17}$$

Using the operator ∇ to obtain $\mathbf{E}$,

$$\frac{\partial V}{\partial R} = \frac{V_m}{\log_e (R_1/R_2)} \frac{1}{R} \tag{18}$$

and

$$\mathbf{E} = \frac{-V_m}{\log_e (R_1/R_2)} \frac{1}{R} \mathbf{r} \tag{19}$$

or

$$\mathbf{E} = \frac{V_m}{\log_e (R_2/R_1)} \frac{1}{R} \mathbf{r} \tag{20}$$

Example 3. In cylindrical coordinates we have also the possibility of the potential being a function of θ alone, as in the field between the conducting planes $\theta = 0$ and $\theta = k$. See Fig. 8.6 and also Fig. 4.6 for the current-field case. Laplace's equation reduces to

$$\frac{d^2V}{d\theta^2} = 0 \tag{21}$$

Two integrations give

$$V = A\theta + B \tag{22}$$

If we maintain the plane $\theta = 0$ at zero potential and the plane $\theta = k$ at the potential V_m, when the constants are evaluated, Eq. (22) becomes

$$V = \frac{V_m}{k} \theta \qquad (23)$$

The field intensity is

$$E = -\nabla V \qquad (24)$$

or

$$\mathbf{E} = -\frac{\partial V}{R\,\partial \theta}\,\mathbf{\theta} = \frac{-V_m}{kR}\,\mathbf{\theta} \qquad (25)$$

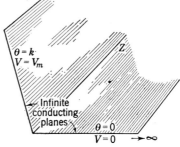

Fig. 8.6 For analysis of the field between intersecting infinite planes, using Laplace's equation.

Example 4. The field between concentric spheres is a one-variable problem in spherical coordinates, with the potential a function of R alone. Laplace's equation reduces to

$$\frac{d^2V}{dR^2} + \frac{2}{R}\frac{dV}{dR} = 0 \qquad (26)$$

This may be written as

$$\frac{d(dV/dR)}{dV/dR} = -2\frac{dR}{R} \qquad (27)$$

The first integration gives

$$\log_e \frac{dV}{dR} = -2\log_e R + \log_e A \qquad (28)$$

and

$$\frac{dV}{dR} = \frac{A}{R^2} \qquad (29)$$

The second integration gives

$$V = -\frac{A}{R} + B \qquad (30)$$

If the sphere at radius R_2 is maintained at zero potential, $V = 0$ when $R = R_2$ and $B = A/R_2$. If the sphere at radius R_1 is maintained at the potential V_m, we may substitute into Eq. (30)

$$V_m = \frac{-A}{R_1} + \frac{A}{R_2} \qquad (31)$$

to find that

$$A = \frac{V_m}{(1/R_2) - (1/R_1)} \qquad (32)$$

Then our solution, Eq. (30), becomes

$$V = \left(\frac{V_m}{\dfrac{1}{R_1} - \dfrac{1}{R_2}}\right)\frac{1}{R} - \left(\frac{V_m}{\dfrac{1}{R_1} - \dfrac{1}{R_2}}\right)\frac{1}{R_2}$$

or

$$V = \frac{V_m}{(1/R_1) - (1/R_2)} \left(\frac{1}{R} - \frac{1}{R_2}\right) \qquad (33)$$

Again, the field intensity is found from the gradient

$$\mathbf{E} = -\boldsymbol{\nabla} V$$

which becomes

$$\mathbf{E} = \frac{V_m}{(1/R_1) - (1/R_2)} \frac{1}{R^2} \mathbf{r} \qquad (34)$$

All these one-variable problems have been solved in previous sections, or in the problems, using Gauss's law and Coulomb's law. We observe that in the present method of solution the work is essentially that of rather simple integrations, and the evaluation of arbitrary constants to fit the boundary conditions. The student may well feel that solving one-dimensional problems by the use of Laplace's equation is somewhat like taking a battleship out on a duck-hunting trip. Gauss's law is much less cumbersome in these simplest problems. However, the evaluation of arbitrary constants to fit the boundary conditions is the idea that is new and unfamiliar. It helps to examine a new idea by first applying it to simple cases.

8.9 Capacitance from Solutions to Laplace's Equation. When the field intensity at the surface of a conductor is known, Gauss's law gives the charge distribution on the surface.

$$\sigma = \epsilon_0 |\mathbf{E}| \qquad (1)$$

From this relation, we can compute the total charge on a conductor.

In the field between infinite parallel planes, $\mathbf{E}$ was found from the potential as Eq. 8.8 (4):

$$\mathbf{E} = (-\mathbf{k}) \frac{V_m}{d}$$

Hence the charge per unit area on the conducting surfaces is

$$\sigma = \frac{\epsilon_0 V_m}{d}$$

and on a given area the charge is

$$\sigma A = \frac{\epsilon_0 A V_m}{d}$$

Since $C = Q/V$, the capacitance is

$$C = \frac{\epsilon_0 A}{d} \qquad (2)$$

Between concentric cylinders we found $\mathbf{E}$ from the potential as Eq. 8.8 (20):

$$\mathbf{E} = \frac{V_m}{\log_e (R_2/R_1)} \frac{1}{R} \mathbf{r} \tag{3}$$

On the cylinder of radius R_1,

$$\sigma = \epsilon_0 \frac{V_m}{\log_e (R_2/R_1)} \frac{1}{R_1}$$

The area of a length L is $2\pi R_1 L$, and it contains a charge of

$$\sigma A = 2\pi \epsilon_0 R_1 L \frac{V_m}{\log_e (R_2/R_1)} \frac{1}{R_1}$$

Hence the capacitance is

$$C = \frac{2\pi \epsilon_0 L}{\log_e (R_2/R_1)} \tag{4}$$

The capacitance of concentric spheres follows as readily.

Obtaining the capacitance as a final step in a problem seems more difficult here than by our previous methods. The reason follows.

In using Coulomb's law and Gauss's law we found it necessary to know or assume a charge distribution. We then found the field intensity and the potential in terms of that assumed or known charge distribution. In using Laplace's equation we are not assuming the charge distribution but are able to find the potential, the field intensity, *and the charge distribution* on the surfaces which we maintain as equipotential surfaces. An engineer seldom thinks of fields in terms of spreading charges over a surface like so much paint. What he does is to establish potential differences between certain boundaries, and Laplace's equation and Poisson's equation are used to solve those boundary-value problems. From the results, he can compute the resulting charge configuration.

8.10   Child's Law, a One-dimensional Solution of Poisson's Equation.
There is little to be gained from using Laplace's equation to solve one-dimensional problems. Each of the results of the previous two sections can be obtained from Gauss's law and careful regard of symmetry conditions. The greater value of the equations of Laplace and Poisson lies in the fact that they may be used to solve problems which we could not hope to solve with Gauss's law. Describing the field in a vacuum tube is just such a problem, and as an illustration, we shall derive Child's law for the potential distribution in a plane diode. To make a one-dimensional problem, we shall assume that the cathode and anode are infinite parallel planes, with the cathode located at $x = 0$ and the anode, or plate, at $x = d$, as in Fig. 8.7. At equilibrium, the potentials and the current density, $\mathbf{J} = \rho \mathbf{U}$, are not functions of time.

In order to provide boundary conditions which can be satisfied by relatively simple expressions, the following assumptions are made:

1. The number of electrons available at the cathode is very much greater than the number reaching the anode. In other words, the current is space-charge-limited rather than temperature-limited.

2. The electrons have a negligible initial velocity.

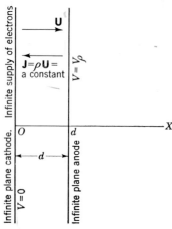

FIG. 8.7 For analysis of the field in a parallel plane diode.

With these assumptions we can establish a boundary condition which simplifies matters considerably: the field intensity is zero at the cathode. For if the field intensity were not zero, and were directed away from the cathode, all electrons would leave the cathode in violation of assumption (1). If it were directed toward the cathode, all electrons would be returned to the cathode and none could reach the anode.

To relate the electron velocity to the potential, we equate the potential and kinetic energies. When e is the charge and m the mass of the electron,

$$eV = \tfrac{1}{2}mU^2 \tag{1}$$

Solving for the magnitude of the velocity,

$$U = \sqrt{\frac{2e}{m}}\,V^{1/2} \tag{2}$$

Since, at equilibrium,

$$\rho = \frac{J}{U} \tag{3}$$

Substituting Eq. (2) into Eq. (3),

$$\rho = J\sqrt{\frac{m}{2e}}\,V^{-1/2} \tag{4}$$

Between infinite parallel planes, the x direction is the only distinguishable direction, and all quantities must be functions of x alone. The symmetry reduces Poisson's equation to an ordinary differential equation

$$\frac{d^2V}{dx^2} = \frac{-\rho}{\epsilon_0} \tag{5}$$

Substituting from Eq. (4) for ρ,

$$\frac{d^2V}{dx^2} = \left[-\frac{J}{\epsilon_0}\sqrt{\frac{m}{2e}}\right]V^{-1/2} \tag{6}$$

$$= kV^{-1/2} \tag{7}$$

The square bracketed quantity on the right is a constant, and to save the writing we may denote it by k.

To solve Eq. (7), we need two integrations, and these can be had by separating the variables. First we substitute the new variable

$$V' = \frac{dV}{dx} \tag{8}$$

In terms of this variable, Eq. (7) may be written

$$\frac{dV'}{dx} = kV^{-\frac{1}{2}} \tag{9}$$

Multiplying both sides by $2V'\,dx$, and rearranging on the right,

$$2V'\,dV' = 2kV^{-\frac{1}{2}}\,dV \tag{10}$$

Integrating both sides and including the necessary arbitrary constant C_1,

$$(V')^2 = 4kV^{\frac{1}{2}} + C_1 \tag{11}$$

Returning to the original variable on the left,

$$\left(\frac{dV}{dx}\right)^2 = 4kV^{\frac{1}{2}} + C_1 \tag{12}$$

We evaluate C_1 from the boundary conditions at equilibrium:
  1. When $x = 0$, $V = 0$
  2. When $x = 0$, $E = -\dfrac{dV}{dx} = 0$

and hence

$$C_1 = 0$$

Taking the square root,

$$\frac{dV}{dx} = -E = \sqrt{4k}\,V^{\frac{1}{4}} \tag{13}$$

We now have the field intensity in terms of the potential, but this is not much help. We seek both the potential and the field intensity as a function of x. Separating the variables again,

$$\frac{dV}{V^{\frac{1}{4}}} = \sqrt{4k}\,dx \tag{14}$$

Integrating both sides,

$$\tfrac{4}{3}V^{\frac{3}{4}} = \sqrt{4k}\,x + C_2 \tag{15}$$

Since, when $x = 0$, $V = 0$, $C_2 = 0$.
Solving for V in terms of x,

$$V = (\tfrac{3}{4})^{\frac{4}{3}}(\sqrt{4k})^{\frac{2}{3}}x^{\frac{2}{3}} \tag{16}$$

The constant terms are getting involved again, but when m and e are given the rather round values of 9 $(10)^{-31}$ kilogram, and 1.6 $(10)^{-19}$ coulomb, the numerical results including the absolute magnitude of the current density J (another constant) is

$$V = 5,670J^{2/3}x^{4/3} \qquad (17)$$

This expression for the potential as a function of the distance from the cathode is Child's law from the field viewpoint. The effect of the space charge is to change this from a linear function of the distance to one involving the $4/3$ power of the distance.

The field intensity can be obtained more easily by differentiating Eq. (17) than by solving Eqs. (13) and (17) simultaneously.

$$E = -\frac{dV}{dx} = 7,560J^{2/3}x^{1/3} \qquad (18)$$

This is in contrast to the uniform field which would be present in the absence of space charge.

In a problem, the student will be asked to solve for ρ and U to complete the analysis. When Eq. (17) is solved for the absolute magnitude of J in terms of the plate potential, V_p at $x = d$, we have Child's law from the external circuit viewpoint, and the conventional form is

$$J = 2.35 \ (10)^{-6} \frac{V_p^{3/2}}{d^2} \qquad (19)$$

This latter result is in accord with experimental observations for plate potentials which are considerably in excess of the emission energy of the electrons expressed in electron volts.

8.11   Product Solutions of Laplace's Equation in Cartesian Coordinates.   One of the ways of solving a partial differential equation is to break it up into a group of ordinary differential equations. To achieve this, we assume that there are solutions which involve the products of functions of each of the variables, as in the following example.

In cartesian coordinates, Laplace's equation is

$$\frac{\partial^2 V}{\partial x^2} + \frac{\partial^2 V}{\partial y^2} + \frac{\partial^2 V}{\partial z^2} = 0 \qquad (1)$$

We assume a solution of the form

$$V = (X)(Y)(Z) \qquad (2)$$

in which X denotes some function of x alone, Y a function of y alone, and Z a function of z alone. This simplifies matters because the partial derivatives required in Eq. (1) involve the total derivatives of the separate functions X, Y, and Z. That is,

$$\frac{\partial^2 V}{\partial x^2} = YZ\frac{d^2X}{dx^2}, \quad \frac{\partial^2 V}{\partial y^2} = XZ\frac{d^2Y}{dy^2}, \quad \frac{\partial^2 V}{\partial z^2} = XY\frac{d^2Z}{dz^2} \qquad (3)$$

Substituting these results into Eq. (1) gives

$$YZ \frac{d^2X}{dx^2} + XZ \frac{d^2Y}{dy^2} + XY \frac{d^2Z}{dz^2} = 0 \tag{4}$$

Dividing by XYZ gives three terms, each of which involves a single variable

$$\frac{1}{X} \frac{d^2X}{dx^2} + \frac{1}{Y} \frac{d^2Y}{dy^2} + \frac{1}{Z} \frac{d^2Z}{dz^2} = 0 \tag{5}$$

Now if y and z are held constant, the second and third terms will be constant since they involve only y and z. This constant will have a numerical value which we could compute if we knew Y and Z. Then for Eq. (5) to be satisfied for every possible value of x, the first term of that equation must also be a constant, and independent of x. Hence, Eq. (5) cannot be satisfied for all values of x, y, and z, unless each of its terms is itself a constant. This allows us to write three separate total differential equations, provided that we add a restriction in the form of the fourth equation below.

$$\frac{1}{X} \frac{d^2X}{dx^2} = a^2 \tag{6}$$

$$\frac{1}{Y} \frac{d^2Y}{dy^2} = b^2 \tag{7}$$

$$\frac{1}{Z} \frac{d^2Z}{dz^2} = c^2 \tag{8}$$

$$a^2 + b^2 + c^2 = 0 \tag{9}$$

In these equations, a, b, and c are called *separation constants*, and we have written their squares to simplify formulating the solutions to Eqs. (6), (7), and (8).

To obtain the solutions to these ordinary differential equations, let us write Eq. (6) in the form

$$\frac{d^2X}{dx^2} = a^2X \tag{10}$$

Now we ask, "What is it that we can differentiate twice and obtain the original function multiplied by a constant squared?" Exponential functions have this property, suggesting that

$$X_1 = A_1 e^{+ax} \tag{11}$$

satisfies Eq. (10). While verifying that Eq. (11) does satisfy Eq. (10), we observe that there is a second solution

$$X_2 = A_2 e^{-ax} \tag{12}$$

It is also evident that either the sum or the difference of Eqs. (11) and (12) is still another solution. These sums and differences suggest the pairs of solutions $\sinh ax$ and $\cosh ax$ if a is a real number, and $\sin ax$ and $\cos ax$ if a is an imaginary number. Whatever form we actually choose is dictated by the ultimate necessity of meeting the boundary conditions in a specific problem.

The solutions to Eqs. (7) and (8) are like those of Eq. (6). To collect our results, including the solutions to Eqs. (7) and (8), let us now write the product solution assumed in Eq. (2) in this form:

$$V = \Sigma A_i e^{\pm ax} e^{\pm by} e^{\pm cz} \qquad a^2 + b^2 + c^2 = 0 \qquad (13)$$

The plus and minus signs on the exponentials may be combined in eight different ways, and with each of the eight we may associate a different value of the arbitrary constant A_i. Further, there is an infinite number of combinations of the separation constants a, b, and c which will satisfy condition $a^2 + b^2 + c^2 = 0$. With each of these combinations, we may associate a still different set of values of A_i.

The need for all this generality arises from the fact that both Eq. (1) and its solution Eq. (13) describe every electrostatic field in those regions which contain no charges. In the next section, we shall adapt the general solution to meet a set of boundary conditions in a specific problem.

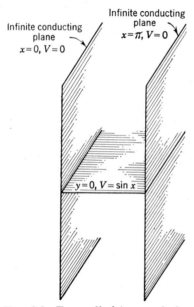

FIG. 8.8 For preliminary analysis of the electrical analogy of Fourier's heat-slab problem.

8.12 An Illustration in Cartesian Coordinates. To illustrate the application of the product solution of Laplace's equation, we shall investigate a field whose symmetry eliminates one of the variables. Such a field lies between planes which are infinite in extent in the z direction, and perpendicular to the x axis.

Here we may set $c = 0$, $a^2 = -b^2$, and $a = +jb$ in which $j = \sqrt{-1}$. Then our solution, Eq. 8.11 (13), takes the form

$$V = \Sigma(A'_1 e^{jbx} + A'_2 e^{-jbx})(B_1 e^{by} + B_2 e^{-by})$$

which is equivalent to

$$V = \Sigma(A_1 \sin bx + A_2 \cos bx)(B_1 e^{by} + B_2 e^{-by}) \qquad (1)$$

As in Fig. 8.8, let two grounded conducting sheets occupy the parallel planes $x = 0$ and $x = \pi$. Let the xz plane be a third surface forming a trough π units wide, infinitely high and infinitely long. The parallel planes forming the sides of the trough are at zero potential, and we arrange potential sources so that the potential on the plane forming the bottom of the trough is given by $V = \sin x$. We also include the reasonable condition that the potential must vanish at points which are at infinitely great distances from the potential sources, where $y = \infty$.

We may list the boundary conditions as

1. $V = 0$ when $x = 0$
2. $V = 0$ when $x = \pi$
3. $V = 0$ when $y = \pm \infty$
4. $V = \sin x$ when $y = 0$

The first two conditions can be met by setting $A_2 = 0$. The third condition requires that $B_1 = 0$ when y is positive and $B_2 = 0$ when y is

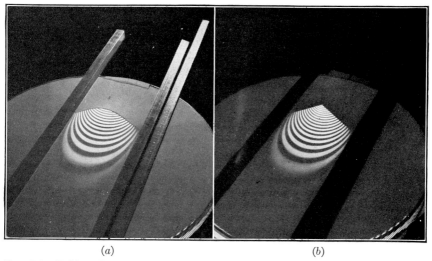

(a)   (b)

Fig. 8.9   Rubber-sheet models of the potential distribution between grounded conducting planes: (a) for a sinusoidal potential source, and (b) for a saw-tooth potential source. Note the similarity in the equipotential contours at the greater distances from sources of displacement.

negative. The fourth condition is satisfied by setting $A_1 B_2 = 1$ and $b = 1$. When these values are substituted, our solution reduces to the simple form

$$V = e^{-y} \sin x \qquad y \gtrless 0 \qquad (2)$$
$$V = e^{+y} \sin x \qquad y \lessgtr 0$$

Determining the field intensity and sketching the resulting field map are left as a fascinating exercise. It is also instructive to determine the surface-charge distribution at the sides of the trough. A contour-lighted rubber-sheet model appears in Fig. 8.9a. A plan view of the shadowlike contours would form a map of the traces of the equipotential surfaces on the planes $z =$ a constant.   The two heavy bars hold the rubber sheet down to create the boundary conditions 1 and 2 above.

We are by no means limited to such specific and simple potential distributions along the bottom of the trough as that given in condition 4 above.   In fact, we may determine the field for any sort of potential distribution by expressing that distribution in the form of a Fourier series. If condition 4 is established as $V = -\frac{1}{9} \sin 3x$ instead of $V = \sin x$, $b = 3$ and $A_1 B_2 = -\frac{1}{9}$, and the solution becomes

$$V = -\frac{1}{9}e^{-3y} \sin 3x \tag{3}$$

and further, the sum of our now two solutions is also a solution.   To express the field which results from a saw-tooth potential distribution along the bottom of the trough, we write the potential distribution in the form of the familiar Fourier series for a saw-tooth wave.

$$V = \sin x - \frac{1}{9} \sin 3x + \frac{1}{25} \sin 5x \cdots \qquad y = 0 \tag{4}$$

We then proceed to evaluate the arbitrary constants for each of these terms and write the expression for the potential field as the Fourier series

$$V = e^{-y} \sin x - \frac{1}{9}e^{-3y} \sin 3x + \frac{1}{25}e^{-5y} \sin 5x \cdots \tag{5}$$

or

$$V = \sum_{n=1}^{n=\infty} \left[\frac{\sin (n\pi/2)}{n^2} \sin nx \right] e^{-ny} \tag{6}$$

A rubber-sheet model of Eq. (6) appears in Fig. 8.9b.   Notice how quickly the elevation of the sheet takes on a sinusoidal cross section as one moves away from the saw-tooth boundary.   This is predicted by the rapid attenuation in the y direction for the higher harmonic terms, e^{-ny}.

The problem we have been studying in this section is a very famous problem indeed.   It has been adapted from Fourier's heat-slab problem. In his problem the two edges of a flat slab were maintained at zero temperature, the face corresponding to that on which we have been maintaining our potentials was maintained at a constant unit temperature, while the top and bottom faces of the slab were insulated so that no heat could flow except in the positive y direction, and to the edges maintained at zero temperature.   Though the problem may have seemed hopeless in its original form, he found that the sinusoidal temperature distributions on the x axis could be solved, that the solutions could be combined as an infinite series of sinusoidal terms, and that their sum represented the solution to the original problem.   His assertion that most periodic functions could be represented by a similar series was sharply criticized by his contemporaries, including Poisson and Laplace.

But the problem was by no means dead and buried when Fourier was. The problem of determining those frequencies at which electromagnetic energy can be propagated in a rectangular wave guide is solved in just this fashion, starting with an equation very similar to Laplace's equation, with a term in time added, to give the wave equation

$$\frac{\partial^2 E}{\partial x^2} + \frac{\partial^2 E}{\partial y^2} + \frac{\partial^2 E}{\partial z^2} = \mu\epsilon\,\frac{\partial^2 E}{\partial t^2}$$

in which E is a component of the electric-field intensity instead of the electrostatic scalar potential. The product solution assumed has the form

$$E = XYZT$$

where T is a function of time alone, and X, Y, Z are functions of x, y, and z alone.

8.13   An Illustration in Polar Coordinates.   When conditions of symmetry are chosen to make the field independent of the z coordinate in cylindrical coordinates, we may write Laplace's equation in two variables, R and θ:

$$\frac{\partial^2 V}{\partial R^2} + \frac{1}{R}\frac{\partial V}{\partial R} + \frac{1}{R^2}\frac{\partial^2 V}{\partial \theta^2} = 0 \tag{1}$$

We may separate the variables if we assume a solution in the form of the product of two functions, each of which contains only one of the variables:

$$V = [F_1(R)][F_2(\theta)] \tag{2}$$

Differentiating, we obtain

$$\frac{1}{R}\frac{\partial V}{\partial R} = \frac{F_2}{R}\frac{\partial F_1}{\partial R}$$

$$\frac{\partial^2 V}{\partial R^2} = F_2\,\frac{\partial^2 F_1}{\partial R^2}$$

$$\frac{1}{R^2}\frac{\partial^2 V}{\partial \theta^2} = \frac{F_1}{R^2}\frac{\partial^2 F_2}{\partial \theta^2}$$

Substituting in Eq. (1),

$$F_2\,\frac{\partial^2 F_1}{\partial R^2} + \frac{F_2}{R}\frac{\partial F_1}{\partial R} + \frac{F_1}{R^2}\frac{\partial^2 F_2}{\partial \theta^2} = 0$$

Multiplying by R^2 and dividing by $F_1 F_2$

$$\frac{R^2}{F_1}\left(\frac{\partial^2 F_1}{\partial R^2} + \frac{1}{R}\frac{\partial F_1}{\partial R}\right) + \frac{1}{F_2}\frac{\partial^2 F_2}{\partial \theta^2} = 0 \tag{3}$$

By the same arguments which followed Eq. 8.11 (3), each of the terms in Eq. (3) must be equal to a constant, and the sum of the constants must be zero. We set the second term equal to the constant $-k^2$ and obtain the ordinary differential equation of simple harmonic motion

$$\frac{d^2 F_2}{d\theta^2} = -k^2 F_2 \tag{4}$$

This equation has the solution when $k \neq 0$

$$F_2 = C \cos k\theta + D \sin k\theta \qquad (5)$$

Setting the first term of Eq. (3) equal to the constant $+k^2$, we obtain the ordinary differential equation

$$R^2 \frac{d^2 F_1}{dR^2} + R \frac{dF_1}{dR} = k^2 F_1 \qquad (6)$$

The solution of this equation, when $k \neq 0$, is

$$F_1 = AR^{+k} + BR^{-k} \qquad (7)$$

and

$$V = (AR^{+k} + BR^{-k})(C \cos k\theta + D \sin k\theta) \qquad (8)$$

When $k = 0$, Eq. (4) becomes

$$\frac{d^2 F_2}{d\theta^2} = 0 \qquad (9)$$

Two integrations give

$$F_2 = C_0 \theta + D_0 \qquad (10)$$

When $k = 0$, Eq. (6) becomes

$$\frac{d^2 F_1}{dR^2} + \frac{1}{R} \frac{dF_1}{dR} = 0 \qquad (11)$$

The variables are separable and two integrations give us the solution as

$$F_1 = A_0 \log_e R + B_0 \qquad (12)$$

and

$$V = (A_0 \log_e R + B_0)(C_0 \theta + D_0) \qquad (13)$$

The resulting expression of our solution to Laplace's equation which includes integer and zero values of the constant k is the sum of Eqs. (8) and (13):

$$V = (A_0 \log_e R + B_0)(C_0 \theta + D_0)$$
$$+ (AR^k + BR^{-k})(C \cos k\theta + D \sin k\theta) \qquad (14)$$

In many physical problems the potential is a single-valued function of position, such that

$$V_{(R,\theta)} = V_{(R,\theta+2\pi)} \qquad (15)$$

In this case, k has integral values only, and the constant $C_0 = 0$. Under these conditions Eq. (14) reduces to

$$V = (A_0 \log_e R + B_0) + (A_k R^k + B_k R^{-k})(C_k \cos k\theta + D_k \sin k\theta) \qquad (16)$$

This is the equation of circular harmonics. The degree of the harmonic is determined by the integral value of k. A circular harmonic of first degree is the solution to the problem of a conducting cylinder in a uniform field.

Example.   A uniform field along the x axis may be written as

$$\mathbf{E}_u = +E_u\,\mathbf{i}$$

Such a field is the gradient of a potential field whose equipotentials are planes parallel to the YZ plane.   If the potential at the origin is taken as zero, the potential due to the uniform field is

$$V_u = -E_u x = -E_u R \cos \theta \qquad (17)$$

When a conducting cylinder of radius a is inserted into the uniform field concentric with the z axis, and maintained at zero potential, the free charges move under the influence of the uniform field until the surface of the cylinder is an equipotential surface on which $V = 0$ (see Fig. 5.11).

The resulting field is given by Eq. (16), and we must determine the arbitrary constants to establish the boundary conditions.   We use Eq. (16) because the potential is a single-valued function of θ.

At great distances from the cylinder, the potential must approach that of the uniform field.   Equation (16) must reduce to

$$V = -E_u R \cos \theta \qquad R \gg a$$

This establishes $A_0 = 0$, $B_0 = 0$, $k = 1$.

The equipotential surfaces have "even" symmetry about the x axis. That is, the potential at the point R, $+\theta$, is the same as that at R, $-\theta$. This establishes $D_k = 0$ and also permits us to set $AC = -E_u$.   Since the potential must be zero when $R = a$, then

$$A_k R^k + B_k R^{-k} = 0 \qquad R = a$$

This determines B in terms of A as

$$B = -Aa^2$$

and

$$BC = -ACa^2$$

We previously found $AC = -E_u$.   We may then write the solution as

$$V = -E_u \left(R - \frac{a^2}{R} \right) \cos \theta \qquad (18)$$

This result was obtained by the method of images and superposition in Sec. 6.6.   In that section the details of obtaining the field intensity from the gradient are given, along with a fluid-flow map and a rubber-sheet model.   A field map is found in Sec. 5.6 as Fig. 5.11.

For a further application of Laplace's equation in cylindrical coordinates, see Probs. 8.15 and 8.16 at the end of this chapter.

8.14   The Theorem of Uniqueness.   When one first studies the solutions to boundary-value problems, he is apt to question the rather ruthless manner in which the arbitrary constants are evaluated to fit the stated boundary conditions. One needs assurance that the particular choice of constants is the one and only one which applies to the case at hand. This is a very legitimate question and has been asked (and answered) by able mathematicians as well as engineering students. The theorem of uniqueness answers this question in a reassuring manner and tells us that when we have obtained a solution which meets the boundary conditions and satisfies Poisson's equation everywhere in the region of interest, we have obtained the one and only solution.

The proof of the theorem requires an extension of two ideas which we have examined only briefly. The extension is rather formal but not very imposing. The first idea is the divergence theorem, stated as Eq. 8.1 (6) in terms of the $\mathbf{D}$ vector

$$\int \mathbf{\nabla} \cdot \mathbf{D} \, dv = \oint \mathbf{D} \cdot \mathbf{n} \, dA \tag{1}$$

The second idea arose in our investigation of a gas undergoing compression, in which we were required, by implication, to evaluate the divergence of a vector function multiplied by a scalar function. In Sec. 8.4, we obtained Eq. (5)

$$\frac{\partial w}{\partial t} = -\mathbf{\nabla} \cdot w\mathbf{U} \tag{2}$$

In one of the problems, the student will be asked to demonstrate the following identity of vector analysis required on the right:

$$\mathbf{\nabla} \cdot w\mathbf{U} = w\mathbf{\nabla} \cdot \mathbf{U} + \mathbf{\nabla}w \cdot \mathbf{U} \tag{3}$$

To adapt Eqs. (1) and (3) to the problem at hand, let $\mathbf{U}$ be replaced by another vector quantity $\mathbf{\nabla}V$, the gradient of a potential function. Let w be replaced by another scalar function V, the potential itself. With this change of variables, Eq. (3) becomes

$$\mathbf{\nabla} \cdot (V\mathbf{\nabla}V) = V(\mathbf{\nabla} \cdot \mathbf{\nabla}V) + \mathbf{\nabla}V \cdot \mathbf{\nabla}V \tag{4}$$

On the right, the first term involves the Laplacian, while the second term is the square of the vector $\mathbf{\nabla}V$; see Sec. 1.5, Eq. (5). Then Eq. (4) becomes

$$\mathbf{\nabla} \cdot (V\mathbf{\nabla}V) = V\mathbf{\nabla}^2V + (\mathbf{\nabla}V)^2 \tag{5}$$

The next step is to treat the vector quantity $V\mathbf{\nabla}V$ like the $\mathbf{D}$ vector in the divergence theorem, Eq. (1), using Eq. (5) in the volume integral. Distributing the volume integration gives

$$\int V\mathbf{\nabla}^2V \, dv + \int (\mathbf{\nabla}V)^2 \, dv = \oint V\mathbf{\nabla}V \cdot \mathbf{n} \, dA \tag{6}$$

Equation (6) is a special case of a more general identity known as *Green's first identity*. It arises in the proof of *Green's theorem*, which is widely used in mathematical physics.   We shall not pursue the general theorem, contenting ourselves with using the special case to prove the theorem of uniqueness.

Let us suppose that in some problem in electrostatics we have obtained two different potential functions as the answer.   Each of these, V_1 and V_2, satisfies Laplace's equation and meets a specific boundary condition on a closed surface.   That is

$$\nabla^2 V_1 = 0 \tag{7}$$
$$\nabla^2 V_2 = 0 \tag{8}$$
$$(V_1 - V_2)_s = 0 \tag{9}$$

where the subscript on the difference in Eq. (9) indicates that the two functions are the same, so far, only on the bounding surface.   To save the writing in what follows, let us now subtract the two solutions, forming a potential function

$$V = V_1 - V_2 \tag{10}$$

Now, applying the Laplacian operator to Eq. (10), and because of our postulates (7) and (8), the difference of our two solutions also satisfies Laplace's equation,

$$\nabla^2 V = 0 \tag{11}$$

Returning now to our form of Green's identity, Eq. (6), let the surface integral on the right be taken over the bounding surface where Eq. (9) applies, giving zero as a result.   Because of Eq. (11), the first integral on the left of Eq. (6) is also zero, leaving us with only

$$\int (\nabla V)^2 \, dv = 0 \tag{12}$$

and this volume integral now applies throughout the entire volume enclosed by the bounding surface.   Regardless of the magnitude or direction of ∇V itself, the quantity $(\nabla V)^2$ is always positive.   The only way that we can obtain the zero result of the volume integral required by Eq. (12) is to have

$$\nabla V = 0 \tag{13}$$

This shows that the difference between our two solutions is a constant at the most.   But if V_1 and V_2 have the same value at any point (and we have specified that they have the same value on the boundary), this constant must be zero.   Therefore

$$V_1 = V_2 \tag{14}$$

and the solutions are identical.

We may extend this conclusion to two possible solutions to Poisson's equation very quickly by noting that if both V_1 and V_2 satisfy Poisson's equation

$$\nabla^2 V_1 = -\frac{\rho}{\epsilon} \tag{15}$$

$$\nabla^2 V_2 = -\frac{\rho}{\epsilon} \tag{16}$$

Then subtracting Eq. (16) from Eq. (15) gives

$$\nabla^2(V_1 - V_2) = 0$$

and this is the same as Eq. (11) in the former proof.

We are at liberty then to determine the value of the arbitrary constants in a solution to Poisson's equation (or Laplace's equation) by any methods which are convenient. If the resulting solution satisfies the boundary conditions and Poisson's equation, it is the one and only solution to the stated physical problem. This is known as the theorem of uniqueness.

Like the Euclidean proof of the proposition that one and only one straight line can be drawn between two points, the theorem of uniqueness is good common sense in formal language. We are pretty sure even without the formal language that if we maintain a given potential on the conductors of a transmission line, for example, the field configuration will be the same on Sundays and holidays as it is during the week, if everything else remains the same. It is helpful, too, to think of the uniqueness of the form of a stretched rubber sheet.

8.15   A Summary and a Criticism. Divergence is the flux gain per unit volume, a scalar concept in which the flux is evaluated with respect to the outward normal of a closed surface. Convergence is the negative of divergence and is the flux gain per unit volume evaluated with respect to the inward normal of a closed surface. In a physical flow problem, convergence is based on the principle that everything which enters a region must cross the walls bounding the region, and in the limit, as the volume becomes vanishingly small, the convergence of a physical flow is the time rate of increase of density of the medium. We have taken as our defining equation for divergence

$$\nabla \cdot \mathbf{D} = \lim_{\Delta v \to 0} \frac{\oint \mathbf{D} \cdot \mathbf{n} \, dA}{\Delta v} \tag{8.1(4)}$$

In terms of this definition, Gauss's law becomes

$$\nabla \cdot \mathbf{D} = \rho$$

The divergence theorem relates a surface integral to a volume integral

$$\oint \mathbf{D} \cdot \mathbf{n} \, dA = \int \nabla \cdot \mathbf{D} \, dv$$

The formula for computing the divergence of a known vector function, in general orthogonal coordinates, is

$$\mathbf{\nabla \cdot D} = \frac{1}{h_1 h_2 h_3} \left\{ \frac{\partial (h_2 h_3 D_1)}{\partial u_1} + \cdots \right\} \qquad 8.3(1)$$

with the other two terms obtained by permuting the subscripts in cyclic order. This is readily adapted to the particular system of coordinates needed.

In Poisson's equation, of which Laplace's equation is a special case for regions in which the charge density is zero, the scalar concepts of flux and potential are tied together. Poisson's equation is Gauss's law in the form of a second-order partial differential equation in which the scalar potential is the dependent variable. The formula for computing the Laplacian of a known potential function, in general orthogonal coordinates, is

$$\mathbf{\nabla}^2 V = \frac{1}{h_1 h_2 h_3} \left[\frac{\partial}{\partial u_1} \left(\frac{h_2 h_3}{h_1} \frac{\partial V}{\partial u_1} \right) + \cdots \right] \qquad 8.7(3)$$

where, again, the other two terms are obtained by permuting the subscripts in cyclic order.

There is an important class of solutions to Laplace's equation which is obtained by assuming a solution in the form of the product of three functions, each of which is a function of a single independent variable. This procedure separates the variables and reduces the partial differential equation to three ordinary differential equations and a restriction on the separation constants. In general, solutions to partial differential equations involve arbitrary functions as opposed to the arbitrary constants which arise in the solution of ordinary differential equations. As an example of these arbitrary functions, we obtained one solution in which a Fourier series was involved.

Regardless of one's familiarity or lack of familiarity with partial differential equations, knowing about Laplace's equation is helpful, because it opens to one's resources the vast literature of potential theory and the branch of applied mathematics called harmonic functions. There is no particular point, in this age, for most of us to seek new and independent solutions, if we know where to find those which are available in this extensive product of some of the finest mathematical minds.

On the other hand, the partial differential equation approach is too general, in a sense. It is quite difficult to satisfy the boundary conditions unless these boundaries can be made to coincide with one of the coordinate surfaces. Sometimes one invents a system of coordinates to meet this need. For many of the common practical problems, a solution from Laplace's equation may be the most cumbersome method rather than the most practical. In symmetrical problems, the use of Gauss's law is much the easier approach.

The viewpoint of the task in fitting solutions of Laplace's equation to the problem at hand is that of the need to *satisfy the boundary conditions*. The theorem of uniqueness tells us that if we can, by any method, obtain a solution which satisfies Poisson's equation and meets the boundary conditions, we have the one and only solution to the problem.

REFERENCES

1. Ware, Lawrence A.: "Elements of Electromagnetic Waves," pp. 26–30, Pitman Publishing Corp., New York, 1949.   Contains examples and physical interpretations of divergence.
2. Weber, Ernst: "Electromagnetic Fields," Vol. I, pp. 72–73, John Wiley & Sons, Inc., New York, 1950.   Shows correspondence of physical quantities in scalar potential fields.
3. Smythe, William R.: "Static and Dynamic Electricity," Chap. V, McGraw-Hill Book Company, Inc., 1939.
4. Bewley, L. V.: "Two-dimensional Fields in Electrical Engineering," pp. 17–21, 138, The Macmillan Company, New York, 1948.   Further treatment of Fourier's heat-slab problem, together with a soap-film model of one formulation.
5. Chaffee, E. L.: "Theory of Thermionic Vacuum Tubes," pp. 64–82, McGraw-Hill Book Company, Inc., New York, 1933.   Elaborate treatment of space charge effects in vacuum tubes.
6. Stratton, J. A.: "Electromagnetic Theory," McGraw-Hill Book Company, Inc., New York, 1941.   Refer to p. 165 for Green's theorem, and to pp. 196, 256, and 486 for more formal treatment of the theorem of uniqueness.

PROBLEMS

*8.1   Interpret the analysis of Sec. 8.4 in terms of the motion of space charge with density ρ, writing Eq. 8.4(5) in terms of the current-density vector $\mathbf{J}$. Under what conditions, then, is $\nabla \cdot \mathbf{J} = 0$?

*8.2   Using the formula for divergence in general orthogonal coordinates, write out the formulas in cylindrical and spherical coordinates.   With the help of these, obtain the divergence of the following vectors: (*a*) the unit vectors of three coordinate systems, individually; (*b*) the field intensity due to a point charge in a vacuum (How about the origin?); (*c*) the field intensity due to a line charge in a vacuum (How about the origin?); (*d*) $y\,\mathbf{i} - x\,\mathbf{j}$; (*e*) $x\,\mathbf{i} - y\,\mathbf{j}$;

$$(f)\ x\,\mathbf{i} + y\,\mathbf{j} + z\,\mathbf{k} = R\,\mathbf{r};\ (g)\ \frac{x\,\mathbf{i} + y\,\mathbf{j} + z\,\mathbf{k}}{(x^2 + y^2 + z^2)^{3/2}} = \frac{\mathbf{r}}{R^2};$$

(*h*) the velocity of a freely falling aggregate of loose particles such as sand or isolated water droplets.

8.3   By expansion in cartesian coordinates, show that

$$\nabla \cdot (w\mathbf{U}) = w(\nabla \cdot \mathbf{U}) + \mathbf{U} \cdot (\nabla w)$$

where w and $\mathbf{U}$ are functions of the coordinates as in Sec. 8.4.   What is the physical significance of ∇w when w is the density of a gas?

*8.4   From the limited viewpoint of the divergence of a one-dimensional vector $\mathbf{M}$, and the resulting expression for its divergence $\nabla \cdot \mathbf{M} = \partial M_x/\partial x$ the statement is sometimes made that divergence is the rate of change of a vector in a direction parallel to itself.   By a study of the field of a point charge or a line charge, show that this statement is not generally true.

8.5   Prepare a field map of the field $V = e^{-y} \sin x$, $y \geq 0$, found in Sec. 8.12. To aid in constructing the direction lines, find their equation.   Compare the shape of the direction lines with the shape of the equipotentials.   Can you find another field map among those we have studied in which this is true?

8.6   From the results of Sec. 8.10, plot the relative magnitudes of ρ, $\mathbf{U}$, V, and $\mathbf{E}$ as a function of x/d in a plane-parallel diode.   Check with curves in a text on vacuum tubes.

*8.7   Show that $V = -E_u R \cos \theta + E_u a^3 (\cos \theta)/R^2$, where E_u is a constant, satisfies Laplace's equation in spherical coordinates.

8.8   The expression in Prob. 8.7 represents the potential distribution outside a conducting sphere of radius a placed in a uniform field E_u along the $+z$ axis, where $\theta = 0$.   (a) Show that the potential is zero on the surface of the sphere. (b) Show that the field-intensity vector is normal to the surface of the sphere, and find an expression for the surface-charge density on the sphere.

8.9   Find the potential due to a conducting sphere in a uniform field by using the method of images.   Show that the resulting field outside the sphere is the superposition of a uniform field on that due to a dipole of moment $4\pi\epsilon_0 E_u a^3$.

8.10   Show that $1/R$ is a solution of Laplace's equation in spherical coordinates. How could such a potential be established?   Show that $1/R$ is not a solution in cylindrical coordinates.   Under what conditions could $1/R$ satisfy Poisson's equation in cylindrical coordinates?

8.11   Show that $\log_e R$ is a solution of Laplace's equation in cylindrical coordinates but not in spherical coordinates.   Under what conditions could $\log_e R$ satisfy Poisson's equation in spherical coordinates?

*8.12   Illustrate the arbitrary nature of the choice of a reference level of potential from the viewpoint of Laplace's equation.   You may use Eq. 8.8(2) as a basis for discussion.

8.13   In cartesian, cylindrical, and spherical coordinates, determine whether or not the coordinates themselves satisfy Laplace's equation.   Apply the same test to the metric coefficients h_1, h_2, and h_3.

*8.14   Equation (14) in Sec. 8.13 gives the solutions to many of our previously solved problems when the arbitrary constants are evaluated.   Evaluate the arbitrary constants for the following fields:

(a) A line charge
(b) Two concentric conducting cylinders
(c) The toroidal current-carrying conductors in Sec. 4.5
(d) A parallel-plane capacitor, neglecting edge effects

8.15   The illustration of Sec. 8.12 has an interesting counterpart in cylindrical coordinates.   On a cylinder of unit radius, infinitely long, the potential is maintained as $V = \sin \theta$.   Evaluate the arbitrary constants in Eq. 8.13(16), obtaining two expressions for the potential, one valid inside the cylinder and the other valid outside.   Show that the two expressions match on the cylinder, and find an expression for the field intensity.

8.16   Extend the results of Prob. 8.15 to the saw-tooth potential distribution given by writing Eq. 8.12(4) in terms of the variable θ.

CHAPTER 9

THE MAGNETOSTATIC FIELD

In this chapter we have more than one job to do. We need to examine magnetic fields which are not changing with time, and we need to gain some of the kind of experience which Maxwell had when he introduced the concept of curl. Our experience with electrostatics has been rather extensive, and while this will aid us in shortening our development of magnetic fields, we have not had an opportunity to see nonconservative fields in action. Our approach, therefore, will be to present magnetic fields in those lights which make most prominent the comparisons between magnetic and electrostatic fields. In addition, we shall use such opportunities as are available to present examples of the kind of thinking which leads to Stokes's theorem and the concept of curl.

9.1 Magnetic Forces on Moving Charges. The electric forces we have been describing are those experienced by charges as a result of their position in space with respect to other fixed charges. When these forces are not changing with time, a description of the electric forces as a function of position describes an electrostatic field. Moving charges experience forces in addition to those forces which can be attributed to the position of other charges, or to gravitational or inertia forces. This additional force due to the velocity of the charge is called a magnetic force. When a moving charge experiences such a force, it is said to be in a magnetic field of force.

Experimentally, magnetic forces are found to act at right angles to the velocity of the moving charge. This introduces a complication in describing the direction of the field. At any one point in a magnetostatic field, it is possible to observe an infinite number of directions of the magnetic force. To describe a direction which can be associated with the point in space and not with the moving charge, the one unique line of direction is that of NO force, as suggested by Fig. 9.1. The experimental observations allow us to define a magnetic field vector **B** in terms of the force experienced by a charge Q moving with velocity **U** by the vector-product relation

$$\mathbf{F} = Q\mathbf{U} \times \mathbf{B} \tag{1}$$

in contrast to the electric-field intensity vector **E**, whose direction was

228

parallel to the direction of the electric force, the magnetic field vector **B** has a direction perpendicular to the force. The units of **E** are newtons per coulomb from the force viewpoint. Correspondingly the units of the **B** vector are newtons per coulomb, divided by meters per second, differing from those of the **E** vector by the units of velocity, meters per second. From the energy viewpoint, the units of **E** are volts per meter. When these are divided by the units of velocity, the corresponding units of the **B** vector are volt-seconds per square meter, commonly called webers per square meter. The name *magnetic flux density* arises from this viewpoint.

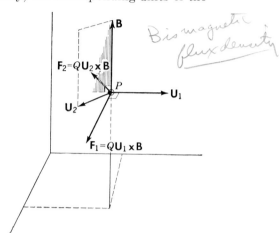

In describing magnetic fields there are many possible starting points. Some begin with compass needles, and others begin with Faraday's law for the interrelations of electric and magnetic fields, while still others begin with the forces between conductors carrying steady currents. Our starting point has been chosen because of its close analogy to the Coulomb's-law viewpoint of electric fields, to enhance thinking about the magnetic field as a vector property associated with a point in space, and to reinforce the very important fact that the **B** vector is everywhere perpendicular to the force. We shall not expect, therefore, to find it re-

FIG. 9.1 The force experienced by a moving charge in a magnetic field does not have a unique magnitude and direction. The one unique direction assignable to a point in the field is the line of no force. This is the direction assigned to the magnetic field vector **B** in the defining equation $F = Q\mathbf{U} \times \mathbf{B}$.

lated simply to the conservation of energy, as is a vector directly proportional and parallel to a physical force.

9.2 Motion of Charged Particles in a Uniform Magnetic Field. Since the magnetic forces acting on a charged particle are perpendicular to the velocity of the particle, they tend to force the particle to move on a circular path. These forces are opposed by the inertia reaction which tends to keep the particle moving in a straight line. While the trajectories can be studied most easily by equating the magnetic force and the inertia reaction, we shall utilize an opportunity to set up and solve an ordinary differential equation.

We shall consider a particle of mass m and charge Q in a uniform magnetic field parallel to the z axis of cartesian coordinates. The vector velocity of the particle is

$$\mathbf{U} = \mathbf{i} \, U_x + \mathbf{j} \, U_y + \mathbf{k} \, U_z \tag{1}$$

The magnetic-field vector is

$$\mathbf{B} = B\,\mathbf{k} \tag{2}$$

Then since the magnetic force $\mathbf{F}_m$ is

$$\mathbf{F}_m = Q\mathbf{U} \times \mathbf{B} \tag{3}$$

we evaluate the vector product as in Chap. 1 to write

$$\mathbf{F}_m = QBU_y\,\mathbf{i} - QBU_x\,\mathbf{j} \tag{4}$$

According to Newton's law

$$\mathbf{F}_m = \frac{d}{dt}\,(m\mathbf{U}) \tag{5}$$

Since the speed is constant, the mass is constant.   (The relativistic mass should be used, however, rather than the rest mass.)   This allows us to differentiate Eq. (5) by treating the unit vectors as constants, also.

$$\frac{d}{dt}\,(m\mathbf{U}) = \mathbf{i}\,m\,\frac{dU_x}{dt} + \mathbf{j}\,m\,\frac{dU_y}{dt} + \mathbf{k}\,m\,\frac{dU_z}{dt} \tag{6}$$

Equating the components of Eqs. (4) and (6),

$$QBU_y = m\,\frac{dU_x}{dt} \tag{7}$$

$$-QBU_x = m\,\frac{dU_y}{dt} \tag{8}$$

$$0 = m\,\frac{dU_z}{dt} \tag{9}$$

When Eqs. (7) and (8) are differentiated and solved for the terms in U_x and U_y, they become

$$\frac{d^2U_x}{dt^2} + \frac{Q^2B^2}{m^2}\,U_x = 0 \tag{10}$$

$$\frac{d^2U_y}{dt^2} + \frac{Q^2B^2}{m^2}\,U_y = 0 \tag{11}$$

These equations describe simple harmonic motion and are more familiar to electrical-engineering students in terms of a lossless resonant circuit in the form

$$\frac{d^2i}{dt^2} + \frac{1}{LC}\,i = 0$$

A solution of the differential equations is

$$U_x = a\,\sin \omega t + b\,\cos \omega t \tag{12}$$

$$U_y = c\,\sin \omega t + d\,\cos \omega t \tag{13}$$

in which a, b, c, and d are arbitrary constants and

$$\omega = \frac{QB}{m} \tag{14}$$

By choosing the y axis tangent to the component of the velocity of the particle which is perpendicular to the z axis at the instant $t = 0$, and denoting the corresponding initial velocity components as U_{x0}, U_{y0}, U_{z0}, Eqs. (12), (13), and (9) become

$$U_x = U_{y0} \sin \omega t \tag{15}$$
$$U_y = U_{y0} \cos \omega t \tag{16}$$
$$U_z = U_{z0} \tag{17}$$

Choosing the origin at the location of the particle when $t = 0$ allows us to convert these equations to three which describe the position of the particle as a function of time by integrating $\frac{dx}{dt} = U_x$, etc.

$$x = \frac{U_{y0}}{\omega} (1 - \cos \omega t) \tag{18}$$

$$y = \frac{U_{y0}}{\omega} \sin \omega t \tag{19}$$

$$z = U_{z0}t \tag{20}$$

By transposing the constant term of Eq. (18), squaring, and adding Eqs. (18) and (19), the time is eliminated. The projection of the trajectory of the particle on the xy plane is

$$\left(x - \frac{U_{y0}}{\omega}\right)^2 + y^2 = \left(\frac{U_{y0}}{\omega}\right)^2 \tag{21}$$

which is the equation of a circle tangent to the y and z axes and having a radius of U_{y0}/ω. The angular velocity of rotation is ω and is independent of the velocity as seen from Eq. (14):

$$\omega = \frac{QB}{m}$$

The time T, for the particle to complete one revolution on the circular path, is $2\pi/\omega$,

$$T = \frac{2\pi m}{QB} \tag{22}$$

This is independent of the velocity! During this length of time, the particle will travel along the z axis a distance given by Eq. (20) as

$$P = U_{z0} \frac{2\pi m}{QB} \tag{23}$$

Thus the path of motion is a helix of radius

$$R = U_{y0} \frac{m}{QB} \tag{24}$$

and a pitch, P, given by Eq. (23).

Magnetic focusing of cathode-ray tubes is accomplished by directing the uniform magnetic field along the axis of the tube. The beam of electrons is only slightly divergent from a direction parallel to the axis of the tube which is our z axis. For an electron which enters the field at the small angle θ with the axis,

$$U_{z0} = \mathbf{U}_0 \cdot \mathbf{k} = U_0 \cos \theta$$
$$U_{y0} = \mathbf{U}_0 \cdot \mathbf{j} = U_0 \sin \theta$$

All such electrons travel to the screen along the z axis in very nearly the same time because the cosine of small angles is essentially unity. Each particle completes a revolution of the helix in the *same time* and thus returns to the z axis at the same instant. If the magnetic-field intensity is properly related to U_0, the divergent beam converges at the screen.

Our defining equation for the magnetic field

$$\mathbf{F} = Q\mathbf{U} \times \mathbf{B}$$

has a considerable and a growing practical importance. It is a part of the equations of motion of the ions in a mass spectrograph used in isotope separation. The magnetron, a high-power microwave generator; the cyclotron; and several other particle accelerators are perhaps the best evidence that we need to know about this equation. As a side light, when the physicist and the engineer speak of the *cyclotron frequency*, as they frequently do, they are referring to the frequency given by dividing the angular velocity of Eq. (14) by 2π.

9.3   The Magnetic Force on a Current Element.   The magnetic force on a moving charge was given by the experimental relation

$$\mathbf{F} = Q\mathbf{U} \times \mathbf{B} \tag{1}$$

The steady current in a conductor is composed of the average drift of great numbers of charges whose motion is confined to the conductor. The distribution of steady currents in conductors is determined almost entirely by the boundaries of the conductor and the electric forces, and not by the forces of the external magnetostatic field which may also be present. The average drift velocities of the electrons in current-carrying conductors are so small that it is difficult to change the current distribution by applying an external magnetic field. Though a small effect, known as the *Hall effect*, can be measured, it will be ignored in these discussions. The restraining forces which confine the moving charges to the conductor itself cause the magnetic forces to be observed as forces on the conductor.

The current density is uniform in a differential volume element of a conductor, and the total force is the sum of the forces on all the moving charges within that volume. If there are n charges Q per unit volume, with an average drift velocity $\mathbf{U}$, the total force on the differential element of volume is

$$dF = (nQ \, dA \, dL)\mathbf{U} \times \mathbf{B} \tag{2}$$

where dA is the cross-sectional area of the differential volume, taken normal to $\mathbf{U}$, and dL is its length taken parallel to $\mathbf{U}$. The volume-charge density ρ is nQ, and the current density vector at every point in the conductor is

$$\mathbf{J} = \rho\mathbf{U}$$

We may then write Eq. (2) as

$$dF = dA \, dL(\mathbf{J} \times \mathbf{B}) \tag{3}$$

Noting that $dA \, dL$ is the volume of the current element, we have for the force per unit volume in a conductor

$$\frac{d\mathbf{F}}{dv} = \mathbf{J} \times \mathbf{B} \qquad \text{per unit volume} \tag{4}$$

The total force on a current-carrying conductor is the vector sum

$$\mathbf{F} = \int \mathbf{J} \times \mathbf{B} \, dv \tag{5}$$

where dv is the differential element of volume, and the integration is to be evaluated throughout the volume of the conductor. This is the general relation for the force on a conductor in a magnetostatic field.

For conductors carrying uniform current densities and having a uniform cross-sectional area, we may rearrange Eq. (3) in the form

$$dF = JA(dL \, \mathbf{j}) \times \mathbf{B} \tag{6}$$

where $\mathbf{j}$ is the unit vector in the direction of $\mathbf{J}$. Then combining the vector $dL \, \mathbf{j}$ into the vector $d\mathbf{L}$, and writing I for JA,

$$dF = I(d\mathbf{L} \times \mathbf{B}) \tag{7}$$

Then the total force on a conductor of uniform cross section and uniform current density is

$$\mathbf{F} = \oint I(d\mathbf{L} \times \mathbf{B}) \tag{8}$$

in which the line integral is to be taken around the entire closed path of the current. For a section of a straight conductor of length $\mathbf{L}$ in a uniform magnetic field

$$\mathbf{F} = I\mathbf{L} \times \mathbf{B} \tag{9}$$

Though strictly a special case, this is the usual form of the expression for "motor action," using vector-analysis notation to describe the direction of the force rather than Fleming's left-hand rule.

To evaluate Eqs. (5) and (8), we must resolve the vector quantity under the integral sign into components and add the components separately as we did in obtaining the sum of the differential contributions of each point charge to the electric-field intensity in Chap. 2. In the following sections we shall examine a few illustrations.

9.4 The Force on a Closed Circuit in a Uniform Magnetic Field. As an illustration of the application of the expression for the force on a differential current element, we shall show that the force on a closed circuit placed in a uniform magnetic field is zero. The force on each current element of length $d\mathbf{L}$ is

$$d\mathbf{F} = I \, d\mathbf{L} \times \mathbf{B} \tag{1}$$

To obtain the total force on a closed circuit we are to obtain the vector sum of all the forces on all the differential line segments forming the closed curve corresponding to the circuit (see Fig. 9.2).

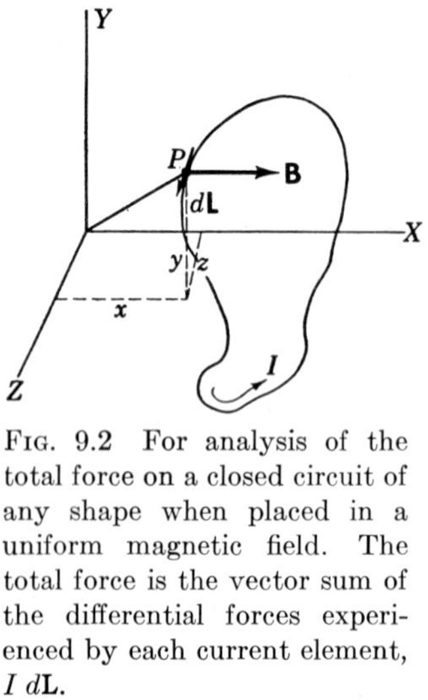

FIG. 9.2 For analysis of the total force on a closed circuit of any shape when placed in a uniform magnetic field. The total force is the vector sum of the differential forces experienced by each current element, $I \, d\mathbf{L}$.

$$\mathbf{F} = I(d\mathbf{L}_1 \times \mathbf{B} + d\mathbf{L}_2 \times \mathbf{B} + d\mathbf{L}_3 \times \mathbf{B} + \cdots) \tag{2}$$

Applying the distributive law of Sec. 1.8, Eq. (3),

$$\mathbf{F} = I(d\mathbf{L}_1 + d\mathbf{L}_2 + d\mathbf{L}_3 + \cdots) \times \mathbf{B} \tag{3}$$

Indicating the summation in the parenthesis by a closed-line integral,

$$\mathbf{F} = I\left(\oint d\mathbf{L}\right) \times \mathbf{B} = 0 \tag{4}$$

The force is zero because

$$\oint d\mathbf{L} = 0 \tag{5}$$

The proof of Eq. (5) is left as a problem.

9.5 Torque on a Plane Closed Loop, and Magnetic Moment. The total force acting on a closed circuit in a uniform field has been found to be zero. The individual forces acting on the line segments must then form a system of couples. The moment of a couple is independent of the choice of axis. For the case of a plane loop, we shall find the moment of the couple as the vector torque

$$\mathbf{T} = \mathbf{R} \times \mathbf{F} \tag{1}$$

Taking the loop in the xy plane with the current counterclockwise, we write, from Fig. 9.3a,

$$dL = i \, dx + j \, dy \tag{2}$$
$$R = i \, x + j \, y \tag{3}$$
$$B = i \, B_x + j \, B_y + k \, B_z \tag{4}$$

and substitute these values into the expression for the force on each current element

$$dF = I \, dL \times B$$

When substituted into Eq. (1), the torque about the origin on each current element is

$$dT = R \times (I \, dL \times B) \tag{5}$$

When this is expanded,

$$dT = [i(B_y y \, dx - B_x y \, dy) + j(B_x x \, dy - B_y x \, dx) \\ - k(B_z x \, dx + B_z y \, dy)]I \tag{6}$$

The total torque is the vector sum of the differential contributions given by this equation. To obtain this sum, we evaluate the line integral of

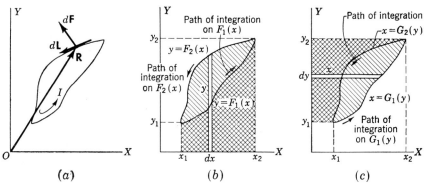

FIG. 9.3 (a) For analysis of the torque on a plane closed loop; (b) and (c) relationships between the line integrals and the area of the loop.

each of scalar differential quantities around the closed path defined by the loop, in the direction indicated by the current. By this process, we are summing the components separately. Now the terms involving $y \, dy$ and $x \, dx$ are independent of the path, and their line integral around a closed path is zero. The terms involving $y \, dx$ and $x \, dy$ depend upon the path, and the path is determined by the loop. In Fig. 9.3b, in the direction of the current around the loop,

$$\oint y \, dx = \int_{x_1}^{x_2} F_1(x) \, dx + \int_{x_2}^{x_1} F_2(x) \, dx \tag{7}$$

If our task were to evaluate the area of the loop A, we should perform this a little differently:

$$A = \int_{x_1}^{x_2} F_2(x)\, dx - \int_{x_1}^{x_2} F_1(x)\, dx \tag{8}$$

Interchanging the limits of integration and the sign of the first integral of Eq. (8), and comparing with Eq. (7), shows that Eq. (8) is the negative of Eq. (7). A similar examination of Fig. 9.3c shows that the line integral of $x\, dy$, taken in the direction of the current, gives the area of the loop directly. The total torque, then, is

$$\mathbf{T} = \oint d\mathbf{T} = (-\mathbf{i}\, B_y + \mathbf{j}\, B_x)AI \tag{9}$$

Since the moment of a couple is independent of the choice of axis, this result should be independent of the system of coordinates used. To divorce the analysis from the coordinate system, let us express the area of the loop as a vector quantity whose magnitude is equal to the area and whose direction is given by the normal to the loop according to the right-hand rule. This is the direction indicated by the thumb of the right hand when the fingers point in the direction of the current, which is also the path of integration. Here

$$\mathbf{A} = A\, \mathbf{k} \tag{10}$$

We now observe that Eq. (9) contains the vector product of Eqs. (10) and (4), which allows us to write

$$\mathbf{T} = I\mathbf{A} \times \mathbf{B} \tag{11}$$

independent of the system of coordinates. For a given current, and a given uniform magnetic field, the torque on a plane closed loop depends only on its area and orientation, and not upon the length of the wire in the loop or upon its shape. It is therefore logical to define the dipole moment of a plane loop as the vector quantity

$$\mathbf{M} = I A\, \mathbf{n} \tag{12}$$

where $\mathbf{n}$ is a unit vector normal to the loop whose sense is given by the right-hand rule. In terms of the magnetic moment, the torque is

$$\mathbf{T} = \mathbf{M} \times \mathbf{B} \tag{13}$$

This is similar in form to the torque on an electric dipole found in Sec. 3.11:

$$\mathbf{T} = \mathbf{P} \times \mathbf{E}$$

Because of this, Eq. (13) is sometimes used as a starting point in defining the magnetic field.

We shall extend this basic result in the next section. Before doing so, however, observe that we have here shown two ways of evaluating a particular line integral around a closed path. One is direct integration, and the other involves finding the area.

9.6 The Torque on a Complete Circuit in a Nonuniform Magnetostatic Field. In the previous section we found that the torque on a plane loop could be written in terms of its magnetic moment. For loops of differential area dA but of any plane shape, the torque is

$$d\mathbf{T} = I \, dA \, \mathbf{n} \times \mathbf{B} \tag{1}$$

This gives us a method of finding the total torque on a complete circuit in a nonuniform magnetic field by finding the sum of the contributions of the differential current loops selected in a very interesting manner. We may consider the closed circuit as the perimeter of a surface consisting of small current loops, each of which carries the circuit current in the same direction, as in Fig. 9.4. Each branch of each mesh carries equal and opposite currents, except at the perimeter. The torque on the complete circuit may be found by performing the vector integration over the surface

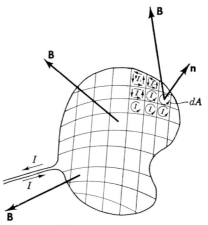

$$\mathbf{T} = \int I \, dA \, \mathbf{n} \times \mathbf{B} \tag{2}$$

FIG. 9.4 The torque on a closed loop of any shape in a magnetic field is the vector sum of the torques on the plane loops of differential area. Each of the differential loops carries the same current as the loop itself.

When the cross-sectional area of the conductor forming the circuit is not negligible, or the current is not uniform, one may break the circuit up into current tubes or filaments like the conductors in Sec. 4.7. The total torque is then found as the sum of the torques on each current tube

$$\mathbf{T} = \int dI \int dA \, \mathbf{n} \times \mathbf{B} \tag{3}$$

Coupled with the relations for the forces given in Sec. 9.3, these torque relations give us the means for computing the magnetostatic forces on any electric circuit, when the magnetic-field configuration is known.

The importance of Eqs. (2) and (3) of this section lies in the fact that they illustrate a powerful method of thinking, rather than in their application to any specific problem. Few problems have sufficient symmetry to allow us to evaluate integrals like these in simple algebraic expressions. Yet it should be possible to evaluate them for any problem. In this day of wonderful computing machines, Eq. (2) or (3) could form a set of instructions for the machine.

9.7   The Magnetic Field Due to a Current Element.   In studying the electrostatic field, we found point charges useful as building blocks. Visualization of the fields was aided by considering the vector summation of the fields due to point charges.   We wrote an expression symbolizing this vector summation for the electric-field-intensity vector

$$\mathbf{E} = \int \frac{\rho \, dv}{4\pi\epsilon_0 R^2} \mathbf{r} \tag{1}$$

In differential form, the contribution of each point charge was

$$d\mathbf{E} = \frac{dQ}{4\pi\epsilon_0 R^2} \mathbf{r} \tag{2}$$

Justified by its results, and here presented by analogy alone, the corresponding relation in the magnetic field due to an element of current isolated in free space is

$$d\mathbf{B} = \frac{\mu_0 I}{4\pi R^2} \, d\mathbf{L} \times \mathbf{r} \tag{3}$$

(We shall derive this equation from the vector potential in Chap. 11.) The current I, in amperes, is in a directed line segment of length $d\mathbf{L}$.   The unit vector $\mathbf{r}$ is directed from the current element to the field point as in Eq. (1).   The constant of proportionality μ_0 here seems to correspond to the reciprocal of the permittivity.   It is called the *permeability*, and in free space it has the numerical value of exactly $4\pi(10^{-7})$.   Its units are called *henries per meter*, a matter to be discussed later.   The relative directions of the three vector quantities are best illustrated by the examples in the following sections.

The relation of Eq. (3) is known as the law of Biot and Savart, who first proposed it.   By combining this relation with that for the force experienced by a differential current element in a magnetic field, we have an expression for the force between two current elements analogous to Coulomb's law for the force between point charges.   From Sec. 9.3, Eq. (7), the force experienced by a current element (number 1) in a magnetic field is

$$d\mathbf{F}_1 = I_1(d\mathbf{L}_1 \times \mathbf{B}) \tag{4}$$

When this magnetic field $\mathbf{B}$ is due to a second current element as given in Eq. (3),

$$d\mathbf{F}_1 = I_1 \, d\mathbf{L}_1 \times \left(\frac{\mu_0 I_2}{4\pi R^2} \, d\mathbf{L}_2 \times \mathbf{r}_{21} \right) \tag{5}$$

The double subscript on the unit vector r_{21} is to remind us that it is to be directed from the current element to the field point which is the location of current element number 1. Collecting the scalar quantities and rewriting Eq. (5),

$$d\mathbf{F}_1 = \frac{\mu_0 I_1 I_2}{4\pi R^2} d\mathbf{L}_1 \times (d\mathbf{L}_2 \times \mathbf{r}_{21}) \tag{6}$$

While the scalar similarity to Coulomb's law is satisfying, this equation is just as cumbersome in use as in appearance. The triple vector product results from our having defined the magnetic field in a direction perpendicular to the force experienced by moving charges, and then finding the magnetic field due to a current element perpendicular to that element. The order of evaluation of the triple vector product is important because if $d\mathbf{L}_1$ and $d\mathbf{L}_2$ are parallel the vector product $d\mathbf{L}_1 \times d\mathbf{L}_2$ is zero, but the force is not.

The numerical value of the permeability of free space is arbitrarily assigned as $4\pi(10^{-7})$. Equation (6) serves as a definition of the absolute ampere. The absolute ampere is that current which produces a force of $2(10^{-7})$ newtons per ampere per meter between infinitely long parallel conductors separated by a distance of 1 meter in a vacuum. In terms of this force expression, the units of permeability are newtons per (ampere)^2. This is equivalent to volt-seconds per ampere-meter, and the combination "volt-seconds per ampere" is called the *henry* to give the units of permeability the name *henries per meter*. This is analogous to the name *farads per meter* for the units of permittivity.

9.8 Some Magnetic Fields Due to Straight Conductors. As an application of the law of Biot and Savart, we here analyze the magnetic field due to a straight conductor, which is, of course, a part of a closed circuit. When we have done this, we shall have a method of obtaining the magnetic field due to any closed circuit formed by straight conductors. We use the notation of Fig. 9.5, which is similar to that used for the analysis of the electric field due to a charged line of finite length. The unit vector from the current element to the field point has been labeled $\mathbf{r}'$ to distinguish it from the unit vector $\mathbf{r}$ of cylindrical coordinates. Each of the current elements lies along the unit vector $\mathbf{k}$, so that for this problem $d\mathbf{L} = \mathbf{k}\, dL$. Each of the current elements is responsible for a differential contribution given by the law of Biot and Savart of the previous section. Adapting to the notation of the figure,

$$d\mathbf{B} = \frac{\mu_0 I\, dL}{4\pi[(z - L)^2 + R^2]} (\mathbf{k} \times \mathbf{r}') \tag{1}$$

The vector product here is directed along the unit vector $\boldsymbol{\theta}$ of our coordinate system and has the magnitude $\sin \alpha$, where α is the angle between

r' and k.   From this observation we may write Eq. (1) as

$$d\mathbf{B} = \frac{\mu_0 I \; dL \sin \alpha}{4\pi[(z - L)^2 + R^2]} \mathbf{\theta} \qquad (2)$$

Guided by our experience with the analysis of the charged line, we here express all the variables in terms of the angle α.   From the figure,

$$z - L = R \cot \alpha \qquad (3)$$

Differentiating, we obtain

$$dL = R \csc^2 \alpha \; d\alpha \qquad (4)$$

With the additional relation

$$\csc \alpha = \frac{\sqrt{(z - L)^2 + R^2}}{R} \qquad (5)$$

substituted into the denominator, Eq. (2) becomes simply

$$d\mathbf{B} = \frac{\mu_0 I}{4\pi R} \sin \alpha \; d\alpha \; \mathbf{\theta} \qquad (6)$$

When this is integrated between the limits α_1 and α_2, we obtain

$$\mathbf{B} = \frac{\mu_0 I}{4\pi R} (\cos \alpha_1 - \cos \alpha_2) \mathbf{\theta} \qquad (7)$$

In this problem, all the differential contributions $d\mathbf{B}$ are parallel.   We have had to sum the components only once, in contrast to the electric-

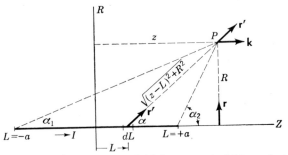

Fig. 9.5   For analysis of the magnetic field due to a straight conductor carrying a current I.   Due to the current element $d\mathbf{L}$, the differential contribution to the field at the point P is directed out of the paper.   The total field is the vector sum of the contributions arising from each current element.

field problem in which two integrations were required.   Also, no analysis is required to obtain the equation of the direction lines.   Since $\mathbf{B}$ is directed along $\mathbf{\theta}$ everywhere, the direction line at every point in the field is the circle which passes through the point and has its center on the axis.

When the length of the line approaches the infinite-length case, α_1 approaches zero and α_2 approaches π, and the field becomes dependent only on the perpendicular distance to the line, as given by

$$\mathbf{B} = \frac{\mu_0 I}{2\pi R} \, \mathbf{\theta} \tag{8}$$

The corresponding expression for the electric field due to an infinitely long, uniformly charged line was found in Chap. 2 as Eq. 2.4(16):

$$\mathbf{E} = \frac{\lambda}{2\pi\epsilon_0 R} \, \mathbf{r}$$

The ratio of the magnetic- to electric-field magnitudes is, for this case,

$$\frac{B}{E} = \mu_0\epsilon_0 \frac{I}{\lambda}$$

When a current is divided by a linear-charge density, the result has the units of velocity. In defining the magnetic-field vector $\mathbf{B}$ in terms of the force on a moving charge, we pointed out that the units of $\mathbf{B}$ were those of $\mathbf{E}$, divided by the units of velocity. This shows that the product of the permittivity and the permeability of a vacuum has the units

$$[\mu_0\epsilon_0] = \left[\frac{1}{\text{velocity}}\right]^2$$

This velocity turns out to be that of light.

With respect to mapping the field for the case in which the line is infinitely long (see Fig. 3.3b), we can use the traces of the equipotential surfaces in the electric field as the direction lines of the magnetic field. We see also that, since the magnitudes of $\mathbf{B}$ and $\mathbf{E}$ are related by a constant, the relative spacing of the equipotential circles which are now the direction lines gives the proper indication of the magnitude of the $\mathbf{B}$ vector.

The planes containing the z axis, $\theta = $ a constant, are surfaces perpendicular to the $\mathbf{B}$ vector, but later we shall examine their nature carefully before applying any such term as equipotential surfaces, because the line integral of the $\mathbf{B}$ vector is not independent of the path.

The magnetic field due to two line currents, infinitely long, is the superposition of the field due to each line. In Fig. 9.6, the current is into the paper on the right and the same current is out of the paper on the left. The notation is identical to that of Fig. 2.11 for the analysis of two line charges. The magnetic field due to the right-hand line is written from Eq. (8) as

$$\mathbf{B}_+ = \frac{\mu_0 I}{2\pi R_2} \, (\mathbf{k} \times \mathbf{r}_2) \tag{9}$$

The field due to the left-hand line, in which the current is along $+\mathbf{k}$, is

$$\mathbf{B}_- = \frac{-\mu_0 I}{2\pi R_1} (\mathbf{k} \times \mathbf{r}_1) \tag{10}$$

The total field at any point is the vector sum of the two contributions, which, when the common terms are collected, is

$$\mathbf{B} = \frac{\mu_0 I}{2\pi} \mathbf{k} \times \left(\frac{\mathbf{r}_2}{R_2} - \frac{\mathbf{r}_1}{R_1} \right) \tag{11}$$

Now the corresponding expression for the electric field was written as Eq. 2.9 (3):

$$\mathbf{E} = \frac{\lambda}{2\pi\epsilon_0} \left(\frac{\mathbf{r}_2}{R_2} - \frac{\mathbf{r}_1}{R_1} \right)$$

Since $\mathbf{r}_1$ and $\mathbf{r}_2$ are in the same plane, and $\mathbf{k}$ is perpendicular to that plane, $\mathbf{B}$ lies in the plane of $\mathbf{r}_1$ and $\mathbf{r}_2$ and is everywhere perpendicular to $\mathbf{E}$,

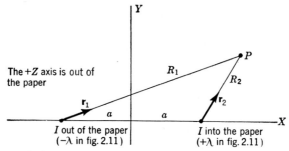

FIG. 9.6   For analysis of the magnetic field due to equal and oppositely directed currents in two infinitely long lines of vanishing radius.   The field map is the same as for the electric field of two line charges, but the direction lines and equipotentials are interchanged.

directed clockwise at all points nearer the right-hand line than the left-hand line.   The equipotential circles in the field map for the electric field, Fig. 3.6, are therefore the direction lines of the magnetic field.   Because the magnitudes of the two fields differ only by a constant, the relative spacing of the direction lines is an indication of the magnitude of the magnetic field.

In two-dimensional problems, the closeness of these analogies stops when the conductors have a finite size.   For such conductors, the electric charge is entirely on the surface of the wire, while the current is distributed over the cross section of the wire.   This means that the magnetic field corresponds to that of a volume-charge distribution instead of a surface-charge distribution.   This is indeed unfortunate because it complicates our pursuit of the analogy between electric and magnetic fields.

In three-dimensional problems, too, the electrostatic and magneto-static fields do not have a direct interchangeability. Comparing the electric and magnetic fields of the finite line, with which we began this section, shows that the electric field has both an axial and a radial component, while the magnetic field has a single component along θ. Reference to Eq. (15) in Sec. 2.4 shows that the θ component of $\mathbf{B}$ has the same magnitude as the radial component of $\mathbf{E}$. The direction lines of the magnetic field do not lie in the hyperboloids of Fig. 2.13.

We here leave the analysis of magnetic fields by the law of Biot and Savart and proceed to develop some of the scalar concepts associated with magnetic fields.

9.9 Some Scalar Concepts in the Magnetostatic Field, and Ampère's Circuital Law. In current-carrying conductors, the current through a surface is related to the current-density vector by the surface integral

$$I = \int \mathbf{J} \cdot \mathbf{n} \, dA$$

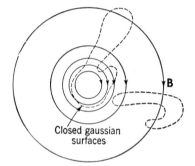

and in discussing this relationship, it was pointed out that more generally the integral of the normal component of a vector over a surface is called a flux. Magnetic flux is the term applied to the flux of the normal component of the $\mathbf{B}$ vector over an open surface

$$\phi = \int \mathbf{B} \cdot \mathbf{n} \, dA \qquad (1)$$

Fig. 9.7 Two closed Gaussian surfaces in the magnetic field of a current element. The net outward flux of the $\mathbf{B}$ vector is zero over each of the closed surfaces.

The units of ϕ are called webers, and from the viewpoint of magnetostatics, ϕ has no more physical significance than does the flux of the $\mathbf{D}$ vector in electrostatics. Indeed, Heaviside called ϕ the "magnetic current."

Electrostatic flux was introduced along with Gauss's law, and through Gauss's law we analyzed electric fields which have a high degree of symmetry. This method is not available to us in magnetic fields, because the flux of the $\mathbf{B}$ vector through all closed surfaces is zero. The magnetic field due to a current element is directed in circles around the axis of the element. In Fig. 9.7, two closed Gaussian surfaces are indicated; one encloses the current element and the other does not. All the flux which enters either region also leaves the region, and none stops inside. Since the flux due to every current element acts the same way, and flux is a scalar like a steady current, regardless of the number or location of the current elements there is no net outward flux through a closed surface. In the magnetic field, we find nothing corresponding to an isolated charge which can provide either a source or a discontinuity in the normal component of the **B** vector at a surface. For magnetic circuits, Gauss's law becomes

$$\oint \mathbf{B} \cdot \mathbf{n}\, dA = 0 \tag{2}$$

At a point in space, rather than over a closed surface of finite area, the limiting process leading to the concept of divergence gives us

$$\nabla \cdot \mathbf{B} = 0 \tag{3}$$

Equations (2) and (3) should recall the corresponding relations in the electric field, Eqs. 5.2 (1) and 8.1 (5):

$$\oint \mathbf{D} \cdot \mathbf{n}\, dA = \int \rho\, dv$$

and

$$\nabla \cdot \mathbf{D} = \rho$$

For the magnetic field in a vacuum, let us now introduce the vector **H**, defined by

$$\mathbf{H} = \frac{\mathbf{B}}{\mu_0} \tag{4}$$

We have stated that the permeability μ_0 is an arbitrary constant of proportionality numerically equal to 4π (10^{-7}), as discussed in Sec. 9.7. From the law of Biot and Savart, or its extensions to the fields of closed circuits, the units of the **H** vector are amperes per meter. Because of this similarity to the units of the **E** vector, volts per meter, the **H** vector is sometimes called *magnetic-field intensity*. When this term is applied to **H**, the **B** vector is called by the name of *magnetic-flux density*, and the two go along together in magnetic circuits very nicely. On the other hand, we related the **B** vector to a force on a moving charge, and there likened **B** to the electric field intensity. It is less confusing to simply call the two magnetic vectors by the names **B** and **H**. The **B** vector is the one which is solenoidal and whose normal component is continuous at a boundary. The helper vector **H** is the one whose tangential component is continuous at a boundary, as we shall see shortly in considering the action of material substances under the influence of magnetic fields.

The magnetic-field vectors do not belong to that special class of vectors in which the line integral is always independent of the path, and in which the line integral around all closed paths is zero. The line integral of the tangential component of a vector quantity gives a scalar result, and the common name of the result with respect to the **H** vector is *magnetomotive force*, abbreviated mmf. The units arise from the product of **H** and a distance, and since the units of **H** are amperes per meter, the units of magnetomotive force are amperes. Magnetomotive force is not a force and it is not work, and later on we shall have more to say about this matter.

As a result of his many experiments in magnetostatics, Ampère proposed the following relationship between steady currents and the magnetic field in the space surrounding them. He stated that *the magnetomotive force is equal to the total current surrounded by the path of integration.* In equation form this basic experimental observation is

$$\oint \mathbf{H} \cdot d\mathbf{S} = I \tag{5}$$

with the path of integration related to the current by the right-hand rule. In closed-line-integral form, this equation is useful. In problems with a high degree of symmetry, we can discover the nature of the field in a manner quite similar to the use of Gauss's law in the electrostatic field.

Many readers will have had some experience with Eq. (5) in other forms and under a variety of names. It has been called Kirchhoff's law for magnetic circuits, Ampère's work law, and Ampère's circuital law, among other names. As an equation it can be written

Magnetomotive force = ampere turns

in MKS rationalized units. To some, the corresponding expression in CGS units is more familiar:

$$\text{mmf} = \frac{4\pi NI}{10}$$

The turns N is merely an aid in computing the total current.

We shall call this experimental observation by the name of Ampère's circuital law for want of a better one. After illustrating its application to fields with a high degree of symmetry, we shall reduce the scalar concept of magnetomotive force to a vector concept which can be defined at a point in space.

There does not seem to be a simple geometric proof of Ampère's circuital law, and we really ought to have one to go along with our proof of Gauss's law. But Gauss's law assumed Coulomb's law as an experimental observation, and as an experiment, Coulomb's law is crude. We really know that because electric fields behave as Gauss's law predicts, the electric field is an inverse-square law with respect to the force between point charges. While it is possible to start with the law of Biot and Savart and derive Ampère's circuital law, direct experiment with isolated current elements is impossible. Before we are through, we shall show through the vector potential that, if we accept Ampère's law as the fundamental experimental relation, then the law of Biot and Savart must follow.

9.10 The Magnetic Field of a Coaxial Cable. As our first illustration of the application of Ampère's circuital law to magnetic-field problems in which there is a high degree of symmetry, we here find the field in a coaxial cable infinitely long. In determining the field due to a long straight wire, we did not investigate the field inside the wire; this time we shall do so. The current configuration is shown in Fig. 9.8. The inner conductor is a solid cylinder of radius R_1, while the outer conductor is a hollow cylinder of inner and outer radii R_2 and R_3 respectively. We shall assume that the two conductors carry the same current in opposite directions and that this current is uniformly distributed in each conductor.

When Ampère's circuital law is evaluated around circular paths in the region between the conductors, the surrounded current is the total current in the inner conductor, and

$$\oint \mathbf{H} \cdot d\mathbf{S} = I \qquad (1)$$

for all closed paths such as number 1 in the figure. This is the same condition which we found in the field due to an isolated wire; hence

$$\mathbf{H} = \frac{I}{2\pi R} \boldsymbol{\theta} \qquad R_1 < R < R_2 \quad (2)$$

For all closed paths completely surrounding the outer conductor, the total current surrounded is zero.

$$\oint \mathbf{H} \cdot d\mathbf{S} = 0$$

and since H_θ is the only component which could contribute to the line integral around a path such as number 2 in the figure,

$$\mathbf{H} = 0 \qquad R_3 < R \qquad (3)$$

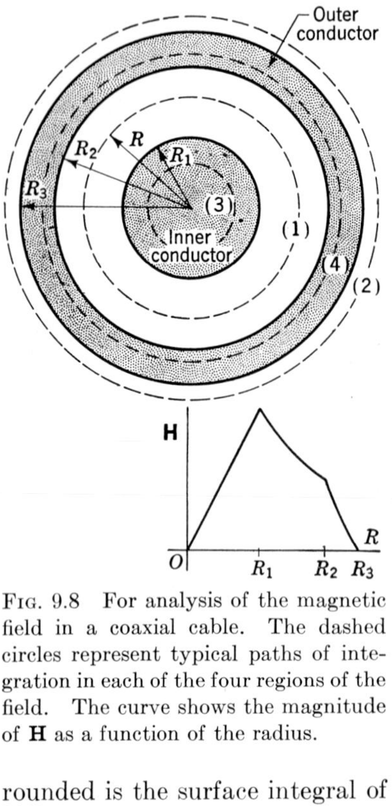

Around concentric circular paths of radius R, taken within the inner conductor where the uniform current density is $\mathbf{J}$, the total current surrounded is the surface integral of $\mathbf{J} \cdot \mathbf{n} \, dA$ and Ampère's circuital law is

$$\oint \mathbf{H} \cdot d\mathbf{S} = \int \mathbf{J} \cdot \mathbf{n} \, dA \qquad (4)$$

Over this carefully chosen surface

$$\mathbf{J} \cdot \mathbf{n} = J = \text{constant}$$

and

$$\mathbf{H} \cdot d\mathbf{S} = HR \, d\theta$$

which is also a constant along the circumference of the circular path labeled 3 in the figure. Substituting in Eq. (4) and writing the constant

FIG. 9.8   For analysis of the magnetic field in a coaxial cable. The dashed circles represent typical paths of integration in each of the four regions of the field. The curve shows the magnitude of $\mathbf{H}$ as a function of the radius.

terms outside the integral signs,

$$HR \oint d\theta = J \int dA = JA \qquad (5)$$

when A is the cross-sectional area of the conductor enclosed by the path of integration. Then

$$2\pi HR = J\pi R^2 \qquad (6)$$

Solving for H,

$$H = \frac{J}{2} R \qquad (7)$$

In vector form, since $\mathbf{H}$ is along $\boldsymbol{\theta}$,

$$\mathbf{H} = \frac{J}{2} R\boldsymbol{\theta} \qquad R < R_1 \qquad (8)$$

When this is written in terms of the total current, since

$$I = J\pi R_1^2$$

$$\mathbf{H} = \frac{I}{2\pi R_1^2} R\boldsymbol{\theta} \qquad R < R_1 \qquad (9)$$

As a final step, when Ampère's circuital law is evaluated in the region within the outer conductor, the total current surrounded is the entire current carried by the inner wire less the portion of the current in the outer wire between the path of integration and R_2. The cross-sectional area of the outer conductor within the path of integration, labeled 4 in the figure, is

$$A = \pi(R^2 - R_2^2)$$

If we denote the current density in the outer conductor as $\mathbf{J}_0$, the current carried by this cross-sectional area is

$$J_0\pi(R^2 - R_2^2)$$

Then Eq. (5) may be written

$$2\pi RH = I - J_0\pi(R^2 - R_2^2) \qquad (10)$$

Writing J_0 as

$$J_0 = \frac{I}{\pi(R_3^2 - R_2^2)}$$

and solving Eq. (10) for H,

$$H = \frac{I}{2\pi R}\left(1 - \frac{R^2 - R_2^2}{R_3^2 - R_2^2}\right) \qquad (11)$$

This may be arranged as

$$H = \frac{IR_3}{2\pi(R_3^2 - R_2^2)}\left(\frac{R_3}{R} - \frac{R}{R_3}\right) \qquad R_3 > R_2, R \lessgtr R_3 \qquad (12)$$

Equation (12) has the form of the curve

$$y = k\left(\frac{1}{x} - x\right)$$

where x = a parameter less than one

k = a constant

Equation (12) reduces to zero when $R = R_3$ and to Eq. (7) when $R = R_2$, as it should.

The results are indicated in the lower part of the figure where the magnitude of **H** is plotted as a function of R. A comparison between this

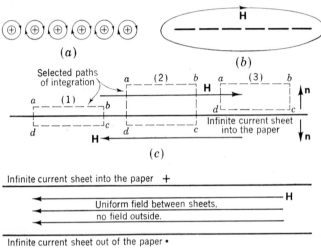

FIG. 9.9   For analysis of the magnetic field due to infinite sheets of current.   (a) The individual contributions of round wires are oppositely directed in the plane of the wires; (b) the wires are flattened into strips, and the total magnetic field is suggested by the elliptical direction line; (c) when a current sheet is infinite in extent, the resulting magnetic field is parallel to the plane of the sheet; (d) two sheets confine the field to the region between the sheets.

field and that due to a cylindrically symmetric volume-charge distribution in Sec. 5.4 should now be made.   In Figs. 5.5b and 5.6a, we did not terminate the electrostatic field with an outer volume charge of opposite polarity, though we could have done so.   Aside from that, observe the correspondence in the magnitudes of the vector quantities in the two problems. The equipotentials in the electrostatic case become the direction lines in the magnetostatic problem, and further, the spacing of the equipotentials correctly shows the magnitude of the magnetic field.

9.11   The Magnetic Field Due to Infinite Sheets of Current.   In studying the electrostatic field, we found that an infinite sheet of charge produced a uniform field normal to the sheet.   While we could determine the magnetic field due to an infinite sheet of current by summing the contributions of individual line currents, an analysis by means of Ampère's circuital law is more interesting and provides a study of symmetry rather than an exercise in the calculus. As a beginning, let us suggest the final result by considering the individual contributions of half a dozen parallel wires as in Fig. 9.9a. In between the wires, these contributions are oppositely directed, so that the components which are vertical on the paper tend to cancel. The components parallel to the plane of the wires tend to add directly. In part b of the figure, the round wires have been flattened until they almost touch each other. One elliptical direction line is shown to suggest the composite field. Recalling that in two-dimensional problems the electrostatic equipotentials correspond to the direction lines of the magnetostatic field, these two parts of the figure suggest the contours on a rubber-sheet model of the electrostatic field due to a linear array of equal line charges of the same polarity. Figure 9.9c represents a section of an infinite sheet of current with a uniform linear distribution of current directed into the paper. The magnitude of the current may be expressed in terms of the number of amperes per unit width of the current sheet, which we shall denote as J_s to distinguish it from a volume distribution of current which we have been denoting by the symbol J. We want to find the nature of the field using Ampère's circuital law.

$$\oint \mathbf{H} \cdot d\mathbf{S} = I \qquad (1)$$

We can select several paths of integration, each of which encloses either the current in a unit width of a sheet or no current at all as suggested by the dashed lines in the figure.

There can be no component of the magnetic field perpendicular to the current sheet because the individual contributions of each segment of the sheet are oppositely directed. The only contributions to the line integral are made along the horizontal parts of the paths of integration. Since the total current enclosed by paths 1 and 2 is the same, and the segments cd are identical, the field must be independent of the distance from the sheet. This is confirmed by considering the path labeled number 3 in which the equal distances bc and da may have any length.

To evaluate the magnitude of the field, we select path 1 or 2 and make the lengths ab and cd unity. Then the total current enclosed by the path of integration is J_s amperes. Breaking the line integral up into four parts,

$$\oint \mathbf{H} \cdot d\mathbf{S} = \int_{x_a}^{x_b} H \, dx + \int_{x_b}^{x_c} 0 + \int_{x_c}^{x_d} H \, dx + \int_{x_d}^{x_a} 0$$

Evaluating the definite integrals, with $x_b - x_a = x_d - x_c = 1$, and using Eq. (1),

$$H = \frac{J_s}{2} \tag{2}$$

When **n** is the unit vector normal to the sheet, the vector expression is

$$\mathbf{H} = \tfrac{1}{2}\mathbf{J}_s \times \mathbf{n}$$

With two parallel, equal, and oppositely directed current sheets, the magnetic fields are in the same direction between the sheets and combine to give

$$\mathbf{H} = \mathbf{J}_s \times \mathbf{n} \tag{3}$$

Elsewhere the fields due to the sheets are equal and opposite and the total field is zero, as in Fig. 9.9d.

Between infinite charged sheets carrying equal surface charge densities σ, the expression for the electric **D** vector was

$$\mathbf{D} = \sigma\,\mathbf{n}$$

Here we see a current sheet providing a boundary for a magnetic field, but it provides a boundary for a *tangential* field, whereas the charged sheets provide a boundary for a *normal* electric field.

Now a sheet of current in a conductor of zero thickness is a physical impossibility, but the concept is a very useful one mathematically. It allows us to ignore the finite thickness of a thin sheet of current, in comparison with all other dimensions in our problems. While our mathematical sheet of current is able to terminate the tangential component of a magnetic field quite abruptly, an actual current does not terminate the magnetic field abruptly but spreads the termination over a finite thickness. To see this as a limiting process, let us refer again to Fig. 9.8 and consider what happens to the graph of the magnitude of **H** as we make the outer conductor thinner and thinner by decreasing the outer radius R_3. In the limit as R_3 approaches R_2, the change in the magnitude of **H** becomes a sudden discontinuity. If the inner radius is an inch or two, and the thickness is a few thousandths of an inch, the graph would appear to have a discontinuity because we could not distinguish between R_2 and R_3 on any reasonable scale.

The current-sheet concept is useful and important in at least two practical cases. Ampère used it to explain the discontinuity in the **H** vector at the surface of a material substance, and we shall investigate this in a following section. In time-varying fields, the induced currents crowd to the surface of conductors, and at high frequencies, most of the current flows in a surface layer so thin that silver plating can change a poor conductor to a good one. Indeed, even at a frequency of 60 cps this *skin effect* attains a magnitude of importance.

9.12   The Magnetic Field of an Infinitely Long Solenoid. One of the ways of finding the magnetic field due to a solenoid is to superimpose the fields due to a number of current rings by means of the calculus. This can be done only on the axis of the solenoid without the use of elliptic integrals. We shall, however, leave this straightforward analysis to the problems and obtain the case of an infinitely long solenoid as a study of symmetry and Ampère's circuital law.

A solenoid wound of closely spaced turns of fine wire may be approximated by a sheet of current flowing in a circular path because the right-hand side of Ampère's circuital law

$$\oint \mathbf{H} \cdot d\mathbf{S} = I \tag{1}$$

indicates that the field is due essentially to the total current enclosed and not its circuit configuration. If the solenoid is wound of n turns per

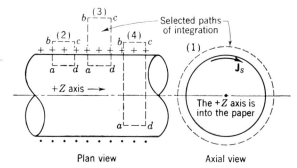

Plan view   Axial view

FIG. 9.10   For analysis of the field of an infinite solenoid. The crosses and dots indicate the current direction in the plan view at the left. The magnetic field is uniform inside the solenoid and is directed into the paper in the axial view at the right. Outside the solenoid, the field is zero.

meter of length, each carrying the same current i, then the equivalent surface current density, J_s, is

$$J_s = ni \qquad \text{amperes per meter} \tag{2}$$

Let us first examine the field outside the infinite solenoid, using cylindrical coordinates to clarify the discussion regarding directions. If the field has a θ component, it must be uniform because of the symmetry. Evaluating it around a closed path entirely outside the solenoid, such as path 1 in Fig. 9.10, tells us that the θ component must be zero because the path encloses no current and therefore when $dS = R \, d\theta$

$$\oint \mathbf{H} \cdot d\mathbf{S} = 0 \tag{3}$$

If the field outside has a radial component, it must be possible to return to the same point by following a closed direction line. This would enable us to distinguish one point on the axis from another, and we cannot do this for an infinite solenoid. Any field outside the solenoid must therefore be directed along the axis. The symmetry of the current requires that this axial component, if it exists, must be unidirectional (along the positive z axis in our figure). Since paths marked 2 and 3 surround the same current, and $\mathbf{H} \cdot d\mathbf{S}$ can have a value other than zero only along the segments bc and ad, the contribution along bc must be identical for each of the paths 2 and 3. If this z component exists, it must be uniform and have the same value at infinite distances from the solenoid as adjacent to the solenoid. All the direction lines outside the solenoid must return inside since they are all closed lines. This would require an infinite field strength inside the solenoid. An infinite field strength inside the solenoid would violate Ampère's circuital law by making the contribution to $\mathbf{H} \cdot d\mathbf{S}$ along the segment da also infinite. Hence the field outside the solenoid must be zero.

The same arguments which eliminated the radial and $\mathbf{\theta}$ components outside may be applied inside. Only the axial component can exist inside, too. In the figure, the paths marked 2 and 4 surround the same current, and around these closed paths, the only contribution to $\oint \mathbf{H} \cdot d\mathbf{S}$ is along segment da. Since the total contribution is independent of the location of da, the field must be uniform throughout the inside of the solenoid. Around paths 2 and 4

$$\oint \mathbf{H} \cdot d\mathbf{S} = \int_a^b \mathbf{H} \cdot d\mathbf{S} + \int_b^c \mathbf{H} \cdot d\mathbf{S} + \int_c^d \mathbf{H} \cdot d\mathbf{S} + \int_d^a \mathbf{H} \cdot d\mathbf{S} \qquad (4)$$

The first three contributions are zero, leaving

$$\oint \mathbf{H} \cdot d\mathbf{S} = \int_{z_d}^{z_a} H \, dz \qquad (5)$$

By choosing a and d to enclose the current carried per unit length of the solenoid, $z_a - z_d = 1$ and

$$H_z = J_s = ni \qquad (6)$$

This is the same result as we obtained for the field between infinite current sheets. Here, too, the current sheet provides a boundary for a tangential magnetic field.

It is unfortunate that there are not a great many types of fields which have enough symmetry to permit their analysis by means of Ampère's circuital law. These three examples together with those in the problems should suffice to verify the statement that Ampère's circuital law plays a role in magnetostatics that is very similar to that played by Gauss's law in electrostatics.

9.13 Magnetic Materials. In studying the action of material substances in magnetic fields, Michael Faraday was able to separate them into two groups. Suspending needlelike samples of materials in the fringing field between two bar magnets, he found that some materials aligned themselves with the direction of the field, and to these he applied the term *magnetic*. Those materials which aligned themselves across the field were termed *diamagnetic*. Later the term *paramagnetic* was applied to the first classification. *Dia-* and *para-* are prefixes from the Greek and mean across and alongside, respectively. All materials exhibit these properties to some degree, but with some notable exceptions, the effect is very slight. These exceptions are iron, nickel, and cobalt as elements, along with some alloys and compounds of other elements, which have pronounced magnetic effects, exhibit hysteresis and nonlinearity and are classified as *ferromagnetic*.

To obtain a quantitative measure of the magnetic properties of the materials themselves, as opposed to the size and shape of the sample, we

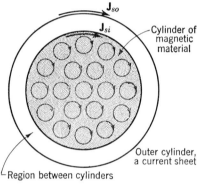

FIG. 9.11 A cylinder of paramagnetic material in a solenoid formed by a current sheet. The induced Amperian currents combine to form an equivalent induced current sheet at the surface of the inner cylinder.

study them under conditions which confine the field to a restricted region of space, and in which there are no appreciable end effects. We have seen that uniform magnetic fields arise from currents in infinite planes, and from a current sheet rolled into a cylinder forming an infinite solenoid. When a long solenoid is bent into the form of a toroid, the field is confined to a restricted region of space, there are no end effects, and while the field is not uniform, it is highly symmetrical and completely predictable from Ampère's circuital law. As a consequence, toroids are used in experimental measurements, but we can arrive at our needed conclusions more quickly by considering the case of the infinite solenoid.

An axial view of the infinite solenoid is shown in Fig. 9.11. The outer circle indicates the equivalent current sheet whose field we analyzed for the case of a vacuum in the previous section. Here we denote the magnitude of the linear-surface-current density in the sheet by the double subscript J_{so} for a reason which appears shortly. We have found that the linear surface current in the current sheet produces a field within the solenoid having the magnitudes $B = \mu_0 J_{so}$ and $H = J_{so}$. If a smaller cylinder of paramagnetic material or ferromagnetic material, also infinitely long, were to be inserted into the solenoid, both the magnetic vectors would be found unchanged in the region between the cylinders. Within the magnetic cylinder, however, the **B** vector is increased.

We are told that the increased flux density within the iron is due to a realignment of electronic spins in the presence of the forces of the magnetic field in a manner similar to the alignment of finite current loops which experience a torque in a magnetic field. Each equivalent current loop is adjacent to another as indicated by the small circles in the figure. Within the material, their contributions to a total current cancel each other because the currents are oppositely directed at the individual boundaries as in Fig. 9.4. On the surface, however, there is no cancellation and the combined effect is the same as that of a surface current, which must be in the same direction as that of the solenoid in order to increase the **B** vector within. We will denote this equivalent, or *Amperian*, current sheet by $\mathbf{J}_{si}$. The **B** vector within the magnetic cylinder is now attributed to the superposition of the two solenoidal current sheets. On the other hand, the **H** vector is attributed to the real, outer current sheet alone. In equation form

$$B_i = \mu_0(J_{so} + J_{si}) \tag{1}$$

and

$$H_i = J_{so} \tag{2}$$

The ratio of B to H in the inner cylinder is

$$\frac{B_i}{H_i} = \mu_0\left(1 + \frac{J_{si}}{J_{so}}\right) \tag{3}$$

The entire right-hand side of Eq. (3) is the permeability of the magnetic material and has the same units as those of μ_0, called henries per meter.

$$\mu = \mu_0\left(1 + \frac{J_{si}}{J_{so}}\right) \tag{4}$$

In terms of Eq. (4), the relationship between B and H in the inner cylinder is

$$B_i = \mu H_i \tag{5}$$

while in the region between the cylinders

$$B_o = \mu_0 H_o \tag{6}$$

By this means, we have attributed the discontinuity in the tangential component of the **B** vector at the boundary surface to a change in the permeability of the medium, rather than to the equivalent induced surface-current sheet. In addition to this, we have retained Ampère's circuital law which calls for a continuous tangential component of the **H** vector at the boundary surface. To achieve this, we specified that, in evaluating the current surrounded by the path of integration, we are to include only the real or heat-producing currents and to exclude the Amperian currents. We made a similar distinction with regard to the charges which are to be included with respect to Gauss's law in dielectric materials.

The ratio of the permeability of the material to the value assigned to free space is called the relative permeability μ_r, a dimensionless number.

$$\mu_r = \frac{\mu}{\mu_0} \tag{7}$$

By analogy with the electrostatic case, there is a temptation to call the relative permeability the magnetic constant. This is seldom done, however, because in ferromagnetic materials, the permeability as given by Eq. (5) for a long solenoid or a toroid is not a constant. A plot of B as a function of H is a magnetization curve which shows a hysteresis loop.

Also by analogy with the field in current-carrying conductors, the permeability may be likened to conductivity, because of the similarity of the expression $\mathbf{B} = \mu\mathbf{H}$ and $\mathbf{J} = \gamma\mathbf{E}$. This is enhanced by the fact that both **J** and **B** are solenoidal and have similar units with respect to an area. Treating the expression $\mathbf{B} = \mu\mathbf{H}$ as a vector formulation like Ohm's law, the first approach to magnetic-current problems is to solve them like current problems. To do this we define the counterparts of resistance and conductance, called reluctance and permeance, respectively. The permeance is also similar to the definition of capacitance.

$$\begin{aligned}\text{Permeance} &= \frac{\phi}{\text{mmf}} \\ &= \frac{\int \mathbf{B} \cdot \mathbf{n}\, dA}{\int \mathbf{H} \cdot d\mathbf{S}}\end{aligned} \tag{8}$$

We shall not pursue magnetic circuits in this book, nor shall we discuss permanent-magnet materials beyond stating that whether or not permanently magnetized materials are present, it is possible to retain Ampère's circuital law for **H**, the solenoidal character of **B**, the continuity of the tangential components of **H** at a boundary, and the continuity of the normal components of **B** at a boundary. It is not always possible to retain the relationship $\mathbf{B} = \mu\mathbf{H}$.

Let us now list and compare the circuit concepts as we have found them in the three types of fields we have studied. Such a comparison will be found in the accompanying table.

Current-carrying conductors	Dielectrics	Magnetic materials
Conductivity, γ $\mathbf{J} = \gamma \mathbf{E}$ $\oint \mathbf{E} \cdot d\mathbf{S} = 0$ $\oint \mathbf{J} \cdot \mathbf{n} \, dA = 0$ $\nabla \cdot \mathbf{J} = 0$	Permittivity, ϵ $\mathbf{D} = \epsilon \mathbf{E}$ $\oint \mathbf{E} \cdot d\mathbf{S} = 0$ $\oint \mathbf{D} \cdot \mathbf{n} \, dA = \int \rho \, dv$ $\nabla \cdot \mathbf{D} = \rho$	Permeability, μ $\mathbf{B} = \mu \mathbf{H}$ $\oint \mathbf{H} \cdot d\mathbf{S} = I$ $\oint \mathbf{B} \cdot \mathbf{n} \, dA = 0$ $\nabla \cdot \mathbf{B} = 0$
Components which are continuous at boundaries		
E_t J_n	E_t D_n	H_t B_n
Conductance	Capacitance	Permeance
$G = \dfrac{\int \mathbf{J} \cdot \mathbf{n} \, dA}{\int \mathbf{E} \cdot d\mathbf{S}} = \dfrac{I}{V_m}$	$C = \dfrac{\oint \mathbf{D} \cdot \mathbf{n} \, dA}{\int \mathbf{E} \cdot d\mathbf{S}} = \dfrac{Q}{V_m}$	$\dfrac{\int \mathbf{B} \cdot \mathbf{n} \, dA}{\int \mathbf{H} \cdot d\mathbf{S}} = \dfrac{\phi}{\text{mmf}}$

9.14   Generalization of Ampère's Circuital Law for Steady Currents.
In its simplest form, Ampère's circuital law is a macroscopic law requiring
a finite current and its associated finite area.   Both the mmf and the current
are scalar quantities, but not the kind of scalar quantities which can
be associated with a point in space.   To apply the law to problems without
out a high degree of symmetry, we require a vector-point relationship
between the **H** vector and the **J** vector.   Let us write Ampère's circuital
law first as

$$\text{mmf} = I \tag{1}$$

We have already associated a vector-point function **J** with the current I,
and **H** with the mmf, but we cannot equate **H** to **J** because they have different
units and different directions.

From one point of view, we could redefine **J** in terms of I in the following
ing way:

$$\mathbf{J} = \lim_{\Delta A \to 0} \frac{\Delta I}{\Delta A} \, \mathbf{n} \tag{2}$$

where **n** is a unit vector normal to ΔA, having the sense of I, when ΔA is
placed in that position which gives the maximum value to ΔI and the limit
in Eq. (2).

Let us treat the mmf in a similar way.   Consider the possibility of
obtaining the limit expressed by

$$\lim_{\Delta A \to 0} \frac{\Delta \, \text{mmf}}{\Delta A} \, \mathbf{n}$$

again when ΔA is placed in such a position as to maximize Δ mmf and the
limit.

With regard to Ampère's circuital law, it is easy to show that this quantity has a definite limit by returning to Eq. (1) and writing it for a small but finite loop whose area is ΔA.

$$\Delta \, \text{mmf} = \Delta I \qquad (3)$$

Dividing by the small but finite area,

$$\frac{\Delta \, \text{mmf}}{\Delta A} = \frac{\Delta I}{\Delta A} \qquad (4)$$

Multiplying Eq. (4) by the identity $\mathbf{n} = \mathbf{n}$ is to express both sides as a vector quantity which is associated with the position of ΔA,

$$\frac{\Delta \, \text{mmf}}{\Delta A} \, \mathbf{n} = \frac{\Delta I}{\Delta A} \, \mathbf{n} \qquad (5)$$

Now to maximize the right-hand side, restrict the position of $\mathbf{n}$ to lie along $\mathbf{J}$, and from Eq. (2) write, after passing to the limit,

$$\lim_{\Delta A \to 0} \frac{\Delta \, \text{mmf}}{\Delta A} \, \mathbf{n} = \mathbf{J} \qquad (6)$$

Equation (6) is equivalent to Eq. (1) but is valid at a point in space. Both sides of the equation involve vector quantities. To measure the value of the quantity on the left, we are instructed to place a small plane loop in that position which maximizes its mmf, and to express the mmf per unit area as a vector quantity in that direction.

This concept is similar to that of gradient, but not so simply evaluated. To find the gradient we are directed to place a differential line segment in that direction which maximizes the potential increase and to express the potential increase per unit length as a vector in that direction. In the notation of this section,

$$\boldsymbol{\nabla} V = \lim_{\Delta S \to 0} \frac{\Delta V}{\Delta S} \, \mathbf{s}$$

here $\mathbf{s}$ is the unit vector whose direction is given by the restriction of the sentence above.

We must now relate the left-hand side of Eq. (6) to the $\mathbf{H}$ vector rather than to the mmf. For the small loop under consideration, the mmf is related to H by

$$\Delta \, \text{mmf} = \oint \mathbf{H} \cdot d\mathbf{S} \qquad (7)$$

where the line integral is evaluated around the perimeter of the loop. If we have only ΔA to look at and are unaware of the direction of $\mathbf{J}$, we can achieve the results of the right-hand rule by traversing the perimeter in that direction which keeps the area on our left. Now using Eq. (7) in Eq. (6),

$$\lim_{\Delta A \to 0} \frac{\oint \mathbf{H} \cdot d\mathbf{S}}{\Delta A} \, \mathbf{n} = \mathbf{J} \qquad (8)$$

The limiting process on the left-hand side of Eq. (8) may be applied to any vector quantity, but we have not done so previously because in conservative fields the line integral around a closed path is zero and the limit is therefore zero. The limit has a shorthand notation in vector analysis involving the operator ∇, read "del cross H" and called the curl. For the H vector, though applicable to any vector, we define

$$\nabla \times \mathbf{H} = \lim_{\Delta A \to 0} \frac{\oint \mathbf{H} \cdot d\mathbf{S}}{\Delta A} \, \mathbf{n} \qquad (9)$$

where the unit vector normal to ΔA is placed in such a direction as to maximize the scalar limit, and the line integral is to be evaluated in that direction which keeps the area on the left.

Since the units of $\mathbf{H}$ are amperes per meter and those of $\mathbf{J}$ are amperes per square meter, we expect that the operation $\nabla \times \mathbf{H}$ will turn out to involve differentiation with respect to distance.

Finally, let us write Ampère's circuital law in terms of $\mathbf{J}$ and $\mathbf{H}$ as

$$\nabla \times \mathbf{H} = \mathbf{J} \qquad (10)$$

for steady currents, and postpone the details of evaluating the curl in a coordinate system.

9.15   A Summary and a Criticism. We defined the magnetic field in terms of the force on a moving charge according to the equation

$$\mathbf{F} = Q\mathbf{U} \times \mathbf{B} \qquad 9.1(1)$$

We applied this relation to motion of an electron in a uniform magnetic field, and then related it to the force on a current-carrying conductor. In the latter case we obtained several expressions for the force, including one which gives the force at a point in a current-region

$$d\mathbf{F} = \mathbf{J} \times \mathbf{B} \, dv \qquad 9.3(4)$$

and

$$\mathbf{F} = \int \mathbf{J} \times \mathbf{B} \, dv \qquad 9.3(5)$$

By investigating the torque on a plane closed loop in a uniform magnetic field, we were led to define the *magnetic moment* as a vector quantity perpendicular to the plane of the loop and with a sense given by the right-hand rule. The moment is given by

$$\mathbf{M} = IA \, \mathbf{n} \qquad 9.5(12)$$

and torque by

$$\mathbf{T} = \mathbf{M} \times \mathbf{B} \qquad 9.5(13)$$

We stated the law of Biot and Savart for the magnetic field of a current element of differential length and finite current

$$dB = \frac{\mu_0 I}{4\pi R^2} dL \times r \qquad 9.7(3)$$

This we applied to the single case of the field of a long straight wire, obtaining, for the infinite-length case,

$$B = \frac{\mu_0 I}{2\pi R} \theta \qquad 9.8(8)$$

For this, and several other two-dimensional fields, we found that the field maps were identical to those of an electrostatic field but with the equipotentials and direction lines interchanged.

The basic experimental relationship between the magnetic field and its sources is Ampère's circuital law. Expanding Eq. 9.9(5), we wrote

$$\oint H \cdot dS = \int J \cdot n \, dA \qquad 9.14(6)$$

This relation is useful in problems having a high degree of symmetry and plays the role of Gauss's law in electrostatics.

Applying Gauss's law to the field of a current element, we found that the B vector is solenoidal

$$\nabla \cdot B = 0 \qquad 9.9(3)$$

Under certain specified conditions, such as exist in a solenoid, infinitely long, or in a uniformly wound toroid, we found it possible to account for the discontinuity in the tangential component of the B vector at a boundary between materials by specifying the permeability of the material. The solenoidal character of B, and Ampère's circuital law determined the general boundary conditions. The normal components of B are continuous and the tangential components of H are continuous.

More as a leader to things to come than as an end in itself, we generalized Ampère's circuital law in a method similar to our generalization of Gauss's law in electrostatics. We obtained the mmf per unit area as a limiting process and found that this was a vector quantity equal to the current density at a point.

$$\nabla \times H = J \qquad 9.14(10)$$

There are many aspects of magnetic fields which we have not treated here. One of them is the use of a scalar potential function from which we can find the magnetic field through the gradient operation. In regions in which there are no currents, and on paths which do not enclose currents, the H vector is conservative, and it is possible to study magnetic fields in terms of Laplace's equation. We have not related B and H when permanent magnets are present, or when any magnetic material is present under conditions producing end effects.

These difficulties with the relationship between **B** and **H** are resolvable in a manner similar to that applied to the relationship between **D** and **E** within a dielectric material. A magnetic polarization vector **M** is defined, which is the magnetic moment per unit volume in a magnetic material. Then **B** and **H** are related by

$$\mathbf{H} = \frac{\mathbf{B}}{\mu_0} - \mathbf{M}$$

REFERENCES

1. Sears, F. W. "Principles of Physics," Vol. II, "Electricity and Magnetism," Chaps. 9, 11, 14, 15, Addison-Wesley Press, Inc., Cambridge, Mass., 1947. Recommended collateral reading on the magnetic field. A part of the discussion is in vector-analysis notation.

PROBLEMS

*9.1 The ring of Fig. 9.12 carries a current I in a clockwise direction. Find the force experienced by the current element labeled dL_1 due to the current element dL_2. Find the force experienced by dL_1 due to the current element dL_3 and vice versa. Compare the results with Newton's third law. (The use of cartesian coordinates is recommended, writing dL_1 as $dL\,\mathbf{i}$ and dL_3 as $-dL\,\mathbf{j}$.)

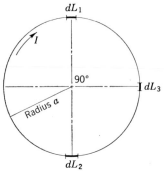

FIG. 9.12   For Prob. 9.1.

*9.2 Using the law of Biot and Savart, find the field on the axis of a current ring.

9.3 Extend the results of Prob. 9.2 to a solenoid of finite length. This procedure will treat the solenoid as a current sheet, thus avoiding the difficulty of including the pitch of the helix. The use of angle variables will simplify the integration and the form of the results. Check by extension to an infinite solenoid.

9.4 Compare the magnitude of the field at the end of a finite solenoid to that at the center, taking both points on the axis.

9.5 Using Ampère's circuital law, find the magnetic field at points within a closed toroid (a transformer core without an air gap.) For constant permeability, compute the permeance for the case of (a) rectangular cross section, and (b) round cross section. Compare the results of (b) with the final result of Sec. 4.5.

*9.6 Develop the law of refraction at a boundary between magnetic materials. In particular, discuss the direction of the magnetic-flux-density vector in air at the surface of a material of high permeability.

9.7 In addition to the arguments following Eq. (3) of Sec. 9.12, there is another way of showing that there can be no radial component in the field of an infinite solenoid. Assume that both radial and axial components of **B** exist. Then show that the radial component must be zero if $\oint \mathbf{B} \cdot \mathbf{n} \, dA$ is to be zero over cylindrical closed surfaces whose axes coincide with the axis of the solenoid.

*9.8 Prove that $\oint d\mathbf{L} = 0$, as stated in Eq. 9.4(5). What is the significance of the similar scalar integral $\oint dL$?

*9.9 Refer to Sec. 3.1 and the accompanying figure. Show that, around a closed path, the work done by this force is directly proportional to the area enclosed by the path of integration, when that path lies in the xy plane. How much work, in foot-pounds per square foot, can be done by this force? How many joules per square meter? (The simplicity of the result is due to the simplicity of the example and is not to be considered as applying to all vectors. Consider, for example, the force vector $\mathbf{F} = y^2 \, \mathbf{i}$.)

9.10 Repeat Prob. 9.9 for the **U** vector in Fig. 2.8b. What are the units of the line integral around a closed path, per unit area, in this field?

9.11 A vector which has a similar equation to that of Prob. 9.10 is $\mathbf{F} = y \, \mathbf{i} + x \, \mathbf{j}$. Show that the line integral of this vector is independent of the path. Obtain a potential function for which $\mathbf{F} = -\nabla V$.

9.12 Find the magnetic field at the center of a current-carrying loop which has the form of an n-sided regular polygon inscribed in a circle of radius a. Check your result by showing that the field approaches that of a circular loop, in the limit, as n becomes infinite.

9.13 Using Ampère's circuital law and the symmetry of the problem, evaluate the magnetic field outside an infinitely long, current-carrying conductor. One of the requirements of this problem is to show that the field cannot have radial or axial components. While the axial component may present difficulties, you will be able to show it to be a constant at most. Consideration of the axial component arising from the current in the return path (in another wire at a remote distance) reduces to zero the combined effects.

*9.14 A circular disk of radius a and negligible thickness t carries a total current I in a circular direction around the center. The current density is directly proportional to the radius. Find the magnetic field at the center in terms of I and a. Compare with that at the center of a current-carrying ring of radius a, from Prob. 9.2.

*9.15 A charged particle enters a uniform magnetic field with an initial velocity $\mathbf{U}_0$. By equating the centripetal and magnetic forces, obtain the trajectory of the particle. Check against Eqs. (23) and (24) in Sec. 9.2.

CHAPTER 10

TIME-VARYING ELECTRIC AND
MAGNETIC FIELDS

In this chapter we examine very briefly some of the characteristics of vectors which are functions of the time. We shall show the similarities between Ampère's circuital law and Faraday's law of induced emf. After generalizing the latter to a vector point relationship between the time-changing electric and magnetic fields, we discuss the concept of curl at greater length than in the previous chapter. After relating the curl to coordinate systems, we summarize most of the material in this book by writing Maxwell's equations.

10.1 The Derivative of a Vector. The derivative of a vector function is quite analogous to the derivative of a scalar function. For a scalar function of a single variable, $y = f(x)$, the derivative is defined by the limit

$$\frac{dy}{dx} = \lim_{\Delta x \to 0} \frac{f(x + \Delta x) - f(x)}{\Delta x}$$

$$= \lim_{\Delta x \to 0} \frac{\Delta y}{\Delta x} \tag{1}$$

For a vector quantity $\mathbf{B}$ which is a function of the single variable t, the derivative is defined as the limit

$$\frac{d\mathbf{B}}{dt} = \lim_{\Delta t \to 0} \frac{\mathbf{B}(t + \Delta t) - \mathbf{B}(t)}{\Delta t}$$

$$= \lim_{\Delta t \to 0} \frac{\Delta \mathbf{B}}{\Delta t} \tag{2}$$

The notation of the definition is illustrated in Fig. 10.1a for a vector changing both in magnitude and direction. *The derivative of a vector is another vector*, having in general a different direction as well as magnitude. It is easiest to examine the two extreme cases in order to discuss the direction of the derivative.

In part *b* of the figure, the vector quantity has a constant direction and only its magnitude is changing. The derivative is parallel to the original vector and has the same sense if the magnitude is increasing and an opposite sense if the magnitude is decreasing. In part *c* of the figure, the vector has a constant magnitude and only its direction is changing. The derivative is perpendicular to the original vector. Observe, too, that the derivative of the magnitude of the original vector is zero.

Part d of the figure is an extension of part a to assist in finding the components of $\Delta\mathbf{B}$ when both the magnitude and direction are changing. Here the component of $\Delta\mathbf{B}$ along $\mathbf{B}$ is, approximately,

$$\Delta\mathbf{B} \cdot \frac{\mathbf{B}}{|\mathbf{B}|} = \Delta B$$

and ΔB is the change in magnitude. Multiplying both sides by B,

$$\Delta\mathbf{B} \cdot \mathbf{B} = B\,\Delta B$$

Dividing by Δt and passing to the limit where the approximation is removed,

$$\frac{d\mathbf{B}}{dt} \cdot \mathbf{B} = B\,\frac{dB}{dt} \tag{3}$$

Now if the vector has a constant magnitude, the term dB/dt on the right is zero.

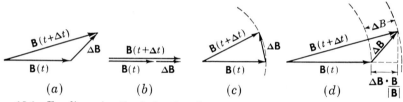

Fig. 10.1   For discussing the derivative of a vector.   In a the vector $\mathbf{B}$ is changing in magnitude and direction.   In b the change is in magnitude alone, while in c the magnitude is constant but the direction is changing.   In the latter case, the derivative is perpendicular to the vector.   The construction of d is used to obtain Eq. (3).

More generally, a vector is a function of the coordinates as well as the time.   At a fixed point of observation, the quantity given by Eq. (2) corresponds to the partial derivative of $\mathbf{B}$ with respect to time.

$$\frac{\partial\mathbf{B}}{\partial t} = \lim_{\Delta t \to 0} \frac{\mathbf{B}(x,y,z,t + \Delta t) - \mathbf{B}(x,y,z,t)}{\Delta t} \tag{4}$$

We evaluate Eq. (4) by treating the coordinates of the point as constants and differentiating with respect to t, just as we do for scalars.   We shall denote the result of Eq. (4) by a shorter notation $\dot{\mathbf{B}} = \partial\mathbf{B}/\partial t$.

The total time derivative of a vector, as measured by a moving particle, or point, which observes changes with respect to the coordinates as well as the time, is given by

$$\frac{d\mathbf{B}}{dt} = \frac{\partial\mathbf{B}}{\partial x}\frac{dx}{dt} + \frac{\partial\mathbf{B}}{\partial y}\frac{dy}{dt} + \frac{\partial\mathbf{B}}{\partial z}\frac{dz}{dt} + \frac{\partial\mathbf{B}}{\partial t} \tag{5}$$

In Eq. (5) the partial derivatives are evaluated by means of Eq. (4), using the appropriate independent variable.

Let us draw our example from the field of alternating current machines. The currents in the polyphase armature produce magnetic fields which, ideally at least, are constant in magnitude and rotate at synchronous speed. In cartesian coordinates, the components are sinusoidal functions of the time.

$$\mathbf{B} = B(\mathbf{i} \cos \omega t + \mathbf{j} \sin \omega t) \tag{6}$$

In cartesian coordinates, the unit vectors are fixed in position and are treated as constants in the differentiation

$$\dot{\mathbf{B}} = \omega B(-\mathbf{i} \sin \omega t + \mathbf{j} \cos \omega t) \tag{7}$$

The derivative is perpendicular to the original vector and its line segment leads that associated with the original vector by $\pi/2$.

There is no reason for treating $\dot{\mathbf{B}}$ in a manner different from any other vector. We can subject it to all the various vector operations without making any changes in our rules.

10.2 Induced Electromotive Force. Moving charges experience forces over and above those which can be attributed to the Coulomb's-law forces, under either of two conditions. The first arises when there is relative motion between a moving charge and the sources of a magnetic field, as in Eq. 9.1(1):

$$\mathbf{F} = q\mathbf{U} \times \mathbf{B} \tag{1}$$

If the magnetic field is due to currents in conductors, there need not be any separation of charge within the conducting circuit. The force per unit of charge is sometimes called the *electromotional* field intensity.

$$\mathbf{E} = \mathbf{U} \times \mathbf{B} \tag{2}$$

This relation is useful when conductors are moving in a magnetic field. The line integral of this electromotional field intensity leads to the familiar relation

$$\text{emf} = BLU$$

used in the study of electrical machinery.

The second condition arises when a time-changing magnetic field is present, whether or not there is relative motion between the test charge and the sources of the magnetic field. Let us now discuss this latter case, restricting ourselves to a study of the effect of the time-changing magnetic field in the absence of relative motion.

The experimental observation known as Faraday's induced emf law is usually written as

$$\text{emf} = -N \frac{d\phi}{dt} \tag{3}$$

A time-changing magnetic field is a reversible source of energy which can be used in many ways. In alternating-current-circuit theory we use Eq. (3) in an energy balance on a per-unit-of-charge basis. If the remainder of the circuit contains resistance only, we write

$$IR = -N\frac{d\phi}{dt} \tag{4}$$

If a capacitor is present to interchange energy with the magnetic field, we write

$$\frac{Q}{C} + IR = -N\frac{d\phi}{dt} \tag{5}$$

These and similar extensions are all in accordance with Kirchhoff's emf law

$$\Sigma emf = 0 \tag{6}$$

From the field viewpoint, we observe that Faraday's law is a relationship which is mathematically like Ampère's circuital law. To compare the two concepts, we first recognize that the turns N is the same sort of aid to evaluating the flux through the relation

$$\phi = \int \mathbf{B} \cdot \mathbf{n} \, dA$$

as it is in Ampère's circuital law in evaluating the total current I by means of

$$I = \int \mathbf{J} \cdot \mathbf{n} \, dA$$

Absorbing the turns into the surface integration process, we write Eq. (3) as

$$emf = -\frac{d\phi}{dt} \tag{7}$$

Now, in Ampère's circuital law,

$$mmf = I \tag{8}$$

let us write I as dQ/dt,

$$mmf = \frac{dQ}{dt} \tag{9}$$

Except for the minus sign, Eqs. (7) and (9) are strikingly similar. The left-hand sides of the equations involve a line integral around a closed path, while the right-hand sides are the time derivatives of a scalar function. This shows that we can do everything with Faraday's law that can be done with Ampère's circuital law, and in problems with identical geometries, the results will be the same. Furthermore, the emf gain per unit area will approach a definite limit, just as did the mmf gain per unit area discussed in Sec. 9.14. Before pursuing the matter, however, we shall associate Eq. (7) with the time derivative of the **B** vector **Ḃ**.

We write the left-hand side of Eq. (7) as the line integral of an electric-field intensity arising from the time-changing magnetic field. We write the right-hand side in terms of the **B** vector, obtaining

$$\oint \mathbf{E} \cdot d\mathbf{S} = -\frac{d}{dt} \int \mathbf{B} \cdot \mathbf{n} \, dA \tag{10}$$

As in Ampère's circuital law, the line integral is to be evaluated around the boundary of the area of the surface integration, keeping the surface on the left. The next step is to interchange the order of differentiation and integration on the right-hand side of the equation. The integral on the right is a definite integral, and in differentiating under the integral sign we are directed, by the rules of calculus, to use partial differentiation. Physically, we are now differentiating at a fixed point in space, at which the coordinates and the unit vectors are constants.

$$\oint \mathbf{E} \cdot d\mathbf{S} = -\int \dot{\mathbf{B}} \cdot \mathbf{n} \, dA \tag{11}$$

Mathematically Eq. (11) is identical in form to Ampère's circuital law written as

$$\oint \mathbf{H} \cdot d\mathbf{S} = \int \mathbf{J} \cdot \mathbf{n} \, dA \tag{12}$$

By retracing the steps of Sec. 9.14, we may obtain the limit of the emf gain per unit area for vanishingly small closed paths as

$$\boldsymbol{\nabla} \times \mathbf{E} = \lim_{\Delta A \to 0} \frac{\oint \mathbf{E} \cdot d\mathbf{S}}{\Delta A} \, \mathbf{n} \tag{13}$$

in which ΔA and its associated unit vector **n** is taken in that direction which maximizes the magnitude of the vector $\boldsymbol{\nabla} \times \mathbf{E}$. The limit in Eq. (13) gives a vector-point relation between the time-changing electric- and magnetic-field vectors at the same point in space, through

$$\boldsymbol{\nabla} \times \mathbf{E} = -\dot{\mathbf{B}} \tag{14}$$

In its integral form Eq. (7), for finite closed paths, Faraday's law does not tell us how the electric field is distributed in a region, or what its direction is. We can discover the magnitude and direction in the easier problems by a study of the symmetry. The differential formulation of Eq. (14) *still* does not tell us the magnitude or direction of the vector **E** itself, but we have achieved a differential equation which will give us the information if we can solve it. We shall write the differential equation when we relate the curl of a vector to a coordinate system.

Equation (14) is one of Maxwell's equations, and this one requires no further modification as we move from static fields to time-changing fields. We arrived at the result essentially because of our experience with a problem in magnetostatics.

10.3 Circulation. To state that in the gravitational field of force there are no closed paths around which the work done by the field is not zero, is to restate the principle of the conservation of energy in a way so thoroughly tied to our experience that it seems redundant if not ridiculous to mention it again. The electrostatic field of force due to fixed configurations of charge is another such field. It was in emphasis of the special nature of the electrostatic field that we first considered the work done by a nonconservative vector in introducing line integrals and the concept of potential in Chap. 3. Fortunately, in the physical world, there are force fields in which the line integral around a closed path is not zero. If this were not so, life would be very uninteresting if possible at all.

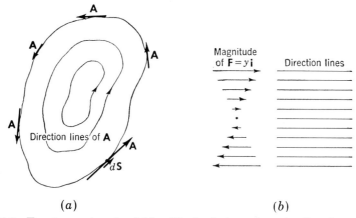

FIG. 10.2 Two types of vector fields with circulation. In *a* the direction lines are closed curves, while in *b* the direction lines are parallel.

At the outset, let us ask just one question about every sort of field. The question is, "Can we, or can we not, find a closed path anywhere in the field, around which the line integral is not zero?" This simple criterion divides fields into two categories. Whenever the answer to our question is "No," we classify that field as a conservative field which can be handled by means of a scalar potential function. Our present interest lies in those fields for which the answer is "Yes." Where do we find them, and under what conditions?

There is one class of fields in which it is very easy to see that there are closed paths available to us on which the line integral of the tangential component of the vector is not zero. These are the fields which we map with direction lines which are closed curves. If we choose a path which coincides with a direction line all the way around the loop as in Fig. 10.2*a*, we can never reverse the sign of the scalar product $\mathbf{A} \cdot d\mathbf{S}$ regardless of how the magnitude of $\mathbf{A}$ varies along the path. These are the vectors which have no divergence and which we have called solenoidal.

Now before proceeding any further in this discussion, we ought to have a good name for the scalar quantity which results from evaluating a line integral around a closed path, for any vector regardless of its nature. Suggested probably by the line of thinking behind the paragraph above, the general term in common use today is *circulation*. For any vector **A**,

$$\text{Circulation of } \mathbf{A} = \oint \mathbf{A} \cdot d\mathbf{S} \tag{1}$$

Now the trouble with this term is a problem in semantics and the psychological tendency to expect that all the properties exhibited by any one member of a class will be found in all members of the class. The stumbling block is this: All vector fields which involve moving materials round and round closed paths have circulation. The current goes round the circuit, and the cooling water in the radiator travels through the system over and over again. Yet there are fields, and lots of them, in which there is nothing going around and yet they have circulation in the sense of Eq. (1).

Because of this difficulty it is perhaps unfortunate that Heaviside's name *circuitation* did not stick, because this term has no other meaning in our language. On introducing the term, Heaviside also said: "Any man who understands the law of circuitation also understands what 'curl' means, though he may not himself be aware of his knowledge, being like the Frenchman who talked prose for many years without knowing it." As to the law of circuitation, he was referring to Ampère's circuital law, Faraday's induced emf law, and Kirchhoff's emf law for circuits.

There is another difficulty with the general term of Eq. (1) regardless of what name is assigned to it, and this arises because almost all of us have had considerable experience with special cases of circulation, calling it by three different names depending on the field under study. In one case we call it work, in the next we call it electromotive force, and then magnetomotive force. If we are now ready to lump together work, electromotive force, and magnetomotive force, calling all of them by the general name of circulation, we are ready to proceed. In what follows we will find an example or two of fields in which there is circulation but nothing going round and round.

Let us first consider steady fields, those in which conditions exist independently of the time, for periods which are long enough for us to study the fields as though time did not matter. In Sec. 3.1 we studied the simple vector $\mathbf{F} = y\,\mathbf{i}$, and computed its circulation in a few cases. The direction lines of this vector, Fig. 10.2b, seem to be all parallel and do not suggest a solenoidal vector at all, yet the field has circulation. In this simple field the circulation is directly proportional to the area enclosed by the path of integration, as is shown by Eq. 3.1 (6). The physical reason for the existence of circulation lies in the fact that the force is changing in

a direction perpendicular to its direction lines. We can take advantage
of this by moving to the right along paths on which the force is large and
to the right, and returning along the x axis where the force is zero, or
indeed by dropping below the axis and getting work out of the field on the
return trip, too.

Velocity fields like this, and force fields, too, are found in the flow of
water in a stream or in a long straight pipe. The simple representation
$\mathbf{F} = y\,\mathbf{i}$ is not adequate to describe these cases completely, but for the
stream the velocity is smaller along the bottom than it is in the main part
of flow. The fish are well aware of this and plunge after the passing food
in the fast part of the stream, returning along the bottom to minimize the
effort.

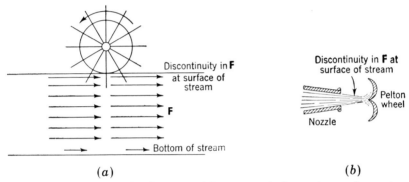

Fig. 10.3 Discontinuities in the tangential component of a vector produce extreme
cases of circulation.

Let us now consider the surface of a river to observe an extreme case of
circulation. The forces which can be exerted by the flowing stream stop
quite suddenly at the surface, and there is a discontinuity, essentially
infinite, in their tangential component. Any device, such as an undershot water wheel, in contact with only a part of the stream, can extract
energy from it. In the undershot water wheel, Fig. 10.3a, only the paddles which are in the stream feel the forces, while the remainder are riding
around in the air doing nothing. A more extreme case of forces which
exist only in a limited region is found in a Pelton water wheel where the
force on the blades comes from a directed jet, Fig. 10.3b.

Now let us consider the case in which fields change either their magnitude or direction as a function of time. Though there is nothing suggestive of circulation at any instant in time, and the field seems to be conservative from its map, it may very well have circulation. If the wind
blows from the west over a very large region with constant velocity and
direction everywhere, the balloonist is quite convinced that he is in a
conservative field at every instant and that he could get back to his start-

ing point only with considerable difficulty. Yet if he waits until another day when the wind blows the other way, back he goes to his starting point, having traveled around a closed path in an apparently conservative field, because his position on the path is also a function of the time.

Those who have thought about circulation for some time can go on with examples like this indefinitely, but to do so obscures the issue. There is nothing profound about circulation; it is all around us, and we all have a feel for it in our daily lives. Now, talking about circulation on a yes-or-no basis is one thing, and characterizing the field by telling how much circulation there is around a given path is another. Electrical engineers with circuit experience should have a good deal of confidence in their ability to do this, because every circuit problem they have ever solved can be said to be an evaluation of circulation.

10.4 Curl in Cartesian Coordinates. Now that we have examined circulation in some detail and generalized two circulations, magnetomotive force and electromotive force, to yield a vector-quantity "curl" associated with a point in space, it is time to investigate the curl of any vector function and to relate it to coordinate systems. The key idea of the curl is the limiting value of the gain in circulation per unit area. This must be expressed as a vector quantity, and specifications of its magnitude and direction are required.

How this is done can be illustrated in terms of the previous work in which we related Faraday's law to the time-changing magnetic field. We began with

$$\oint \mathbf{E} \cdot d\mathbf{S} = -\frac{d\phi}{dt} = -\int \dot{\mathbf{B}} \cdot \mathbf{n} \, dA \tag{1}$$

and established the results for differential loops as

$$\lim_{\Delta A \to 0} \frac{\oint \mathbf{E} \cdot d\mathbf{S}}{\Delta A} \, \mathbf{n} = -\dot{\mathbf{B}} \tag{2}$$

Then we introduced the shorthand notation of vector analysis to write Eq. (2) as

$$\nabla \times \mathbf{E} = -\dot{\mathbf{B}} \tag{3}$$

To write Eq. (3) in terms of a coordinate system, we have to evaluate Eq. (2) in that coordinate system. The unit vector $\mathbf{n}$ has to be taken along $-\dot{\mathbf{B}}$. This tells us how to place the differential loop whose area is ΔA. At any one point we can choose a coordinate system with one of the axes along $-\dot{\mathbf{B}}$ in order to simplify the details. The shape of the path of integration can be anything we like, but the normal to ΔA must be taken parallel to $-\dot{\mathbf{B}}$. In cartesian coordinates we get a picture like Fig. 10.4a. If it helps we can also break the square loop and insert an ideal voltmeter to measure the electromotive force induced in the little loop. but our

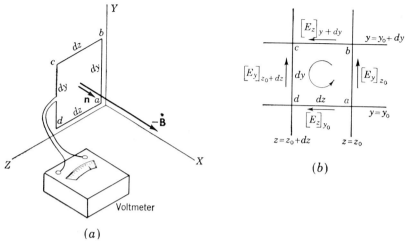

FIG. 10.4 (a) A small plane loop whose plane is perpendicular to a time-changing magnetic field, the induced emf being measured by a voltmeter; (b) a mathematical loop placed in the same physical position.

formal task is a mathematical problem. We shall do this as indicated in Fig. 10.4b by writing, as in Sec. 3.1,

$$\oint \mathbf{E} \cdot d\mathbf{S} = \int_a^b \mathbf{E} \cdot d\mathbf{S} + \int_b^c \mathbf{E} \cdot d\mathbf{S} + \int_c^d \mathbf{E} \cdot d\mathbf{S} + \int_d^a \mathbf{E} \cdot d\mathbf{S} \quad (4)$$

Along the path ab, $d\mathbf{S} = \mathbf{j}\,dy$, and

$$\int_a^b \mathbf{E} \cdot d\mathbf{S} = \int_a^b (E_x \mathbf{i} + E_y \mathbf{j} + E_z \mathbf{k}) \cdot \mathbf{j}\,dy = [E_y\,dy]_{z_0} \quad (5)$$

where $E_y\,dy$ is to be evaluated at z_0. Then along the path cd,

$$\int_c^d \mathbf{E} \cdot d\mathbf{S} = [-E_y\,dy]_{z_0+dz}$$

where $E_y\,dy$ is to be evaluated at $z_0 + dz$. Along the path bc

$$\int_b^c \mathbf{E} \cdot d\mathbf{S} = [E_z\,dz]_{y_0+dy}$$

where $E_z\,dz$ is to be evaluated at $y_0 + dy$. Finally, along the path da

$$\int_d^a \mathbf{E} \cdot d\mathbf{S} = [-E_z\,dz]_{y_0}$$

where $E_z\,dz$ is to be evaluated at y_0. Substituting these relations into Eq. (3),

$$\oint \mathbf{E} \cdot d\mathbf{S} = [E_y\,dy]_{z_0} - [E_y\,dy]_{z_0+dz} + [E_z\,dz]_{y_0+dy} - [E_z\,dz]_{y_0} \quad (6)$$

The last two brackets are

$$\frac{\partial(E_z\,dz)}{\partial y}\,dy$$

When this is evaluated by the product rule, it gives

$$\frac{\partial E_z}{\partial y} \, dy \, dz$$

The first two brackets are the negative of a similar expression, so that Eq. (6) becomes

$$\oint \mathbf{E} \cdot d\mathbf{S} = \left(\frac{\partial E_z}{\partial y} - \frac{\partial E_y}{\partial z}\right) dy \, dz \qquad (7)$$

This is the circulation around the loop. When divided by the area it gives the curl, directed along the normal to the loop

$$\nabla \times \mathbf{E} = \left(\frac{\partial E_z}{\partial y} - \frac{\partial E_y}{\partial z}\right) \mathbf{i} \qquad (8)$$

This applies to the special case in which $-\dot{\mathbf{B}}$ was directed along $\mathbf{i}$. It is not always convenient to choose a new coordinate system for every point. Furthermore, $-\dot{\mathbf{B}}$ may vary in magnitude and direction from point to point. If this is the case, $\mathbf{B}$ can be resolved into its components at the point and a curl vector obtained for each of the components. We can write the results for the other two components by permuting the subscripts in Eq. (8) and adding the results according to the parallelogram law. When this is done,

$$\nabla \times \mathbf{E} = \left(\frac{\partial E_z}{\partial y} - \frac{\partial E_y}{\partial z}\right) \mathbf{i} + \left(\frac{\partial E_x}{\partial z} - \frac{\partial E_z}{\partial x}\right) \mathbf{j} + \left(\frac{\partial E_y}{\partial x} - \frac{\partial E_x}{\partial y}\right) \mathbf{k} \qquad (9)$$

This expression is valid only in cartesian coordinates. It relates the curl vector to the $\mathbf{E}$ vector through a partial differential equation. It may also be used as an expansion in cartesian coordinates for the curl of any vector. In retrospect we recognize that carrying $\dot{\mathbf{B}}$ along was just a crutch to help us keep our directions straight.

To explain the notation for the curl symbol in terms of the cartesian vector operator ∇, we take the vector product of ∇ and the $\mathbf{E}$ vector

$$\nabla \times \mathbf{E} = \left(\mathbf{i} \frac{\partial}{\partial x} + \mathbf{j} \frac{\partial}{\partial y} + \mathbf{k} \frac{\partial}{\partial z}\right) \times (\mathbf{i} E_x + \mathbf{j} E_y + \mathbf{k} E_z) \qquad (10)$$

This may be written in the readily remembered determinant form, valid for cartesian coordinates only,

$$\nabla \times \mathbf{E} = \begin{vmatrix} \mathbf{i} & \mathbf{j} & \mathbf{k} \\ \dfrac{\partial}{\partial x} & \dfrac{\partial}{\partial y} & \dfrac{\partial}{\partial z} \\ E_x & E_y & E_z \end{vmatrix} \qquad (11)$$

The expansion of Eq. (11) gives Eq. (9).

In any orthogonal coordinate system one proceeds in similar fashion to evaluate the component of the curl due to each of the components of the vector whose curl is to be related to the coordinates of the point of observation. We shall do this in the next section.

Before we leave this line of thinking, it would be well to examine the physical significance of the presence of the ideal voltmeter in Fig. 10.4a. A small plane loop of wire, containing one or a great many turns, is an *electrical engineer's curl meter*. When such a loop is placed in a time-changing electric field, in that position which gives the maximum induced voltage, that induced voltage is directly proportional to the curl of the electric field intensity and the area of the loop. When the loop is placed in any position in the field, the induced voltage in the loop is directly proportional to the component of the curl of the field in a direction taken along the normal to the loop.

Such loops are commonly used in measuring the magnitude of the electric fields radiated from antennas, and many who use them do not seem to realize that their response is proportional to the curl of the electric field intensity and not to the field intensity itself. It happens that there is a special case (plane waves) in which the magnitude of the field-intensity vector is simply related to the magnitude of its curl, but in general the two are not simply related at all. This sometimes causes gross misinterpretations of the readings of commercial field-strength meters when measurements are made near the source of the radiated energy.

10.5   The Curl of a Vector in General Orthogonal Coordinates.   In the previous investigations of circulation and curl, we have been dealing with the special cases in which the direction of the curl vector is known by its association with another vector whose direction has been specified. We have found that

$$\nabla \times \mathbf{H} = \mathbf{J} \quad \text{and} \quad \nabla \times \mathbf{E} = -\dot{\mathbf{B}}$$

We should now like to determine the curl of any vector from the vector itself. That is, when we are given a general vector $\mathbf{F}$ in terms of the coordinates at the point of observation, we are required to find the curl of $\mathbf{F}$, which is another vector function of position. We have written a defining equation for the curl of a vector

$$\nabla \times \mathbf{F} = \lim_{\Delta A \to 0} \frac{\oint \mathbf{F} \cdot d\mathbf{S}}{\Delta A} \mathbf{n}$$

We no longer have $\mathbf{J}$ or $\mathbf{B}$ to specify the direction of $\mathbf{n}$ but must rely on the appended part of the definition requiring that ΔA be so chosen that the magnitude of the vector $\nabla \times \mathbf{F}$ is maximized. Rather than hunt around for this direction, we can find the components of the curl in each of three mutually perpendicular directions and combine the results according to the parallelogram law.   By resolving the vector itself into three mutually perpendicular components, we can eliminate the contribution of one of the components to the line integral by making the plane of the loop perpendicular to that component.

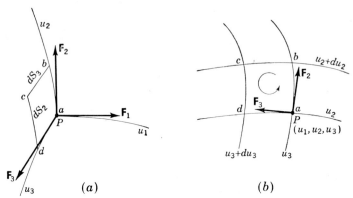

FIG. 10.5   For analysis of the curl of a vector in general orthogonal coordinates.

Figure 10.5 has the same arrangement as Fig. 10.4.   Here we are to consider the simultaneous effects of the varying field and varying path lengths.   We shall compute the circulation around the differential loop. When this is divided by the area of the loop, we shall have the component of the curl along the normal to the differential area.

$$\oint \mathbf{F} \cdot d\mathbf{S} = \int_a^b \mathbf{F} \cdot d\mathbf{S}_2 + \int_b^c \mathbf{F} \cdot d\mathbf{S}_3 + \int_c^d \mathbf{F} \cdot d\mathbf{S}_2 + \int_d^a \mathbf{F} \cdot d\mathbf{S}_3 \quad (1)$$

Using brackets and subscripts to denote the coordinates at which the products are to be evaluated, Eq. (1) becomes

$$\oint \mathbf{F} \cdot d\mathbf{S} = [F_2 \, dS_2]_{u_3} - [F_2 \, dS_2]_{u_3+du_3} + [F_3 \, dS_3]_{u_2+du_2} - [F_3 \, dS_3]_{u_2} \quad (2)$$

Writing the right-hand side in terms of differential quantities

$$\oint \mathbf{F} \cdot d\mathbf{S} = - \frac{\partial(F_2 \, dS_2)}{\partial u_3} \, du_3 + \frac{\partial(F_3 \, dS_3)}{\partial u_2} \, du_2 \quad (3)$$

Now expressing the increments of the path lengths in terms of the corresponding increments in the coordinates,

$$dS_1 = h_1 \, du_1 \qquad dS_2 = h_2 \, du_2 \qquad dS_3 = h_3 \, du_3$$

Substituting, and writing the positive term first, we have

$$\oint \mathbf{F} \cdot d\mathbf{S} = \frac{\partial(h_3 F_3 \, du_3)}{\partial u_2} \, du_2 - \frac{\partial(h_2 F_2 \, du_2)}{\partial u_3} \, du_3 \quad (4)$$

When the partial derivatives are evaluated by the product rule and the common terms are factored, the circulation is

$$\oint \mathbf{F} \cdot d\mathbf{S} = \left(\frac{\partial (h_3 F_3)}{\partial u_2} - \frac{\partial (h_2 F_2)}{\partial u_3} \right) du_2 \, du_3 \tag{5}$$

The area of the loop is

$$dS_2 \, dS_3 = h_2 h_3 \, du_2 \, du_3 \tag{6}$$

When the circulation in Eq. (5) is divided by the area of the loop, we have the component of the curl which is normal to the loop.

$$(\nabla \times \mathbf{F}) \cdot \mathbf{i}_1 = \frac{1}{h_2 h_3} \left[\frac{\partial}{\partial u_2} (h_3 F_3) - \frac{\partial}{\partial u_3} (h_2 F_2) \right] \tag{7}$$

We may now evaluate the other two components by permuting the subscripts to write

$$(\nabla \times \mathbf{F}) \cdot \mathbf{i}_2 = \frac{1}{h_3 h_1} \left[\frac{\partial}{\partial u_3} (h_1 F_1) - \frac{\partial}{\partial u_1} (h_3 F_3) \right] \tag{8}$$

$$(\nabla \times \mathbf{F}) \cdot \mathbf{i}_3 = \frac{1}{h_1 h_2} \left[\frac{\partial}{\partial u_1} (h_2 F_2) - \frac{\partial}{\partial u_2} (h_1 F_1) \right] \tag{9}$$

The final step is to express the components of the curl given by Eqs. (7), (8), and (9) as component vectors, and write the result in the form of the determinant

$$\nabla \times \mathbf{F} = \begin{vmatrix} \dfrac{\mathbf{i}_1}{h_2 h_3} & \dfrac{\mathbf{i}_2}{h_1 h_3} & \dfrac{\mathbf{i}_3}{h_1 h_2} \\ \dfrac{\partial}{\partial u_1} & \dfrac{\partial}{\partial u_2} & \dfrac{\partial}{\partial u_3} \\ h_1 F_1 & h_2 F_2 & h_3 F_3 \end{vmatrix} \tag{10}$$

In cylindrical coordinates,

$$u_1 = R, \; u_2 = \theta, \; u_3 = z$$
$$\mathbf{i}_1 = \mathbf{r}, \;\; \mathbf{i}_2 = \boldsymbol{\theta}, \;\; \mathbf{i}_3 = \mathbf{k}$$
$$h_1 = 1, \; h_2 = R, \; h_3 = 1$$

In spherical coordinates,

$$u_1 = R, \; u_2 = \theta, \; u_3 = \phi$$
$$\mathbf{i}_1 = \mathbf{r}, \;\; \mathbf{i}_2 = \boldsymbol{\theta}, \;\; \mathbf{i}_3 = \boldsymbol{\phi}$$
$$h_1 = 1, \; h_2 = R, \; h_3 = R \sin \theta$$

Physical interpretations of curl usually involve fluids. In hydrodynamics, the terms *rotation* and *vorticity* are used as frequently as is the term curl. The motion of incompressible fluids involves translation and rotation. Expansion and divergence make things a little more complicated in the flow of gases. In rotation about a tiny circular path, the velocity is $R\omega$, the length of the circumference is $2\pi R$ so that the line integral of the velocity around the circumference is $2\pi R^2\omega$. The area of the loop is πR^2 and the curl is therefore 2ω, twice the angular velocity of rotation. As a vector, the direction is along the axis of rotation with a sense given by the right-hand rule.

Let us imagine a cold winter day and consider the water in a stream under freezing conditions. At one point in the stream, a tiny sphere of ice is suddenly formed. If it were not for the friction with the surface of the surrounding fluid, the angular velocity of the tiny sphere, or its spin, would be half the curl at that point. If at the instant of freezing we could remove the surrounding fluid, we could watch the little sphere of ice and actually see its rotation unimpeded by the friction. This illustration has

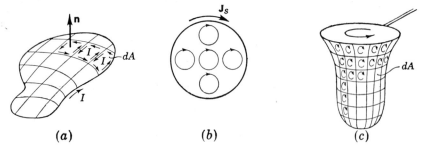

FIG. 10.6   The mesh–current method of obtaining the total torque on a closed loop in a magnetic field (part a) and the Amperian currents in a paramagnetic material (part b) are suggestions leading to Stokes's theorem. Suggestive of a basketball net and hoop, or a fisherman's dip net, part c represents a surface of any shape, bounded by a closed curve. Because of the common boundaries, the sum of the circulations around the perimeters of the individual meshes is equal to the circulation around the bounding curve.

been given by Milne-Thomson, whose superb book on hydrodynamics is included in the references listed at the end of this chapter.

The present author's teaching experience is that fluid analogies leave as many students cold as they leave helped, probably because electrical engineers have not had the opportunity to give a lot of thought to the flow of fluids. However, if the circulation, or circuitation, is grasped, curl comes along as readily as does the velocity from the average speed. The most frequent comment from students whose grasp of curl was delayed is this: "I was trying to make something hard out of it."

10.6   Some General Theorems Involving Curl.   One of the best ways of examining the concept of curl is to carry it backward into our experience with other vector operations. In Chap. 9, Sec. 9.6, we found it helpful to relate the total torque on a closed circuit to the magnetic **B** vector integrated over a surface bounded by the closed circuit, as in Fig. 10.6a. We observed that the circuit current could be considered as a superposition of mesh currents, each mesh having an area dA, and a magnetic moment of $I\,dA\,\mathbf{n}$.

We also attributed the increase in the magnetic vector, $\mathbf{B}$, in paramagnetic materials to the superposition of similar mesh currents, resulting in an equivalent surface current on the boundary of the material (Fig. 10.6b). When this *kind of thinking* is applied to the concept of curl, the result is Stokes's theorem, which is very important in vector analysis.

When the circulation of a vector is evaluated over a surface divided into meshes (such as a basketball net closed at the bottom, or a fisherman's dip net), adjacent meshes have common boundaries. When the circulation is evaluated successively around two adjacent meshes and the results are added, that part of the circulation along the common boundary cancels, as in Fig. 10.6c. When the circulation over the whole surface is evaluated, the results are identical to the circulation around the boundary of the surface. For each mesh, the circulation per unit area, when the mesh is oriented to maximize the circulation, is $\nabla \times \mathbf{E}$. Multiplying by the area of the mesh gives the maximum circulation as $(\nabla \times \mathbf{E})\,dA$. The actual circulation is the component along the normal to dA, $(\nabla \times \mathbf{E}) \cdot \mathbf{n}\,dA$. Integrating this over the whole surface gives the circulation around the entire boundary of the surface. In mathematical form,

$$\oint \mathbf{E} \cdot d\mathbf{S} = \int (\nabla \times \mathbf{E}) \cdot \mathbf{n}\,dA \tag{1}$$

where $\mathbf{E}$ can be any vector. This equation is known as Stokes's theorem and is much used in vector analysis. It serves to convert a surface integration of the curl of a vector to a line integral of the vector itself, and vice versa. Its use gives the easiest way of arriving at Ampère's circuital law or Faraday's induction law in integral form, starting with the differential forms. Given

$$\nabla \times \mathbf{H} = \mathbf{J}$$

we take the scalar product of both sides with $\mathbf{n}\,dA$ and integrate over an open surface:

$$\int (\nabla \times \mathbf{H}) \cdot \mathbf{n}\,dA = \int \mathbf{J} \cdot \mathbf{n}\,dA$$

Applying Stokes's theorem on the left and recognizing the term on the right as the current, we have immediately

$$\oint \mathbf{H} \cdot d\mathbf{S} = I$$

Another theorem states that the divergence of the curl of a vector is zero, and the commonest proof is presented in the form of an expansion in cartesian coordinates. The theorem is

$$\nabla \cdot (\nabla \times \mathbf{F}) = 0 \tag{2}$$

The expansion is unnecessary in the light of Stokes's theorem. Equation (2) may be written as divergence was defined,

$$\lim_{\Delta v \to 0} \frac{\oint (\nabla \times \mathbf{F}) \cdot \mathbf{n} \, dA}{\Delta v} = 0$$

in terms of the limiting value of the flux gain per unit volume. But the surface integration is equivalent to the circulation around the perimeter of an open surface. As the perimeter is shrunk to zero to form a closed surface, the circulation must go to zero, so the curl of a vector cannot have divergence.

A third theorem states that the curl of the gradient of a single-valued scalar function is zero.

$$\nabla \times (\nabla V) = 0$$

Though expansion in a coordinate system also verifies this statement, expansion is unnecessary. If the scalar function has a gradient, then the scalar function is a conservative potential function, and the line integral of its gradient must be independent of the path. Hence there can be no circulation, and if there is no circulation, there can be no curl.

10.7 Displacement Current and the Equation of Continuity. In considering the flow of steady currents where no charge may accumulate at a point, it was possible to show, as we did in Chap. 4, that since

$$I = \int \mathbf{J} \cdot \mathbf{n} \, dA$$

and I is continuous, then

$$\oint \mathbf{J} \cdot \mathbf{n} \, dA = 0$$

This is another way of saying that, when no charge can accumulate within any volume,

$$\nabla \cdot \mathbf{J} = 0$$

When time-varying conduction currents flow in circuits containing capacitors, charge can accumulate on the surface of the conductors forming the capacitor, in addition to any conduction currents which may be present in the dielectric. Under these conditions we have no basis for the conclusions indicated by the above equations, but must apply the equation of continuity first presented in Sec. 8.4.

We are also unable to resolve a contradiction between Ampère's circuital law and the law of Biot and Savart when capacitors form a part of a closed circuit.

In Fig. 10.7, a capacitor has been inserted into a circuit formed in part by a long straight wire. The law of Biot and Savart predicts that the magnetic field at all points on the circle enclosing the capacitor is due to the contributions of all the differential current elements in the long wire, and that removing a short section of the wire will not essentially change the magnetic field if the current in the wire is not changed. According to the law of Biot and Savart, if the wire is infinitely long the field will be

$$\mathbf{B} = \int_{-\infty}^{\infty} \frac{\mu_0 I \, d\mathbf{L} \times \mathbf{r}}{4\pi R^2}$$

when the capacitor is not present. When the capacitor is present, the field will be

$$B = \int_{-\infty}^{a} \frac{\mu_0 I \, d\mathbf{L} \times \mathbf{r}}{4\pi R^2} + \int_{b}^{\infty} \frac{\mu_0 I \, d\mathbf{L} \times \mathbf{r}}{4\pi R^2}$$

and these two results cannot differ very much.

Ampère's circuital law, on the other hand, predicts that

$$\oint \mathbf{H} \cdot d\mathbf{S} = I$$

around all closed paths enclosing the conduction current in the wire, and that

$$\oint \mathbf{H} \cdot d\mathbf{S} = 0$$

around a path enclosing the capacitor.

However, if the changing electric field within the capacitor is capable of establishing the same contribution to the magnetic field as that due to

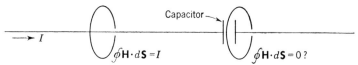

Fig. 10.7 For discussion of the magnetic field around a long wire when a capacitor is present.

the conduction current in the wire, then this difficulty can be resolved. The experimental observation is that the presence of the capacitor does not affect the magnetic field appreciably.

Maxwell studied the rearrangement of the dipole molecules in a dielectric when a field was being established within the dielectric, and on finding this equivalent to a current within the material, proposed the term "displacement current."

In Fig. 10.8a, a potential difference has just been applied to a parallel-plate capacitor containing a dielectric material. No charge has appeared on the plates, and the dipoles in the dielectric are in utter disorder. As charge accumulates on the plates, the dipoles align themselves with the field. The uniform motion of charge is a current through every cross-sectional area of the dielectric. The realignment of the dipoles is sketched in part b of the figure, and an enlarged view of the two successive positions of a dipole is shown in part c. As indicated in this figure, there is a net motion of positive charge from left to right, and of negative charge from right to left, through every cross-sectional area which can be established within the dielectric.   This is the basis for the term "displacement current" introduced by Maxwell.   It is not difficult to go to the next step in reasoning that the displacement current in the dielectric is as effective in producing a magnetic field as is a true conduction current.

The bold hypothesis of the existence of a displacement current when material substances are not present is much more difficult to accept physically.   There is perhaps no satisfactory explanation in terms of a physical model.   In an attempt to make the concept reasonable to his colleagues and students, Maxwell attributed to free space the dielectric properties of a physical medium, the ether.   At that time, propagation of electromagnetic waves through space had not been demonstrated.   The

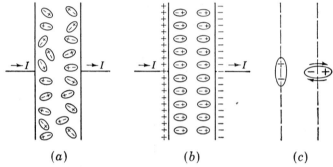

(a)   (b)   (c)

Fig. 10.8   For discussion of displacement current in a dielectric.

mathematical model, as opposed to a physical model perhaps, requires the displacement current to explain electromagnetic waves.   The mathematical model also requires the displacement current in free space to satisfy the conservation of electric charge.

The equation of continuity is a mathematical formulation of the self-evident principle that the rate of accumulation of material in a given region is equal to the net rate at which material crosses the walls of the region.   As previously mentioned, we investigated this formulation in Sec. 8.4 for the motion of a gas.   Extending these ideas to the volume density of charge at a point in a region, we write the equation of continuity, Eq. 8.4(5), as

$$\frac{\partial \rho}{\partial t} = -(\nabla \cdot \rho \mathbf{U}) \tag{1}$$

The terms $\rho \mathbf{U}$ on the right represent the conduction current density.   On the left we utilize Gauss's law

$$\nabla \cdot \mathbf{D} = \rho \tag{2}$$

to write Eq. (1) in the form

$$\frac{\partial}{\partial t}(\nabla \cdot \mathbf{D}) = -\nabla \cdot \mathbf{J} \tag{3}$$

In evaluating the divergence on the left, a definite integral is involved.

As previously stated in connection with Faraday's law, to interchange the order of differentiation and integration, we are directed to differentiate **D** partially with respect to time.

$$\mathbf{\nabla} \cdot \dot{\mathbf{D}} = -\mathbf{\nabla} \cdot \mathbf{J} \tag{4}$$

Collecting and distributing the operator **∇** gives

$$\mathbf{\nabla} \cdot (\mathbf{J} + \dot{\mathbf{D}}) = 0 \tag{5}$$

Now **D**, we recall, has the units of coulombs per square meter, and its time derivative has the same units as current density. $\dot{\mathbf{D}}$ is the displacement-current density.

Maxwell reasoned that the displacement-current density should be included in Ampère's circuital law. In the differential formulation he wrote

$$\mathbf{\nabla} \times \mathbf{H} = \mathbf{J} + \dot{\mathbf{D}} \tag{6}$$

If the equation of continuity is to hold along with Gauss's law in regions in which time-changing electric fields are present, this form is required. Further, if time-changing electric fields are present, then there is also a time-changing magnetic field present, whether or not there is actually any motion of charge in the region to give a finite value to **J** in Eq. (6). Unfortunately, Eq. (6) does not tell us directly the magnitude and direction of the time-changing magnetic field vector **H**. Instead, it gives us the magnitude and direction of its curl.

In good conductors, the contribution of the displacement current density to the magnetic field is negligible in comparison to the contribution of the conduction current. We establish a time-varying electric field, $E = E_{\max} \sin \omega t$, and write $J = \gamma E$ and $D = \epsilon_0 E$. Now the conductivity has the order of magnitude of 10^7, while the permittivity ϵ_0 is 0.885 (10^{-12}). Even at the highest radio frequencies, $\dot{D} = \epsilon_0 \omega E_{\max} \cos \omega t$ can be ignored in comparison with J. In dielectrics or in a vacuum, on the other hand, the important contribution arises from $\dot{D}$.

10.8 Maxwell's Equations. This section serves as a summary of the material of this chapter. It also provides us a summary of most of the material in the preceding chapters as well.

The equations known as Maxwell's equations are four partial differential equations between the five vector quantities, **E**, **J**, **D**, **B**, and **H**, together with the scalar concept of the volume density of electric charge. Maxwell sought the most succinct statement of our knowledge of electricity, and he succeeded in expressing this knowledge in a manner which is independent of a system of coordinates. He achieved this by specifying both the divergence and curl of an electric-field vector and a magnetic-field vector. A theorem of vector analysis, due to Helmholtz, states that a vector is specified when its divergence and curl have been specified.

The first of Maxwell's equations is a differential formulation of Faraday's induced emf law, with which we may still be most familiar in the form

$$\text{emf} = -N\frac{d\phi}{dt}$$

As an aid to computation, we have written this in integral form as

$$\oint \mathbf{E} \cdot d\mathbf{S} = -\frac{d}{dt}\int \mathbf{B} \cdot \mathbf{n}\, dA$$

By defining a vector quantity called the curl of $\mathbf{E}$ through the limit of the emf gain per unit area, we obtained the differential formulation as

$$\nabla \times \mathbf{E} = -\dot{\mathbf{B}} \tag{1}$$

While this equation does not give us the magnitude and direction of $\mathbf{E}$ itself if $\dot{\mathbf{B}}$ is known, it is a relation valid at a fixed point in space and independent of any coordinate system.

The second of Maxwell's equations is a differential formulation of Ampère's circuital law, in which the displacement current is included, as required by the equation of continuity. Most of us are most familiar with Ampère's circuital law in the form which is most useful in magnetic circuits,

$$\text{mmf} = NI$$

In the integral form which is useful in problems with a high degree of symmetry, we wrote

$$\oint \mathbf{H} \cdot d\mathbf{S} = \int \mathbf{J} \cdot \mathbf{n}\, dA$$

for those cases in which there were no time-changing electric fields present. The corresponding differential formulation, including the displacement-current density contribution, is

$$\nabla \times \mathbf{H} = \mathbf{J} + \dot{\mathbf{D}} \tag{2}$$

These first two relations specify the curl of the vectors $\mathbf{E}$ and $\mathbf{H}$. The divergence of the electric and magnetic field vectors is usually specified in terms of the $\mathbf{D}$ and $\mathbf{B}$ vectors. The divergence is specified by Gauss's law in unmodified form. In problems with a high degree of symmetry, we used Gauss's law in integral form

$$\oint \mathbf{D} \cdot \mathbf{n}\, dA = \int \rho\, dv$$

The differential formulation, which we later associated with the potential and called Poisson's equation, is Maxwell's third equation:

$$\nabla \cdot \mathbf{D} = \rho \tag{3}$$

The fourth equation also comes from Gauss's law, applied to the $\mathbf{B}$ vector of the magnetic field:

$$\nabla \cdot \mathbf{B} = 0 \tag{4}$$

Let us now list these relations in tabular form, including the source and the several forms in which they may be written. Such a listing is shown in the accompanying table.

Source	Circuit form	Integral form	Differential formulation
Faraday..........	$emf = -N \dfrac{d\phi}{dt}$	$\oint E \cdot dS = -\dfrac{d}{dt}\int B \cdot n\, dA$	$\nabla \times E = -\dot{B}$
Ampère..........	$mmf = NI$	$\oint H \cdot dS = \int (J + \dot{D}) \cdot n\, dA$	$\nabla \times H = J + \dot{D} = \gamma E + \epsilon \dfrac{\partial E}{\partial t}$
Gauss...........	....	$\oint D \cdot n\, dA = \int \rho\, dv$	$\nabla \cdot D = \rho$
Gauss and Ampère	....	$\oint B \cdot n\, dA = 0$	$\nabla \cdot B = 0$

Under the simplest conditions, the vector quantities are related at each point by three Ohm's-law-like equations:

$$J = \gamma E \qquad D = \epsilon E \qquad B = \mu H$$

We have investigated the methods of solution of the third relation, in the form of Poisson's equation. Our problem was to select a particular solution which met the boundary conditions imposed by our physical problem. The other three equations are subject to the same interpretation. They are solved by associating them with both scalar and vector potentials. The potentials are obtained first, and the field quantities evaluated by differentiation. In the next chapter we shall introduce the concept of vector potential.

REFERENCES

1. Heaviside, Oliver: "Electromagnetic Theory," pp. 33–36, Dover Publications, Inc., New York, 1950.
2. Milne-Thomson, L. M.: "Theoretical Hydrodynamics," 2d ed., pp. 45–49, The Macmillan Company, New York, 1949.
3. Jordan, E. C.: "Electromagnetic Waves and Radiating Systems," pp. 12–18, Prentice-Hall, Inc., New York, 1950.
4. Skilling, H. H.: "Fundamentals of Electric Waves," 2d ed., pp. 23–36, John Wiley & Sons, Inc., New York, 1948.
5. Ware, Lawrence A.: "Elements of Electromagnetic Waves," pp. 32–37, Pitman Publishing Corp., New York, 1949.
6. Cullwick, E. G.: "The Fundamentals of Electro-magnetism," The Macmillan Company, New York, 1939.

References 2 to 5 contain physical interpretations of curl. Reference 6 discusses the limitations of the macroscopic formulation of Faraday's law in considerable detail.

PROBLEMS

*10.1 A ring of radius a and conductance G is placed in a time-changing magnetic field which is perpendicular to the plane of the ring and constant in magnitude over the plane surface. Ignoring the magnetic field of the current in the ring, find the current in the ring. Is there a charge separation and its accompanying electrostatic field? Can potentials be assigned to points on the ring?

*10.2   In Prob. 10.1, replace the ring with a circular disk of radius a, thickness t, and conductivity γ. Find the induced field intensity and the current density at every point in the disk, and the total current. To what magnetostatics problem is this analogous? Does the problem have a practical application?

10.3   A simplified water wheel consists of four planes of width $2a$ intersecting in a small hub, thus placing a plane "paddle" every 45° around the hub. Place the hub across and at the surface of a stream which exerts a horizontal force which is independent of the depth and also independent of the velocity of the paddles. Under these simplified conditions, evaluate the line integral of the normal force per unit area around the closed path followed by a point on one of the paddles (see Fig. 10.3a).

*10.4   In a river 10 meters in depth, the velocity varies uniformly from zero at the bottom to 2 meters per second at the top. Find the curl of the velocity vector. What is its value at the surface? Sketch the field, letting the length of the line segment represent the magnitude of the vector. Assuming that the stream can exert forces directly proportional to the velocity, sketch the traces of the surfaces of no work which are perpendicular to the forces. Are these surfaces equipotential surfaces, and if not, why not?

*10.5   An infinite conducting plane parallel to the yz plane and of thickness $2d$ carries a steady current of uniform density along k. Using Ampere's circuital law, find the magnetic field inside the plane. Sketch the field and compare with Prob. 10.4 above.

10.6   Find the differential equation which relates the curl of a vector to its components in cylindrical coordinates by applying the analytical methods of Fig. 10.5b to this special case, rather than by substituting the appropriate metric coefficients into Eq. 10.5(10).

*10.7   Using the formula for computing curl in general orthogonal coordinates, write out the determinant form in cylindrical and spherical coordinates. Simplify the results as far as possible, and be sure to replace all the general notations with the appropriate values in these specific systems. With the help of these results, find the curl of the following vectors: (a) the individual unit vectors of three coordinate systems; (b) $y\,\mathbf{i}$; (c) $y\,\mathbf{i} - x\,\mathbf{j}$; (d) $y\,\mathbf{i} + x\,\mathbf{j}$; (e) the velocity of a point on a wheel.

*10.8   By expansion in cartesian coordinates, verify the identities

$$\nabla \cdot (\nabla \times \mathbf{A}) = 0$$

and

$$\nabla \times (\nabla V) = 0$$

10.9   Write Maxwell's equations in terms of the $\mathbf{B}$ and $\mathbf{E}$ vectors alone for an evacuated region free of charges.

*10.10   Letting the length of the line segments represent the magnitude, sketch the fields of (a) $\mathbf{F} = \mathbf{i} \sin y$; (b) $\mathbf{G} = \nabla \times \mathbf{F}$, where $\mathbf{F}$ is given in (a).

CHAPTER 11

VECTOR POTENTIAL

In this chapter we shall associate a vector potential with the magneto-static field. It is the purpose of this book to present only those aspects of the concept which are the easiest to understand on first contact with the subject. This is done in the hope that the reader will turn from this book to more advanced material with a feeling of confidence in his understanding of vector potential.

11.1 Energy Functions and Potential Functions. Throughout this book the new concepts have been introduced as easier ways of solving problems. We first learned a little vector-analysis shorthand and gained some experience in expressing some of our everyday experiences in the language of this shorthand. We then began our study of electrostatics in terms of a single experimental relationship, Coulomb's law. We learned how to describe a vector field in terms of electric-field intensity. We learned that the Coulomb's-law approach to field problems was physically satisfying but mathematically difficult.

In seeking easier ways of solving problems, we "invented" some scalar concepts which were easier to handle than vector quantities, and the first of these scalar concepts was electrostatic scalar potential. Fortunately the relationship between the scalar potential and the field intensity was readily obtained from energy considerations. There it was possible to discuss the potential in terms of the work done by the forces of the field, and this added enough physical reality to the concept to enable us to accept it and proceed to use it without asking too much in the way of explanation. Regardless of the simplicity of the relationship between the electrostatic potential and the field intensity expressed by the differential equation

$$dV = -\mathbf{E} \cdot d\mathbf{S} \tag{1}$$

we must recall our viewpoint that if this is all we know about the potential, there is very little excuse for its existence. Our purpose is to find the $\mathbf{E}$ vector, and if this is known already, we do not need the potential very much in electrostatics. We learned to find the potential distribution in other ways, and then to find the field intensity from the potential by taking its gradient, a process of differentiation. Of all the methods of finding the potential function, using Laplace's equation and Poisson's equation is probably the most basic and certainly the most direct. An engineer establishes a field by making connections to a source of energy and thus establishes the boundary conditions which the Laplacian solution must satisfy. He frequently neither knows nor cares what the distribution of charge is, and the Coulomb's-law approach requires that the charge distribution be known before the problem can be started.

One of the reasons why the scalar potential proved readily acceptable to us is because of long familiarity with the concept of energy and long experience in working mechanics problems and the like. As a bookkeeping tool, the concept of energy has so pervaded our economic life that people in all walks of life feel perfectly familiar with it. The accountant, the housewife, the mechanic, and the politician speak glibly of kilowatt-hours and horsepower. Engineers and physicists learn to draw field maps and to think of the equipotential lines as pictures of the potential—but no one has drawn a picture of energy itself, and who can? He who has not thought of the truly abstract basis of the energy concept should try to explain it to a child and then perhaps overhear the story as the child retells it to his playmates.

For the purpose of analogy in introducing vector potential, the following review is made of electrostatic potential. Because the electric field was defined in terms of a physically measurable force, and the forces must satisfy the conservation of energy, it is possible to associate with the field an energy function known as the potential. Mathematically this requires that the line integral of the forces be independent of the path, that the line integral around closed paths be zero, and that the curl of the electric field intensity be zero. In vector-analysis shorthand, we say that since

$$\mathbf{\nabla} \times \mathbf{E} = 0 \tag{2}$$

it is possible to define a scalar function V such that

$$\mathbf{E} = -\mathbf{\nabla}V \tag{3}$$

Of the many ways of finding the potential function V, we here record the two which lead us to the vector-potential concept. The first is the integral formulation, Eq. 3.6 (4),

$$V = \int \frac{\rho \, dv}{4\pi\epsilon R} \tag{4}$$

and the second is Poisson's equation, Eq. 8.5 (5),

$$\mathbf{\nabla}^2 V = -\frac{\rho}{\epsilon} \tag{5}$$

11.2 The Relationship between Magnetostatic Vector Potential and the Field Vectors. In a mathematical study of physical science there ultimately comes a point at which it is necessary to stop drawing pictures and making physical models to explain mathematical concepts. One gains confidence and learns to accept the mathematics by applying it to problems. Most of the writers on field theory stop drawing pictures and making physical models at the concept of curl, and those who do not stop there almost invariably omit pictures of vector potential. Vector potential may be explained briefly and succinctly by mathematics alone, and its utility in solving problems provides familiarity through use. However, this is seldom satisfactory at the outset of one's experience, and we shall find it possible to draw some pictures of vector potential. It is the mathematical significance which is important, and pictures and models are just to assist our understanding. In what follows we shall speak of magnetostatic vector potential to indicate that we are not considering displacement currents. We shall, however, apply the results to slowly varying fields in which radiation is negligible. To further simplify matters we shall not consider ferromagnetic materials.

The magnetic-field vectors are not parallel to the force on charges but are perpendicular to them. Hence the magnetic-field vectors need not satisfy that mathematics peculiar to conservative fields. The curl of the **H** vector is given in the differential formulation form of Ampère's circuital law as

$$\mathbf{\nabla \times H = J} \tag{1}$$

Since the **H** and **B** vectors do not have line integrals independent of the path, in general, we cannot establish a scalar potential function ψ except in regions containing no currents. We could try to relate a potential function ψ to the **H** vector by

$$\mathbf{H} = -\mathbf{\nabla}\psi \tag{2}$$

as we did in electrostatics. If we do this, we find that there is a contradiction with the nature of the field in current-carrying regions. Taking the curl of Eq. (2) gives us a result which is identically zero

$$\mathbf{\nabla \times H = \nabla \times} (-\mathbf{\nabla}\psi) = 0 \tag{3}$$

because the curl of the gradient of single-valued scalar potential functions is always zero.

It would be very convenient to have a potential concept which is frequently easier to find than the magnetic-field vectors, and which will yield the magnetic vectors by a process of differentiation. Though the gradient operation fails us here, we still have the curl operation available to produce a vector by a process of differentiation. This suggests to us that we may be able to find a vector potential which will yield the magnetic vectors when we take its curl. This would relate the vector potential **A** and the magnetic field vectors by the equation

$$\mathbf{H} = \nabla \times \mathbf{A} \tag{4}$$

There is another suggestion for a vector potential in Maxwell's form of Faraday's law.

$$\nabla \times \mathbf{E} = -\frac{\partial \mathbf{B}}{\partial t} \tag{5}$$

When we look at this equation closely, we are apt to pursue this line of reasoning: "I know what **E** is; I have some experience with it through solving problems and drawing field maps. I know what **B** is for the same reason. I would like to be able to compute **E** from **B**, but this one of Maxwell's equations is not in the form I wish it were, because even though I know **B** and can differentiate it with respect to time, this equation does not give me the **E** vector but gives me its curl. I am not as interested in its curl as in the vector itself. Isn't there some vector associated with the magnetic field which will give me the **E** vector directly?"

If the magnetic field had a vector quantity **A**, such that

$$\mathbf{E} = -\frac{\partial \mathbf{A}}{\partial t} \tag{6}$$

then taking the curl of both sides would give

$$\nabla \times \mathbf{E} = -\frac{\partial}{\partial t}(\nabla \times \mathbf{A}) \tag{7}$$

and in order to satisfy Eq. (5) the **A** vector would be related to the **B** vector through

$$\mathbf{B} = \nabla \times \mathbf{A} \tag{8}$$

On comparing Eqs. (4) and (8), we seem to have a choice between relating **A** to either **B** or **H** directly. Under the simplest conditions, when we can write $\mathbf{B} = \mu\mathbf{H}$ and μ is a constant, either is satisfactory. Because the equations in the next six sections will be made slightly more compact by doing so, we shall use Eq. (4) in what follows. We could not make this choice if we were considering ferromagnetic materials. It would be necessary to use Eq. (8). If we take the divergence of both Eqs. (4) and (8), on the right-hand side we have the divergence of the curl, and this is identically zero. For Eq. (8), this result is not in conflict with a requirement given by Maxwell's equation $\nabla \cdot \mathbf{B} = 0$. On the other hand, when nonlinear materials or permanent magnets are present, the divergence of **H** is not zero.

In examining Eq. (4) we are led to inquire whether or not we can compute the vector potential **A** when we know the field vector **H**, just as we first computed the scalar potential V, from a known vector **E** through

$$V = \int - \mathbf{E} \cdot d\mathbf{S} + \text{a constant} \tag{9}$$

We can do this, after a fashion, by equating the components of the two vectors of Eq. (4) in a system of coordinates. In cartesian coordinates, expansion of Eq. (4) gives the scalar equations

$$H_x = \frac{\partial A_z}{\partial y} - \frac{\partial A_y}{\partial z} \tag{10}$$

$$H_y = \frac{\partial A_x}{\partial z} - \frac{\partial A_z}{\partial x} \tag{11}$$

$$H_z = \frac{\partial A_y}{\partial x} - \frac{\partial A_x}{\partial y} \tag{12}$$

These partial differential equations are not easy to solve for **A**. One of the difficulties is that there is no simple recipe or formula for driving the answer out of them. Another difficulty is that there are no unique solutions, so we have to select one which suits our purpose.

As an illustration, consider a uniform magnetic field of 1 ampere per meter, directed along the x axis.

$$H_x = 1 \qquad H_y = 0 \qquad H_z = 0$$

For this case, Eqs. (10) to (12) become

$$\frac{\partial A_z}{\partial y} - \frac{\partial A_y}{\partial z} = 1 \tag{13}$$

$$\frac{\partial A_x}{\partial z} - \frac{\partial A_z}{\partial x} = 0 \tag{14}$$

$$\frac{\partial A_y}{\partial x} - \frac{\partial A_x}{\partial y} = 0 \tag{15}$$

Now to guide us in our selection from the many solutions of these equations, we can explore this field with the electrical engineer's curl meter—a plane loop connected to an ideal voltmeter. If

$$\mathbf{H} = \nabla \times \mathbf{A}$$

then the curl meter must be placed with the normal to the loop along the x axis as in Fig. 10.4a, to which reference should now be made. Since the curl is the circulation per unit area, the circulation of the **A** vector can arise from differences in its magnitude in the sides ab and cd, or in sides bc and ad, or both. Suppose we assume that **A** has the same magnitude in sides bc and ad. Mathematically, we are assuming that A_z is a constant, and we can just as well make that constant zero. Further, any x component of **A** cannot contribute to the circulation when the loop is normal to the x axis, so we can just as well set A_x equal to zero also. The curl-meter viewpoint has helped us to simplify our equations to

$$\frac{\partial A_y}{\partial z} = -1 \tag{16}$$

$$\frac{\partial A_y}{\partial x} = 0 \tag{17}$$

We are now one equation short of our needs, since we have no information about the rate of change of the y component of $\mathbf{A}$ with respect to y. Help now comes from considering the divergence of A. There is a theorem due to Helmholtz which states that a vector is specified when its

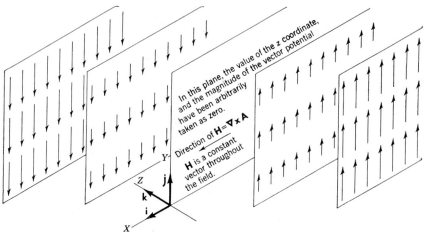

In this plane, the value of the z coordinate, and the magnitude of the vector potential have been arbitrarily taken as zero.

Direction of $\mathbf{H} = \mathbf{\nabla} \times \mathbf{A}$

$\mathbf{H}$ is a constant vector throughout the field.

FIG. 11.1   The vector potential of a uniform magnetic field directed along the x axis. The vector potential, $\mathbf{A} = -z\,\mathbf{j}$, has a constant magnitude in the planes, $z = $ a constant. In this illustration, the length of the line segment represents the magnitude of the vector.

divergence and curl are specified.   Here we have no concern about the divergence of A; any divergence will do, so we can just as well set it equal to zero.   Since

$$\mathbf{\nabla} \cdot \mathbf{A} = \frac{\partial A_x}{\partial x} + \frac{\partial A_y}{\partial y} + \frac{\partial A_z}{\partial z} = 0 \tag{18}$$

and we have set A_x and A_z equal to zero, then Eq. (18) gives us

$$\frac{\partial A_y}{\partial y} = 0 \tag{19}$$

Equations (17) and (19) tell us that A_y is not a function of x or y, and therefore Eq. (16) is a total differential equation

$$\frac{dA_y}{dz} = -1 \tag{20}$$

This integrates at once to

$$A_y = -z + C \tag{21}$$

The arbitrary constant cannot affect the curl of **A**, so if we set it equal to zero we have finally

$$A_x = 0 \qquad A_y = -z \qquad A_z = 0 \tag{22}$$

To this solution we could add any other vector whose curl is zero. We have selected, however, one of the simplest vector potentials, and we can draw a sketch of it rather easily. In all planes parallel to the xy plane it appears as in Fig. 11.1. The student should compare this with his solution to Prob. 3.6 for the corresponding problem in electrostatics.

What we have been doing here is not a practical use for the vector potential, and except for the possibility that it can enhance our understanding of the concept, there is little excuse for trying to find **A** from the equation

$$\nabla \times \mathbf{A} = \mathbf{H}$$

for if we know **H** already, there is little need for knowing **A**. What we really want to do is to find **A** from the current distribution so we can compute **H** from **A** by differentiation.

11.3 The Vector Potential from Poisson's Equation. We have stated that the most powerful method of obtaining the electrostatic scalar potential is to solve Poisson's equation or Laplace's equation. We shall now examine the possibility of obtaining the magnetic vector potential from Poisson's equation. If we define the relationship between the vector potential and the field vectors through Eq. (4) of the previous section

$$\mathbf{H} = \nabla \times \mathbf{A} \tag{1}$$

and substitute into Maxwell's form of Ampère's circuital law for the static case, we have

$$\nabla \times (\nabla \times \mathbf{A}) = \mathbf{J} \tag{2}$$

Now the curl of the curl of a vector is something we have not met before. It involves successive applications of the operator to yield a vector whose components are a function of the second partial derivatives of the components of the original vector. Fortunately we do not need to deal with the curl of the curl directly because we can convert it to another form which is quite easy to interpret. If one expands the left-hand side of Eq. (2) in cartesian coordinates, he obtains the difference of two vectors. The expansion gives

$$\nabla \times \nabla \times \mathbf{A} = \left[\mathbf{i} \left(\frac{\partial^2 A_x}{\partial x^2} + \frac{\partial^2 A_y}{\partial x\,\partial y} + \frac{\partial^2 A_z}{\partial x\,\partial z} \right) + \mathbf{j} \left(\frac{\partial^2 A_x}{\partial x\,\partial y} + \frac{\partial^2 A_y}{\partial y^2} + \frac{\partial^2 A_z}{\partial y\,\partial z} \right) \right.$$
$$+ \mathbf{k} \left(\frac{\partial^2 A_x}{\partial x\,\partial z} + \frac{\partial^2 A_y}{\partial y\,\partial z} + \frac{\partial^2 A_z}{\partial z^2} \right) \right] - \left[\mathbf{i} \left(\frac{\partial^2 A_x}{\partial x^2} + \frac{\partial^2 A_x}{\partial y^2} + \frac{\partial^2 A_x}{\partial z^2} \right) \right.$$
$$\left. + \mathbf{j} \left(\frac{\partial^2 A_y}{\partial x^2} + \frac{\partial^2 A_y}{\partial y^2} + \frac{\partial^2 A_y}{\partial z^2} \right) + \mathbf{k} \left(\frac{\partial^2 A_z}{\partial x^2} + \frac{\partial^2 A_z}{\partial y^2} + \frac{\partial^2 A_z}{\partial z^2} \right) \right] \tag{3}$$

The first of the two vectors on the right may be obtained by taking the gradient of the divergence of the original vector.   The second of the two vectors on the right in Eq. (3) has components suggestive of the Laplacian operator.   The shorthand notation for this vector is the Laplacian operator applied to a vector, $\nabla^2\mathbf{A}$.   Reverting to shorthand again, we write Eq. (3) in the form of a famous identity of vector analysis

$$\nabla \times (\nabla \times \mathbf{A}) = \nabla(\nabla \cdot \mathbf{A}) - \nabla^2\mathbf{A} \tag{4}$$

Many vectors have the same curl, and we cannot specify a vector function by defining its curl alone.   For magnetostatics or slowly varying fields, we again make the simplest choice and specify that the vector $\mathbf{A}$ have zero divergence.   We may then substitute from Eq. (4) into Eq. (2) to write Maxwell's form of Ampère's circuital law in terms of the vector potential as

$$\nabla^2\mathbf{A} = -\mathbf{J} \tag{5}$$

Mathematically this is very similar to Poisson's equation except that vectors are involved instead of scalars.

To make clear what we mean by the Laplacian operator applied to a vector, we shall again expand in cartesian coordinates, transpose the minus sign, and obtain three scalar equations by equating the components of the vectors in Eq. (5)

$$\frac{\partial^2 A_x}{\partial x^2} + \frac{\partial^2 A_x}{\partial y^2} + \frac{\partial^2 A_x}{\partial z^2} = -J_x \tag{6}$$

$$\frac{\partial^2 A_y}{\partial x^2} + \frac{\partial^2 A_y}{\partial y^2} + \frac{\partial^2 A_y}{\partial z^2} = -J_y \tag{7}$$

$$\frac{\partial^2 A_z}{\partial x^2} + \frac{\partial^2 A_z}{\partial y^2} + \frac{\partial^2 A_z}{\partial z^2} = -J_z \tag{8}$$

Each of these relations is in the form of Poisson's equation.   The importance of this lies in the fact that the components of the vector potential may be found by the methods of electrostatics.   We see that every magnetostatic problem has an analogy in electrostatics, and the solution to the magnetostatic problem may sometimes be found rather easily by solving the corresponding problem in electrostatics.   We further may employ the theorem of uniqueness to justify obtaining the solution to the electrostatics problem in any way we wish, and this includes such techniques as Coulomb's law, Gauss's law, the method of images, circuit techniques, or direct integration.

Before summarizing the mathematical steps of this discussion, it is suggested that the reader refer to the summary of the mathematical steps described in Sec. 11.1 so that he may see their similarity with the following, which are the key steps in relating the vector potential $\mathbf{A}$ to its sources:

1. We associate a vector potential $\mathbf{A}$ with the magnetic vector $\mathbf{H}$ through the relation

$$\mathbf{H} = \boldsymbol{\nabla} \times \mathbf{A} \tag{1}$$

2. We relate the vector $\mathbf{A}$ to its sources rather than to the $\mathbf{H}$ vector through Maxwell's form of Ampère's circuital law for magnetostatics

$$\boldsymbol{\nabla} \times \mathbf{H} = \mathbf{J}$$

which yields

$$\boldsymbol{\nabla} \times \boldsymbol{\nabla} \times \mathbf{A} = \mathbf{J} \tag{2}$$

3. From an identity of vector analysis, we write Eq. (2) as

$$\boldsymbol{\nabla}(\boldsymbol{\nabla} \cdot \mathbf{A}) - \boldsymbol{\nabla}^2 \mathbf{A} = \mathbf{J}$$

4. If we now specify that

$$\boldsymbol{\nabla} \cdot \mathbf{A} = 0$$

the relationship between the vector potential and its sources is

$$\boldsymbol{\nabla}^2 \mathbf{A} = -\mathbf{J} \tag{5}$$

This relation allows us to compute the components of $\mathbf{A}$ from Poisson's equation or by any of the methods of electrostatics. Examples of such computations follow.

11.4   Vector Potential of a Current Element.   When we began our study of electrostatics we first described the field of the simplest possible configuration of charge, a point charge. The simplest possible configuration of current is a hypothetical current element, which is a differential length of a small current-carrying wire. We shall find its vector potential and its magnetic field, and draw a picture of its vector potential field. For convenience we shall place the current element at the origin of our coordinate system and let the z axis coincide with the direction of the current element. The z component of the vector potential is given by an equation similar to Poisson's equation, Sec. 11.3, Eq. (8).

$$\frac{\partial^2 A_z}{\partial x^2} + \frac{\partial^2 A_z}{\partial y^2} + \frac{\partial^2 A_z}{\partial z^2} = -J_z \tag{1}$$

Poisson's equation for electrostatics is

$$\frac{\partial^2 V}{\partial x^2} + \frac{\partial^2 V}{\partial y^2} + \frac{\partial^2 V}{\partial z^2} = -\frac{\rho}{\epsilon_0} \tag{2}$$

Now we know the electrostatic scalar potential V, due to a point charge, and that it satisfies Eq. (2). From Chap. 3, the potential of a point charge is

$$V = \frac{Q}{4\pi\epsilon_0 R} \tag{3}$$

The magnitude of the point charge is the charge density ρ times the volume of the point charge dv. This allows us to write Eq. (3) as

$$V = \frac{\rho \, dv}{4\pi\epsilon_0 R} \tag{4}$$

In terms of the variables of the magnetostatics problem, to convert the form of Eq. (2) to that of Eq. (1) requires only the change of variables

$$V = A_z \tag{5}$$

and

$$\frac{\rho}{\epsilon_0} = J_z \tag{6}$$

Substituting these new variables into Eq. (4), the solution to Eq. (1) is

$$A_z = \frac{J_z \, dv}{4\pi R} \tag{7}$$

The current density in the current element is its total current I divided by its cross-sectional area a. (Here we use the lower-case letter to avoid confusion with the vector potential symbol.)

$$J = \frac{I}{a}$$

The volume of the differential current element is

$$dv = a \, dL$$

In terms of these quantities, Eq. (7) becomes

$$A_z = \frac{I \, dL}{4\pi R} \qquad A_x = 0 \qquad A_y = 0 \tag{8}$$

To justify setting the x and y components of $\mathbf{A}$ equal to zero as we have done in Eq. (8), the following statements are made. Just as we could add any arbitrary constant to Eq. (4), to this solution we could also add any other solution which satisfies Laplace's equation, not Poisson's equation. All such solutions are independent of the presence or absence of the current element itself. They represent the contributions of sources other than our current element, and what we seek is that potential due to the current element alone. The vector potential due to the current element may be written in the vector equation

$$\mathbf{A} = \frac{I \, dL}{4\pi R} \mathbf{k} \tag{9}$$

The magnitude of this vector at every point in space is the same as the magnitude of the scalar potential of an equivalent point charge. The direction of the vector coincides with that of the current element and is the same throughout all space. This is illustrated in Fig. 11.2. The reader may easily construct a model of this vector field by inserting a number of pins into a tennis ball in such a manner that all the pins are parallel (not perpendicular to its surface).

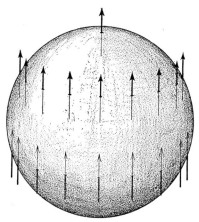

FIG. 11.2 In the magnetic field of a differential current element, the locus of all points whose vector potential is a constant is a sphere whose center coincides with the location of the current element. The vector potential is directed along the current element. Compare with the concentric spherical surfaces of equipotential in the electric field of a point charge (Fig. 3.4). A model of this figure may be constructed by pushing a number of pins into a tennis ball in such a way that the pins are all parallel.

We shall now find the **H** vector by taking the curl of the vector potential **A**. To do this we shall write Eq. (9) in spherical coordinates. The needed relations between the unit vectors were listed in Sec. 1.14:

$$\mathbf{k} \cdot \mathbf{r} = \cos\theta$$
$$\mathbf{k} \cdot \boldsymbol{\theta} = -\sin\theta$$
$$\mathbf{k} \cdot \boldsymbol{\phi} = 0$$

The expression for the vector potential of Eq. (9) in spherical coordinates is then

$$\mathbf{A} = \frac{I\,dL}{4\pi}\left(\frac{\cos\theta}{R}\,\mathbf{r} - \frac{\sin\theta}{R}\,\boldsymbol{\theta}\right) \tag{10}$$

Taking the curl to find **H** gives

$$\mathbf{H} = \boldsymbol{\nabla} \times \mathbf{A} = \frac{I\,dL}{4\pi R^2}\sin\theta\,\boldsymbol{\phi} \tag{11}$$

An inspection of Fig. 1.10 reveals that

$$\mathbf{k} \times \mathbf{r} = \sin\theta\,\boldsymbol{\phi} \tag{12}$$

Equation (11) may therefore be written in the form

$$\mathbf{H} = \frac{I}{4\pi R^2} (d\mathbf{L} \times \mathbf{r}) \tag{13}$$

This is the law of Biot and Savart. We were unable to derive this law from more elementary considerations, and the use of the vector potential is probably the easiest way to derive it.

11.5   Integral Formulation of the Relation of Vector Potential to Its Sources.   We obtained an integral formulation of the relationship between the electrostatic scalar potential and the charges which produced it by considering any charge configuration to be made up of equivalent point charges. We found that the potential at a point due to a single point charge was

$$V = \frac{Q}{4\pi\epsilon_0 R} \tag{1}$$

and that the potential due to several point charges could be written

$$V = \frac{Q_1}{4\pi\epsilon_0 R_1} + \frac{Q_2}{4\pi\epsilon_0 R_2} + \cdots + \frac{Q_n}{4\pi\epsilon_0 R_n} \tag{2}$$

For a continuous distribution of charge throughout a whole region, we extended Eq. (2) to the integral form

$$V = \int \frac{\rho\, dv}{4\pi\epsilon_0 R} \tag{3}$$

where the integral sign tells us that, to compute the potential at a point in space, we are to find the scalar sum of the contributions of all the little point charges.

Previous to this we had also established an integral formulation for a vector, the electric-field intensity. We found that the field intensity due to a single point charge was

$$\mathbf{E} = \frac{Q}{4\pi\epsilon_0 R^2} \mathbf{r} \tag{4}$$

where $\mathbf{r}$ is a unit vector drawn from the point charge to the point at which the field is described. For several such point charges we wrote the expression for the field intensity as the summation of the vectors

$$\mathbf{E} = \frac{Q_1}{4\pi\epsilon_0 R_1{}^2} \mathbf{r}_1 + \frac{Q_2}{4\pi\epsilon_0 R_2{}^2} \mathbf{r}_2 + \cdots + \frac{Q_n}{4\pi\epsilon_0 R_n{}^2} \mathbf{r}_n \tag{5}$$

To cover distributed charges we wrote Eq. (5) as

$$\mathbf{E} = \int \frac{\rho\, dv}{4\pi\epsilon_0 R^2} \mathbf{r} \tag{6}$$

in which the integration, a process of addition, is a vector integration, involving a summation of the components separately, as in Chap. 2.

Let us extend this kind of thinking. We have found that the vector potential due to a single current element is

$$\mathbf{A} = \frac{I\, d\mathbf{L}}{4\pi R} \tag{7}$$

or the alternative form

$$\mathbf{A} = \frac{\mathbf{J}\, dv}{4\pi R} \tag{8}$$

For several such current elements, we can write the vector potential as the vector summation

$$\mathbf{A} = \frac{I_1\, d\mathbf{L}_1}{4\pi R_1} + \frac{I_2\, d\mathbf{L}_2}{4\pi R_2} + \cdots + \frac{I_n\, d\mathbf{L}_n}{4\pi R_n} \tag{9}$$

or in the alternative form

$$\mathbf{A} = \frac{\mathbf{J}_1\, dv}{4\pi R_1} + \frac{\mathbf{J}_2\, dv}{4\pi R_2} + \cdots + \frac{\mathbf{J}_n\, dv}{4\pi R_n} \tag{10}$$

For an infinite number of differential current elements, the corresponding integral formulations are

$$\mathbf{A} = \int \frac{I\, d\mathbf{L}}{4\pi R} \tag{11}$$

and

$$\mathbf{A} = \int \frac{\mathbf{J}\, dv}{4\pi R} \tag{12}$$

in which the integration, a process of addition, is a vector integration involving a summation of the components separately as in Eq. (6).

There is, however, another method of finding the components of $\mathbf{A}$ which is sometimes easier than evaluating Eqs. (11) and (12). Noting the similarity of each of the scalar summations of these components to the integral formulation of the electrostatic potential

$$V = \int \frac{\rho\, dv}{4\pi\epsilon_0 R} \tag{3}$$

we see that we do not have to evaluate the components if *we have already solved, or can solve, the corresponding problem in electrostatics.* If we know the value of Eq. (3) due to the corresponding charge configuration, we can obtain the value of Eq. (11) or (12), component by component, by a successive change of variables

$$\frac{\rho_1}{\epsilon_0} = J_x \qquad \frac{\rho_2}{\epsilon_0} = J_y \qquad \frac{\rho_3}{\epsilon_0} = J_z \tag{13}$$

This very interesting comparison tells us that, to find a component of the vector potential due to a given distribution of steady currents, we can set up the corresponding electrostatics problem, in which the charges have the same volume distribution as one of the components of the current. An example follows.

11.6   The Vector Potential of a Straight Wire, Infinitely Long. As an example of how we may find the vector potential in a magnetostatic problem by solving the corresponding problem in electrostatics we shall obtain the vector potential of a long straight wire. Let a round wire carry a total current I, and let the current density be uniform over its cross section. The corresponding problem in electrostatics will then be a cylindrical region containing a uniform volume charge density ρ. The electrostatics problem was solved by using Gauss's law in Sec. 5.4. For a wire of radius b, the electrostatic potential inside the cylinder was found as Eq. 5.4 (7):

$$V = - \frac{\rho R^2}{4\epsilon_0} \qquad R \lessgtr b \tag{1}$$

The potential outside the cylinder was Eq. 5.4 (11):

$$V = - \frac{b^2 \rho}{4\epsilon_0} - \frac{b^2 \rho}{2\epsilon_0} \log_e \frac{R}{b} \qquad R \gtrless b \tag{2}$$

Since the current-density vector has a single component, the vector potential will also have a single component, and both are along the wire. Taking this direction as along the positive z axis of cylindrical coordinates and substituting into Eqs. (1) and (2), the variables

$$V = A_z$$

and

$$\frac{\rho}{\epsilon_0} = J_z$$

as in the previous section, the vector potential becomes

$$A_z = - \frac{J_z R^2}{4} \qquad R \lessgtr b \tag{3}$$

inside the wire, and

$$A_z = - \frac{b^2 J_z}{4} - \frac{b^2 J_z}{2} \log_e \frac{R}{b} \qquad R \gtrless b \tag{4}$$

outside the wire. In terms of the total current I, we have the equivalent expressions

$$A_z = \frac{-I}{4\pi b^2} R^2 \qquad R \lessgtr b \tag{5}$$

and

$$A_z = \frac{-I}{4\pi} - \frac{I}{2\pi} \log_e \frac{R}{b} \qquad R \gtrless b \tag{6}$$

In order to find the magnetic field in terms of the **H** vector, we find the curl of the vector whose one component is given by Eqs. (5) and (6) respectively.

$$\mathbf{H} = \boldsymbol{\nabla} \times \mathbf{A} = \frac{IR}{2\pi b^2} \, \boldsymbol{\theta} \qquad R \lessgtr b \qquad (7)$$

and

$$\mathbf{H} = \boldsymbol{\nabla} \times \mathbf{A} = \frac{I}{2\pi R} \, \boldsymbol{\theta} \qquad R \gtrless b \qquad (8)$$

These results match those obtained in other ways in Sec. 9.10, Eqs. (9) and (2).

The surfaces in which the vector potential is constant in magnitude are concentric cylinders, as shown in Fig. 11.3. The magnitude of the vector

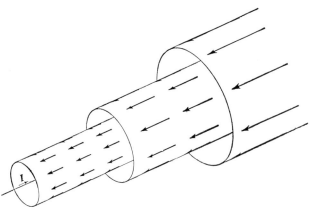

FIG. 11.3 In the magnetic field of a long straight wire, the vector potential is a constant in concentric cylinders. The reference level has been chosen at the center of the wire, so that the direction of the vector potential is opposite to that of the current, while the magnitude increases as the logarithm of the distance from the wire. Compare with the equipotential surfaces in the electric field of a charged line (Fig. 3.4).

potential as a function of position is the same as that of the electrostatics problem and is sketched in Fig. 5.5c, along with other interpretations, to which reference should now be made. The vector potential is oppositely directed to the current in the wire because we arbitrarily assigned its zero reference level to the center of the wire. For this same reason, the electrostatic potential was negative in Sec. 5.4.

11.7 Vector Potential of Two Round Wires, Infinitely Long, with Uniform Current Density. In the previous section we studied the vector potential field due to a single conductor, obtaining the results by analogy with the corresponding electrostatics problem of Sec. 5.4. The present study would have been shortened a good deal had we solved the electrostatic analogy in Chap. 5. There, however, our emphasis was on Gauss's law and the study of symmetry, rather than on extending the results by superposition.

Our choice of reference level at the center of the space charge is not convenient in the present case, because we cannot arbitrarily assign the zero potential level to two regions unless they happen to be at the same potential. We now assign the zero potential level to an arbitrary point at a distance R_0 from the center of a single cylinder of space charge. For

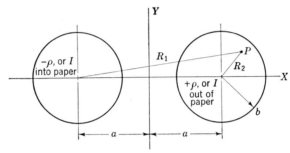

FIG. 11.4   Analysis of the vector potential due to equal currents, oppositely directed, in two round wires, infinitely long.

points inside the cylinder, we return to Eq. 5.4(6) and modify the limits of integration accordingly.

$$V = \frac{\lambda}{2\pi\epsilon_0}\left(\int_R^b \frac{R\,dR}{b^2} + \int_b^{R_0}\frac{dR}{R}\right) \qquad R \lessgtr b \qquad (1)$$

Integrating, substituting limits, and collecting, we obtain

$$V = \frac{\lambda}{4\pi\epsilon_0}\left(1 - \frac{R^2}{b^2} + 2\log_e\frac{R_0}{b}\right) \qquad R \lessgtr b \qquad (2)$$

From a similar analysis outside the cylinder, we obtain

$$V = \frac{\lambda}{2\pi\epsilon_0}\log_e\frac{R_0}{R} \qquad R \gtrless b \qquad (3)$$

For two cylinders, using the notation of Fig. 11.4 instead of that of Sec. 5.4, we have for points inside the right-hand cylinder, the sum of the potentials given by Eq. (2), and Eq. (3) with λ negative.

$$V = \frac{\lambda}{4\pi\epsilon_0}\left(1 - \frac{R_2^2}{b^2} + 2\log_e\frac{R_0}{b}\right) - \frac{\lambda}{2\pi\epsilon_0}\log_e\frac{R_0}{R_1} \qquad R_2 \lessgtr b \qquad (4)$$

Collecting the logarithmic terms,

$$V = \frac{\lambda}{4\pi\epsilon_0}\left(1 - \frac{R^2}{b^2} + \log_e\frac{R_1^2}{b^2}\right) \qquad R_2 \lessgtr b \qquad (5)$$

For points outside both cylinders, the sum of the potentials is

$$V = \frac{\lambda}{2\pi\epsilon_0} \log_e \frac{R_1}{R_2} \qquad R_1 \gtrless b, R_2 \gtrless b \qquad (6)$$

Observe the difference here between the points to which the distances are measured in comparison with the line charges of Chap. 3. There the distances were to be measured to the line charges; here the distances are measured to the center of the cylinders of space charge.

The corresponding vector potential has only a z component which is obtained by replacing the variables according to $J = \dfrac{\rho}{\epsilon_0}$ as in the previous section. This is equivalent to writing here

$$\frac{I}{2\pi} = \frac{\lambda}{2\pi\epsilon_0}$$

Then we have, for the vector potential in the magnetic field, the equations

$$A_z = \frac{I}{4\pi}\left(1 - \frac{R_2{}^2}{b^2} + \log_e \frac{R_1{}^2}{b^2}\right) \qquad R_2 \lessgtr b \qquad (7)$$

and

$$A_z = \frac{I}{2\pi} \log_e \frac{R_1}{R_2} \qquad R_1 \gtrless b, R_2 \gtrless b \qquad (8)$$

The surfaces in which the vector potential is constant coincide with the surfaces in which the electrostatic potential is a constant. Outside the regions of space charge or current, the equipotential surfaces are cylinders corresponding to those in the field of two line charges located at the *centers* of the cylinders of space charge. This is depicted in the isometric drawing, Fig. 11.5a.

Inside the wires, the equipotential surfaces are not circular cylinders, but surfaces of oval-shaped cross section whose equation is obtained by setting Eq. (7) equal to a constant. These surfaces are mapped in Fig. 11.5b, together with the stream lines of the corresponding electrostatics problem. The stream lines converge on, or diverge from, *kernels* which are displaced from the centers. These stagnation points represent a maximum of potential, and their location depends on the relative spacing and diameter of the wires, as detailed in the paragraph below. The field map of Fig. 11.5b is for the case in which the diameter of the wires is six-tenths of the spacing between centers.

From the symmetry, any maximum of potential must lie on the x axis, where $R_2 = a - x$ and $R_1 = a + x$. This reduces Eq. (7) to

$$A_z = \frac{I}{4\pi}\left(1 - \frac{(a-x)^2}{b^2} + \log_e \frac{(a+x)^2}{b^2}\right) \qquad (9)$$

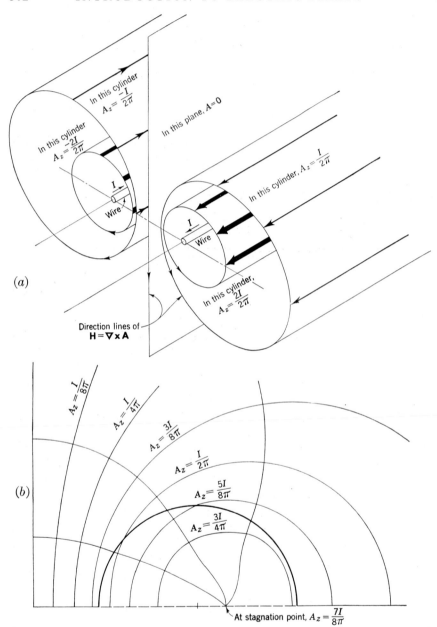

FIG. 11.5   Vector potential due to equal currents, oppositely directed, in two round wires, infinitely long.   Part *a* is an isometric drawing of the surfaces in which the vector potential is constant in magnitude, for regions outside the wires.   Part *b* shows the traces of the equipotential surfaces both inside and outside the wires, and it also shows three of the stream lines in the corresponding electrostatics problem meeting at the stagnation point or kernel, at which the potential is a maximum.   In part *a*, the width of the line segment represents the magnitude of the vector potential.

FIG. 11.6   Fluid-flow models of the stream lines in the electric field of cylindrical uniform space charges, (*above*) for the case of opposite polarities; (*below*) for the case of like polarities.   The stagnation points are on opposite sides of the centers of the cylinders.

Differentiating with respect to x and setting the result equal to zero gives the location of the maximum at

$$x = \sqrt{a^2 + b^2} \qquad (10)$$

for the case of equal and opposite currents. This is outside the center, at the kernel or stagnation point.

A fluid-flow map has been included as Fig. 11.6 to demonstrate the kernels. The two darker circular regions correspond to the current-carrying regions. The upper part of the figure is the map for a distributed source and sink, while the lower part maps the field of two distributed sources, corresponding to currents in the same direction. Observe that in the latter case the kernels are displaced in the opposite direction with respect to the centers of the circles.

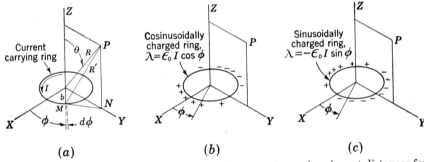

(a) $\qquad\qquad\qquad$ (b) $\qquad\qquad\qquad$ (c)

FIG. 11.7 Analysis of the vector potential of a current-carrying ring, at distances far from the ring. Parts b and c show the corresponding charged rings in an electrostatic analogy which is found in the analysis of the vector potential.

11.8 Vector Potential of a Differential Current Loop. We shall find the vector potential of a small plane loop, evaluating the integrals only in the case of vanishingly small loops. Let the z axis coincide with the axis of the loop, taken in the right-hand sense with respect to the current I. Because of symmetry about this axis, we can select a point in the yz plane for the analysis, as sketched in Fig. 11.7a. It will simplify matters if we evaluate the distance from the field point P to each part of the loop as a geometry problem, prior to beginning the analysis of the field. In the figure, we require the distance MP. This we shall obtain in terms of MN as a first step. From the law of cosines,

$$\overline{MN}^2 = R^2 \sin^2 \theta + b^2 - 2\,bR \sin \theta \cos\left(\frac{\pi}{2} - \phi\right) \qquad (1)$$

Expanding the last term,

$$\overline{MN}^2 = R^2 \sin^2 \theta + b^2 - 2\,bR \sin \theta \sin \phi \qquad (2)$$

Then, from the figure,

$$\overline{MP}^2 = \overline{MN}^2 + R^2 \cos^2 \theta = R^2 + b^2 - 2\,bR \sin \theta \sin \phi \qquad (3)$$

To obtain the vector potential, we shall require the value of $1/MP$ when $R \gg b$. Expanding by the binomial theorem and retaining only the first term,

$$\frac{1}{MP} = \frac{1}{R}\left(1 + \frac{b}{R}\sin\theta\sin\phi\right) \tag{4}$$

The vector potential due to each current element is

$$d\mathbf{A} = \frac{I\,d\mathbf{L}}{4\pi R'} = \frac{Ib\,d\phi}{4\pi R'}\boldsymbol{\phi} \tag{5}$$

where the prime on R' reminds us to use the distance to the current element MP. Resolving the vector potential $d\mathbf{A}$ into its x and y components,

$$dA_x = d\mathbf{A}\cdot\mathbf{i} = \frac{Ib\,d\phi}{4\pi R'}\boldsymbol{\phi}\cdot\mathbf{i} \tag{6}$$

$$dA_y = d\mathbf{A}\cdot\mathbf{j} = \frac{Ib\,d\phi}{4\pi R'}\boldsymbol{\phi}\cdot\mathbf{j} \tag{7}$$

Since $\boldsymbol{\phi}\cdot\mathbf{i} = -\sin\phi$ and $\boldsymbol{\phi}\cdot\mathbf{j} = \cos\phi$, Eqs. (6) and (7) may be written as

$$dA_x = \frac{-Ib\sin\phi\,d\phi}{4\pi R'} \tag{8}$$

$$dA_y = \frac{Ib\cos\phi\,d\phi}{4\pi R'} \tag{9}$$

At this point, we can help our understanding of the analysis, and save the evaluation of an integral in the bargain, by examining the equivalent electrostatics problems suggested by Eqs. (8) and (9). Equation (9) is mathematically identical to the equation which would arise in finding the scalar potential due to a charged ring of radius b and carrying a charge of density

$$\lambda = \epsilon_0 I \cos\phi \tag{10}$$

The charge configuration is shown in Fig. 11.7b, and because the point P is symmetrically located with respect to the charge distribution, the electrostatic potential at P would be zero. Correspondingly, Eq. (9) must vanish when integrated around the ring, and $A_y = 0$.

The charge configuration suggested by Eq. (8), on the other hand, is

$$\lambda = -\epsilon_0 I \sin\phi \tag{11}$$

This is shown in Fig. 11.7c. To evaluate Eq. (8), we substitute for R' from Eq. (4), writing

$$dA_x = \frac{-Ib\sin\phi}{4\pi R}\left(1 + \frac{b}{R}\sin\theta\sin\phi\right)d\phi \tag{12}$$

Integrating between the limits of 0 and 2π gives

$$A_x = \frac{-I\pi b^2}{4\pi R^2} \sin \theta \tag{13}$$

Let us now eliminate the restriction that the point P lie in the yz plane. One of the ways of doing this is to revert to the spherical coordinate system. Regardless of our choice of x axis, $\mathbf{A}$ must lie parallel to the xy plane and be perpendicular to the z axis and to the unit vector $\mathbf{r}$. Hence A must lie along $\boldsymbol{\phi}$. At a general point, then,

$$\mathbf{A} = \frac{I(\pi b^2)}{4\pi R^2} \sin \theta\, \boldsymbol{\phi} \tag{14}$$

To eliminate the restriction that the loop lie in the xy plane, we can use the magnetic moment of the loop $\mathbf{M}$, defined in Sec. 9.5, Eq. (12), as

$$\mathbf{M} = I(\pi b^2)\mathbf{n} \tag{15}$$

Here, $\mathbf{n} = \mathbf{k}$, and reference to Fig. 1.10 reveals that

$$\mathbf{k} \times \mathbf{r} = \sin \theta\, \boldsymbol{\phi} \tag{16}$$

Through Eqs. (15) and (16), we may write Eq. (14) as

$$\mathbf{A} = \frac{\mathbf{M} \times \mathbf{r}}{4\pi R^2} \tag{17}$$

This expression is similar in form to that for the scalar potential of an electric dipole of moment $\mathbf{P}$ as found in Sec. 3.11, Eq. (8):

$$V = \frac{\mathbf{P} \cdot \mathbf{r}}{4\pi \epsilon_0 R^2} \tag{18}$$

To map the field, it is convenient to retain the form of Eq. (14). The vector potential has a constant magnitude in the toroidal surfaces of revolution whose equation is

$$R^2 = C \sin \theta \tag{19}$$

where C is a constant. An isometric view of two such surfaces is shown in Fig. 11.8. The direction lines of $\mathbf{A}$ are circles around the axis of the loop.

As a problem, the student will be asked to obtain the magnetic-field vectors from the vector potential and to show that the direction lines of $\mathbf{H}$ have the same equation as the direction lines of $\mathbf{E}$ in the electric dipole field.

11.9 Coefficients of Inductance and Some Energy Considerations. The material presented in this section is familiar to those with a little experience in alternating-current circuit theory. In a following section we shall recast these formulations, as required by our present studies.

The interrelations of a circuit with its magnetic flux are investigated most easily by relating the induced emf to the currents which produce the flux, rather than by using Faraday's law directly. This is achieved through an intermediary called *coefficients of inductance*. With several circuits, the flux through each will be the scalar sum of that arising from

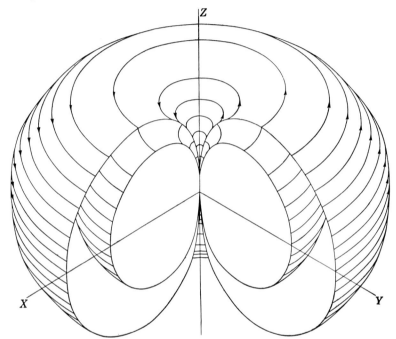

FIG. 11.8 Isometric drawing of two of the surfaces in which the vector potential is constant, in the magnetic field of a current-carrying ring, vanishing small. One quadrant has been cut away to show the cross section of the toroidal surfaces. The cross sections are not circles, but have the equation $R^2 = C \sin \theta$. The direction lines of the vector potential coincide with that of the current in the ring and are circles about the axis. The direction lines which are shown have been selected at equal increments of elevation above the ring, and thus correspond to contour lines on the equipotential surfaces.

the several currents. We shall use numbered subscripts to identify the various quantities associated with each circuit. The differential change in flux in circuit number 1 is

$$d\phi_1 = \frac{\partial \phi_1}{\partial I_1} dI_1 + \frac{\partial \phi_1}{\partial I_2} dI_2 + \cdot \cdot \cdot + \frac{\partial \phi_1}{\partial I_n} dI_n \qquad (1)$$

The partial derivatives are the coefficients of inductance. The coefficient of self-inductance is usually denoted by the letter L

$$L = \frac{\partial \phi_1}{\partial I_1} \tag{2}$$

The others are mutual coefficients denoted by the letter M.

$$M_{12} = \frac{\partial \phi_1}{\partial I_2}, \; \ldots \; , M_{1n} = \frac{\partial \phi_1}{\partial I_n} \tag{3}$$

This removes the flux from Faraday's law, which is now written as

$$\text{emf}_1 = - \left(L \frac{dI_1}{dt} + M_{12} \frac{dI_2}{dt} + \cdots + M_{1n} \frac{dI_n}{dt} \right) \tag{4}$$

In linear systems (those which do not contain ferromagnetic materials), the various contributions to the flux depend only on the geometry, and the coefficients of inductance are constants.

$$L_1 = \frac{\phi_{11}}{I_1} \tag{5}$$

$$M_{12} = \frac{\phi_{12}}{I_2}, \; \ldots \; , M_{1n} = \frac{\phi_{1n}}{I_n} \tag{6}$$

The double subscripts here introduced are interpreted as follows: the first subscript indicates the circuit through which the flux is evaluated, and the second indicates the circuit whose current is responsible for the contribution. Under the conditions of a linear system, the quantities in Eqs. (5) and (6) are known as self-inductances and mutual inductances, dropping the term coefficient.

By considering two closed circuits carrying steady currents I_1 and I_2, we may simultaneously relate the inductances to the energy and demonstrate the equivalence of the mutual coefficients which have the same subscripts. For the two circuits, we write Eq. (4) in the specific equations

$$\text{emf}_1 = - \left(L_1 \frac{dI_1}{dt} + M_{12} \frac{dI_2}{dt} \right) \tag{7}$$

$$\text{emf}_2 = - \left(M_{21} \frac{dI_1}{dt} + L_2 \frac{dI_2}{dt} \right) \tag{8}$$

Let us now find the energy exchanged in collapsing the field. We maintain I_2 constant by adjusting its source, thus holding its time derivatives at zero. We reduce I_1 to zero by short-circuiting its source. The work done by the magnetic field due to I_1 is

$$W' = \int_0^t (\text{emf}_1) I_1 \, dt + \int_0^t (\text{emf}_2) I_2 \, dt \tag{9}$$

This is readily evaluated by a change of variable from t to I from Eq. (7). The results are

$$W' = \tfrac{1}{2} L_1 I_1{}^2 + M_{21} I_2 I_1 \tag{10}$$

We now short-circuit the source of I_2, after having opened the circuit number 1 to keep its current at zero. The work done by the remainder of the field is found similarly as

$$W'' = \tfrac{1}{2} L_2 I_2{}^2 \tag{11}$$

The total energy is the sum of Eqs. (10) and (11):

$$W = \tfrac{1}{2} L_1 I_1{}^2 + M_{21} I_2 I_1 + \tfrac{1}{2} L_2 I_2{}^2 \tag{12}$$

Now, had we interchanged the order of operations, or changed the labels on the circuits, we should have obtained the mutual term M_{12} rather than M_{21}. Since the energy[1] must be the same in the two cases,

$$M_{21} = M_{12} \tag{13}$$

In Eq. (12) we attribute the terms containing L_1 and L_2 to the individual circuits as self-energy and the mutual term to the mutual energy, as suggested by Eq. (11).

For any number of circuits, Eq. (12) may be written in summation form

$$W = \frac{1}{2} \sum_{i=1}^{i=n} \sum_{j=1}^{j=n} M_{ij} I_i I_j \tag{14}$$

By this equation, we mean, for n circuits,

$$W = \tfrac{1}{2}(M_{11} I_1 I_1 + M_{12} I_1 I_2 + \cdots + M_{1n} I_1 I_n + M_{21} I_2 I_1$$
$$+ M_{22} I_2 I_2 + \cdots M_{2n} I_2 I_n + \cdots + M_{nn} I_n I_n) \tag{15}$$

The values of M with like subscripts are self-inductances. Since the terms involving two different subscripts will occur twice, the factor $\tfrac{1}{2}$ may be applied to all terms in the summation. The necessity for this is in accordance with the absence of the factor of $\tfrac{1}{2}$ in the central term of Eq. (12).

Utilizing the formulation of Eqs. (5) and (6) to relate the energy to the flux again, Eq. (15) may be written

$$W = \tfrac{1}{2}(\phi_{11} I_1 + \phi_{12} I_1 + \cdots + \phi_{1n} I_n + \phi_{21} I_2 + \phi_{22} I_2$$
$$+ \cdots + \phi_{2n} I_n + \cdots + \phi_{nn} I_n) \tag{16}$$

This is equivalent to

$$W = \tfrac{1}{2}(\phi_1 I_1 + \phi_2 I_2 + \cdots + \phi_n I_n) \tag{17}$$

and

$$W = \frac{1}{2} \sum_{i=1}^{i=n} \phi_i I_i \tag{18}$$

[1] A more formal demonstration is given in the following section.

By evaluating Eq. (18) in a uniform field, or in one in which the field vectors are easily determined from the geometry, we find that Eq. (18) may be expressed in terms of the field vectors by

$$W = \int \frac{1}{2} \mathbf{B} \cdot \mathbf{H} \, dv \qquad (19)$$

in complete analogy with the electrostatic case. This is subject to the interpretation that the energy is distributed throughout the field with an energy density of

$$w = \tfrac{1}{2}\mathbf{B} \cdot \mathbf{H} \qquad (20)$$

per unit volume. While the total energy is given by Eq. (19), the distribution interpretation is somewhat hypothetical and is not unique. We shall soon find another energy relation which is subject to the interpretation that the magnetic energy is confined to the current-carrying regions.

11.10   The Inductance of Circuits of Finite Cross Section, and Flux Linkages. Following the custom of the circuit approach, we defined coefficients of inductance and the self-inductance and mutual inductance without any regard as to how they might be calculated. Let us now consider this problem. For the self-inductance of a linear system we wrote, as Eq. (5) of the previous section,

$$L = \frac{\phi}{I} \qquad (1)$$

To evaluate this, consider the problem of evaluating the flux from the **B** vector:

$$\phi = \int \mathbf{B} \cdot \mathbf{n} \, da \qquad (2)$$

We are required to bound the area of the surface of integration with a line which is a closed curve. If the circuit is formed by a wire of finite cross section, we are unable to say just which part of the wire forms the boundary of the surface of integration. If the wire is round, we might consider it plausible that the center of the wire bounds the area. We could also justify the statement that, if the wire is small compared to the other dimensions in the circuit, the whole argument is numerically unimportant. More generally, it is necessary to redefine our concepts of inductance.

We retain the energy formulation for self-inductance, Eq. 11.9 (11):

$$W = \tfrac{1}{2}LI^2 \qquad (3)$$

We combine this with the expression for the total energy of any number of circuits, Eq. 11.9 (18):

$$W = \frac{1}{2} \sum_{i=1}^{i=n} \phi_i I_i \qquad (4)$$

Our task now becomes that of computing the self-energy and mutual energy of the circuit, considering it as made up of an infinite number of current filaments or current tubes, each of which carries an equal share of the total current dI. One such current filament is diagrammed in Fig. 11.9, for a part of a closed circuit of finite cross section. Equation (4)

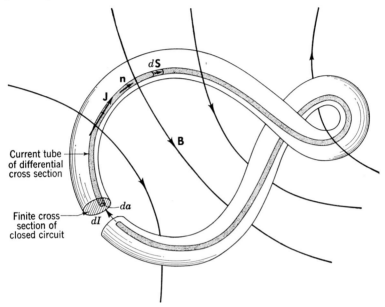

FIG. 11.9   For discussion of the problem of evaluating the inductance of a circuit of finite cross section. The inductance is found by evaluating the self and mutual inductances of current tubes of differential cross section, one of which is shown lying inside the conductor.

may then be evaluated as an integral taken over any convenient cross section of the current-carrying conductor

$$W = \frac{1}{2} \int \phi \, dI \qquad (5)$$

There are several ways of evaluating this energy integral. If we know the value of **B** everywhere, we can use Eq. (2) to evaluate the flux through each current tube.   If we can somehow express the results in terms of our coordinate system, we can then perform a second integration to evaluate Eq. (5).   However, if we know the vector potential **A** *we need not compute either* **B** *or* ϕ *in order to evaluate the energy and the inductance.*

   To see this, we write our previous form of the vector potential,

$$\mathbf{H} = \mathbf{\nabla} \times \mathbf{A}$$

as

$$\mathbf{B} = \mu_0(\mathbf{\nabla} \times \mathbf{A}) \qquad (6)$$

Then Eq. (2) may be written in terms of **A** as

$$\phi = \int \mu_0 (\nabla \times \mathbf{A}) \cdot \mathbf{n} \, da \tag{7}$$

Applying Stokes's theorem, we change the surface integral to a line integral

$$\phi = \oint \mu_0 \mathbf{A} \cdot d\mathbf{S} \tag{8}$$

Here, happily, the line integral is to be evaluated around a closed path which coincides with a current filament. Replacing dI by $\mathbf{J} \cdot \mathbf{n} \, da$, Eq. (5) becomes

$$W = \frac{1}{2} \int \left[\oint \mu_0 \mathbf{A} \cdot d\mathbf{S} \right] \mathbf{J} \cdot \mathbf{n} \, da \tag{9}$$

Within a current filament, $\mathbf{J}$, $\mathbf{n}$, and $d\mathbf{S}$ are all parallel. Also, $dS \, da$ is the differential element of volume. These simplifications reduce Eq. (9) to

$$W = \frac{1}{2} \int \mu_0 \mathbf{A} \cdot \mathbf{J} \, dv \tag{10}$$

Here the integration is to be performed throughout the volume of the conductor. Now equating Eq. (10) to Eq. (3), the self-inductance of a circuit becomes

$$L = \frac{\int \mu_0 \mathbf{A} \cdot \mathbf{J} \, dv}{I^2} \tag{11}$$

In a similar manner, the mutual inductance of two circuits may be obtained from the mutual energy as

$$M_{12} = \frac{\int \mu_0 \mathbf{A}_2 \cdot \mathbf{J}_1 \, dv_1}{I_1 I_2} \tag{12}$$

Here, the subscript on $\mathbf{A}_2$ distinguishes the contribution of I_2 to the vector potential, as opposed to the total vector potential and the contribution of I_1 to that total.

These two equations are the goal of this section, and in the following two sections we shall illustrate their use in evaluating self-inductance and mutual inductance. Further comments are in order, however, before leaving this general examination.

By analogy with Eq. (1), $L = \phi/I$, the self-inductance of a circuit of finite cross section may be written in terms of the flux linkages Λ, which have the same units as those of flux.

$$L = \frac{\Lambda}{I} \tag{13}$$

The flux linkages may be determined, and defined, in either of two equivalent forms. When we are using the concept of vector potential, Eq. (11)

tells us that the flux linkages may be computed by means of

$$\Lambda = \frac{\int \mu_0 \mathbf{A} \cdot \mathbf{J} \, dv}{I} \tag{14}$$

While this is occasionally the easiest, and always the most straight-forward, method of evaluating the flux linkages, a physical interpretation is more readily achieved by replacing the volume integral of Eq. (14) with its equivalent from Eq. (5),

$$\Lambda = \frac{\int \phi \, dI}{I} \tag{15}$$

Recalling that dI is the current in each of the current filaments, we may interpret the flux linkages as the *average value of the flux through all the surfaces which are bounded by current filaments*. The difficulty of evaluating the flux linkages by using Eq. (15) is not to be underestimated. The reader may verify this by reference to any of the standard electrical engineering texts in which the inductance of a circuit of finite cross section is evaluated without the use of the vector potential. Even in the relatively symmetrical problem of two parallel round wires, there is an uncertainty in the limits of integration.

A more formal procedure for computing mutual inductance arises from writing the vector potential of a current element in its integral formulation, as in Sec. 11.4:

$$A_2 = \int \frac{I_2 \, d\mathbf{L}_2}{4\pi R} \tag{16}$$

Also, by writing $\mathbf{J}_1 \, dv_1$ as $I_1 \, d\mathbf{L}_1$, Eq. (12) becomes

$$M_{12} = \frac{\mu_0}{4\pi} \int \frac{d\mathbf{L}_1 \cdot d\mathbf{L}_2}{R} \tag{17}$$

While this shows the equivalence of the mutual inductance terms with interchanged subscripts, we shall use Eqs. (11) and (12) in our illustrations. By doing this, we can apply the vector potentials already obtained in the first part of this chapter. It is easier to break some tasks up into two separate parts.

Finally, let us observe that the magnetic energy of a circuit due to its own current can be written from Eqs. (5) and (11) as

$$W = \frac{1}{2} \int \mu_0 \mathbf{A} \cdot \mathbf{J} \, dv \tag{18}$$

This is subject to the interpretation that the magnetic energy is entirely within the conductors themselves and is distributed with a volume density

$$w = \mu_0 \frac{\mathbf{A} \cdot \mathbf{J}}{2} \tag{19}$$

This is in contrast to the interpretation involving the magnetic-field vectors which was discussed at the end of the previous section.

11.11   Mutual Inductance of Two Parallel Transmission Lines.   To illustrate the application of the vector potential to inductance calculations, it is well to examine the mutual terms separately from the self-inductance.   Accordingly, we here dispose of the details of obtaining the mutual terms arising in round wires, infinitely long.   In the following section we shall extend the results one step more in order to obtain the self-inductance of a two-wire line.

In Fig. 11.10a, four numbered round conductors are shown.   The pairs 1-2 and 3-4 each form a complete circuit with equal and opposite currents.

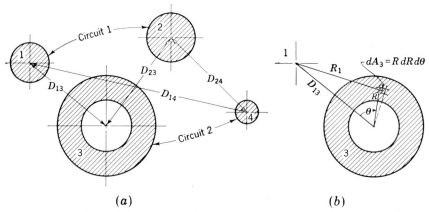

(a)   (b)

FIG. 11.10   Analysis of the mutual inductance of two circuits.   The notation for the distances between the centers of the long round conductors is depicted in a.   In b is shown the local coordinate system needed in the analysis.

In equation form, using subscripts to distinguish the conductors rather than the circuits, temporarily, we have $I_2 = -I_1$ and $I_3 = -I_4$; hence

$$J_3 a_3 = J_4 a_4 \tag{1}$$

where J = current density

a = cross-sectional area of conductor

We shall focus our attention on one part of the entire problem, as illustrated in part b of the figure.   The remaining results can be written by permuting the subscripts.   From Sec. 11.7, we write the vector potential due to the current in conductor 1, using an indefinite reference level, R_{01}, which is very remote from our conductors.

$$A_1 = \frac{I_1}{2\pi} \log_e \frac{R_{01}}{R_1} \tag{2}$$

All the vector potentials and current densities are in the axial direction, perpendicular to the paper in the figure.   To keep our signs straight, let

I_1 and I_3 both be into the paper (though in the end it will make no difference). Under this condition, $\mathbf{A}_1 \cdot \mathbf{J}_3 = A_1 J_3$. We have now to evaluate the integral

$$\int \mathbf{A}_1 \cdot \mathbf{J}_3 \, dv = \int A_1 J_3 R \, dR \, d\theta \, dz \tag{3}$$

By integrating with respect to z at once, all the following *are expressed on a per-unit-length basis*. Writing the constant J_3 outside and using Eq. (2),

$$\int \mathbf{A}_1 \cdot \mathbf{J}_3 \, dv = \frac{J_3 I_1}{2\pi} \int \left(\log_e \frac{R_{01}}{R_1} \right) R \, dR \, d\theta \tag{4}$$

Separating the logarithmic terms,

$$\int \mathbf{A}_1 \cdot \mathbf{J}_3 \, dv = \frac{J_3 I_1}{2\pi} \left[\int \int (\log_e R_{01}) R \, dR \, d\theta - \int (\log_e R_1) R \, dR \, d\theta \right] \tag{5}$$

The first integration gives the area of the conductor.

$$\int \mathbf{A}_1 \cdot \mathbf{J}_3 \, dv = \frac{J_3 I_1 a_3}{2\pi} \log_e R_{01} - \frac{J_3 I_1}{2\pi} \int (\log_e R_1) R \, dR \, d\theta \tag{6}$$

To evaluate the remaining integral, we use the law of cosines in part b of the figure and a temporary cylindrical coordinate system with the axis at the center of the conductor.

$$R_1{}^2 = D_{13}{}^2 + R^2 - 2 D_{13} R \cos \theta \tag{7}$$

Dividing by $D_{13}{}^2$ and taking the logarithm of both sides,

$$\log_e R_1{}^2 - \log_e D_{13}{}^2 = \log_e \left(1 + \frac{R^2}{D_{13}{}^2} - \frac{2R}{D_{13}} \cos \theta \right) \tag{8}$$

The remaining integral in Eq. (6) becomes

$$\int (\log_e R_1) R \, dR \, d\theta = \frac{1}{2} \int \left[\log_e \left(1 + \frac{R^2}{D_{13}{}^2} - \frac{2R}{D_{13}} \cos \theta \right) \right] R \, dR \, d\theta$$
$$+ \int (\log_e D_{13}) R \, dR \, d\theta \tag{9}$$

The second integral on the right gives the area a_3 again. As for the remaining integral, we are fortunate to find in a table of definite integrals (Pierce 523)

$$\int_0^\pi [\log_e (1 + b^2 + 2b \cos \theta)] \, d\theta = 0 \qquad 1 + b^2 > 2b \tag{10}$$

Collecting our results gives

$$\int \mathbf{A}_1 \cdot \mathbf{J}_3 \, dv = \frac{J_3 a_3 I_1}{2\pi} \log_e \frac{R_{01}}{D_{13}} \tag{11}$$

Within conductor number three, the vector potential due to the current in number two is oppositely directed to that due to the current in number one

$$A_2 = -I_1 \log_e \frac{R_{02}}{R_2} \tag{12}$$

Here R_2 is the distance from conductor number two, and R_{02} is the distance to the reference point. Within conductor number three, $A_2 J_3$ is negative since $A_1 J_3$ was taken as positive. Comparing Eq. (12) with Eq. (2) shows that by advancing the subscript 1 to 2 and changing the sign we can write the relation corresponding to Eq. (11) as

$$\int \mathbf{A}_2 \cdot \mathbf{J}_3 \, dv = \frac{-J_3 a_3 I_1}{2\pi} \log_e \frac{R_{02}}{D_{23}} \tag{13}$$

Then the total contribution of conductors one and two to the volume integral within conductor number three is the sum of Eqs. (12) and (13). Combining the logarithmic terms,

$$\int (\mathbf{A}_1 + \mathbf{A}_2) \cdot \mathbf{J}_3 \, dv = \frac{-J_3 a_3 I_1}{2\pi} \log_e \frac{D_{23}}{D_{13}} \tag{14}$$

The reference-level terms cancel, in the limit, as the reference point is taken at a distance sufficiently remote from the conductors.

Turning now to conductor number four, we can write the contributions of both $\mathbf{A}_1$ and $\mathbf{A}_2$ by advancing the subscript 3 and 4 and again changing the sign because the current in four is in the opposite direction.

$$\int (\mathbf{A}_1 + \mathbf{A}_2) \cdot \mathbf{J}_4 \, dv = \frac{J_4 a_4 I_1}{2\pi} \log_e \frac{D_{14}}{D_{24}} \tag{15}$$

Observing Eq. (1) again and adding Eqs. (14) and (15) gives the total volume integral per unit length.

$$\int (\mathbf{A}_1 + \mathbf{A}_2) \cdot (\mathbf{J}_3 + \mathbf{J}_4) \, dv = \frac{I_1 I_3}{2\pi} \log_e \frac{D_{14} D_{23}}{D_{13} D_{24}} \tag{16}$$

From Eq. 11.10 (12), the mutual inductance is

$$M = \frac{\mu_0}{2\pi} \log_e \frac{D_{14} D_{23}}{D_{13} D_{24}} \qquad \text{henries per meter} \tag{17}$$

This result is perhaps simpler than we had a right to expect. For long round wires, the mutual inductance depends only on the spacing of the wires and not on their size. Further, the conductors may be solid or hollow as long as their individual circular symmetry is preserved. From another interpretation, the mutual inductance of long round-wire circuits is the same as though the currents were concentrated at the center of the wires.

For wires which are not round, the definite integral of Eq. (10) has different limits. The method of evaluating the integral is beyond the scope of this book. See Reddick and Miller, listed in the references at the end of this chapter.

11.12   Self-inductance of a Two-wire Transmission Line. In Sec. 11.7 we evaluated the vector potentials of a two-wire line. To obtain the self-inductance we use these vector potentials in evaluating the volume integrals illustrated in the previous section. We shall use the notation of Fig. 11.11, which differs from Fig. 11.4 in that the two conductors have

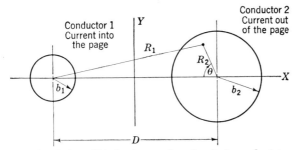

FIG. 11.11   Analysis of the self-inductance of a circuit formed of two round wires, infinitely long.

different radii and the distance between centers is labeled D instead of $2a$. Properly accounting for the two different radii in the steps leading to Eq. 11.7 (7), we have for the vector potential within conductor number two (on the right in the figure)

$$A = \frac{I}{4\pi}\left(1 - \frac{R_2{}^2}{b_2{}^2} + \log_e \frac{R_1{}^2}{b_1{}^2}\right) \qquad R_2 \lessgtr b_2 \qquad (1)$$

Within the conductor, $\mathbf{J}_2$ and $\mathbf{A}$ are parallel. The volume integral of their scalar product, on a per-unit-length basis, is written from Eq. (1) after separating the logarithmic terms

$$\int \mathbf{A} \cdot \mathbf{J}_2 \, dv = \frac{IJ_2}{4\pi}\left[\int da_2 - \int \frac{R_2{}^2}{b_2{}^2} \, da_2 \right.$$
$$\left. + 2\int (\log_e R_1) \, da_2 - 2\int (\log_e b_1) \, da_2 \right] \qquad (2)$$

Of the four integrals in Eq. (2), the third and fourth arise from the contributions of the current in the other conductor and were evaluated in the previous section. Adapting Eqs. 11.11 (9) and (10) to the present notation, the third integral in Eq. (2) has the value

$$\int (\log_e R_1) \, da_2 = a_2 \log_e D \qquad (3)$$

All the other integrals give the area of the conductor multiplied by a constant. Collecting the results and writing $J_2 a_2$ as I,

$$\int \mathbf{A} \cdot \mathbf{J}_2 \, dv = \frac{I^2}{4\pi} \left(\frac{1}{2} + \log_e \frac{D^2}{b_1{}^2} \right) \qquad \text{per unit length} \qquad (4)$$

Permuting the subscripts gives, for the other conductor,

$$\int \mathbf{A} \cdot \mathbf{J}_1 \, dv = \frac{I^2}{4\pi} \left(\frac{1}{2} + \log_e \frac{D^2}{b_2{}^2} \right) \qquad \text{per unit length} \qquad (5)$$

The total volume integration is the sum of Eqs. (4) and (5), which may be written as

$$\int \mathbf{A} \cdot \mathbf{J} \, dv = \frac{I^2}{\pi} \left(\frac{1}{4} + \log_e \frac{D}{\sqrt{b_1 b_2}} \right) \qquad \text{per unit length} \qquad (6)$$

The self-inductance is given by using Eq. (6) in Eq. 11.10 (11):

$$L = \frac{\mu_0}{\pi} \left(\frac{1}{4} + \log_e \frac{D}{\sqrt{b_1 b_2}} \right) \qquad \text{henries per meter} \qquad (7)$$

For equal wire radii, let $b_1 = b_2 = r$; then

$$L = \frac{\mu_0}{\pi} \left(\frac{1}{4} + \log_e \frac{D}{r} \right) \qquad \text{henries per meter} \qquad (8)$$

If the current is concentrated in the surface of the cylinder, as a current sheet, an analysis shows that the constant term within the parentheses disappears from these formulas.

These results assume uniform current densities, and this can occur only with direct currents. At power frequencies, the formulas are excellent approximations when the spacing of the wires is large compared to their radii. Usually there are greater uncertainties which arise from the nature of the construction of a practical transmission line.

For paramagnetic wires, in which the permeability is a constant, Eq. (7) is modified to include the permeability μ of the wire material.

$$L = \frac{\mu_0}{\pi} \left(\frac{\mu}{4\mu_0} + \log_e \frac{D}{\sqrt{b_1 b_2}} \right) \qquad \text{henries per meter} \qquad (9)$$

With appreciation of the nonlinearity, this may be used for ferromagnetic wires. To obtain this result from the vector potential requires that we reformulate the vector potential to include the Amperian currents, or equivalent induced currents, in the wires themselves. We shall not do this in this book, the reader being referred to a very painstaking explanation of the procedure in Pender and Warren, included in the references at the end of this chapter.

REFERENCES

1. Skilling, H. H.: "Fundamentals of Electric Waves," 2d ed., pp. 46–50, 91–95, John Wiley & Sons, Inc., New York, 1948.
2. Pender, Harold, and S. Reid Warren, Jr.: "Electric Circuits and Fields," pp. 481–509, McGraw-Hill Book Company, Inc., New York, 1943.
3. Reddick, H. W., and F. H. Miller: "Advanced Mathematics for Engineers," pp. 233–237, John Wiley & Sons, Inc., New York, 1938.
4. Ware, Lawrence A.: "Elements of Electromagnetic Waves," pp. 48–61, Pitman Publishing Corp., New York, 1949.
5. Weber, Ernst: "Electromagnetic Fields," Vol. I, pp. 39–60, 152–164, John Wiley & Sons, Inc., New York, 1950.
6. Boast, Warren B.: "Principles of Electric and Magnetic Fields," pp. 305–308, Harper & Brothers, New York, 1948.
7. Hague, B.: "An Introduction to Vector Analysis," 4th ed., Chaps. VII and VIII, John Wiley & Sons, Inc., New York, 1950.

PROBLEMS

11.1 Verify the results given as Eq. 11.6(7) and (8), by evaluating the curl of the vector potential given in Eqs. 11.6(5) and (6).

11.2 By expansion, verify Eq. 11.3(3).

11.3 Find the vector potential on the axis of a current loop of finite radius but vanishing cross section. Compare with Eq. 11.8(17). What does the result mean with respect to the magnetic field vector evaluated in Prob. 9.2? Describe the analogous situation in the field of a dipole as given by Eq. 11.8(18).

11.4 Find the magnetic field vectors in the field of a differential current loop, from the vector potential given by Eq. 11.8(14). Compare with the electric field as given by the gradient of Eq. 11.8(18), for the corresponding electric dipole.

11.5 Assume that the current in long round wires can be confined to the surface of the wires, as a current sheet. Define the self-inductance of a circuit of two such wires in terms of the surface-current density, and then show that the self-inductance per unit length is given by Eq. 11.12(8) with the constant term in the brackets set equal to zero.

*11.6 Evaluate the vector potential which would arise from a single long straight wire of length L and vanishing cross section. Find the equation of the surfaces in which the magnitude of the vector potential is a constant. From this, prepare a sketch of the vector potential field, letting the length of the line segment represent the magnitude of **A**.

11.7 Verify Eq. 11.12(1).

APPENDIX 1

RUBBER-SHEET MODELS OF
TWO-DIMENSIONAL POTENTIAL FIELDS

The deflection h of a thin elastic membrane under constant surface tension obeys a differential equation identical to Laplace's equation in two dimensions:

$$\frac{\partial^2 h}{\partial x^2} + \frac{\partial^2 h}{\partial y^2} = 0$$

Holding for small deflections only, this relation is widely used in mechanics in studying vibrations of membranes such as drumheads. Differential equations for larger deflections are given by Spangenberg, by Zworykin, by Weber, and by Kleynen,[1] for uniform pressure on both sides of the membrane. In an appendix to a book by Bewley, Hiltner discusses the case in which the membrane is dilated by a uniform pressure, giving an equation which reduces to Poisson's equation for small deflections.

Hiltner states that the membrane gives a good approximation to the potential field if the maximum slope of the surface is not greater than 30°. On the basis of his experience with modeling electron trajectories, Zworykin finds the sheet useful without serious error for angles as large as 15°.

Photographs of rubber-sheet models showing the method of construction will be found in Spangenberg, Zworykin, Kleynen, and Pierce. Zworykin stretched surgical rubber over a square frame, wrapped the sheet around the frame, and from the appearance of the photographs, apparently fastened the sheet with thumbtacks. In Spangenburg's model, the edge tension seems to arise from spring-loaded clips somewhat like clothespins. Kleynen supported a heavy sheet on a round hoop by lashing it with a rope looped through reinforced holes in the sheet, much like rigging a sail. Pierce has used sheets a yard wide and several yards long on an elaborate frame of I beams, fastening the sheet with a contrivance which seems to be more like a garter than anything else. Weber shows a drawing of a technique which uses heavy weights on the sheet to achieve the boundary conditions. Using a soap film, Hiltner modeled Fourier's heat-slab problem and presents a photograph.

[1] All the references mentioned in this discussion are listed at the end of Appendix 1.

The author has found that round frames are better than square ones when it comes to stretching the sheet uniformly. For classroom demonstration, a simple, inexpensive, portable frame can be bought ready-made in the form of a quilting hoop. These hoops are similar to embroidery hoops but are considerably larger. They are available at department stores and through mail-order catalogues. Figure 6.20 shows a quilting hoop in use.

For most of the photographs in this book, the author used a large, heavy steel toroid. The cross section is 1 inch square and the diameter is 32 inches. This was used because it was already on hand, and there is no particular reason for its being so heavy. Anything which is stiff enough to provide an accurate plane boundary and which will remain quite level when the rubber sheet is displaced upward would be satisfactory. The rubber sheet is held by an outer clamping ring with a tension screw which is tightened as the sheet is stretched. By marking the rubber sheet with a circle before stretching, it is not difficult to achieve uniform tension, but care is necessary in the final stages if the sheet is not to be torn.

It is also interesting and instructive to discuss this modeling problem with a musician familiar with drums. An old snare or bass drum can be modified to carry rubber sheeting, which takes a good deal more stretching than does the usual drum head.

All the rubber-sheet materials that the author has tried have been disappointingly fragile. Surgical rubber, or rubberdam, varies greatly in cost and quality. Some of it is filled with tiny holes which can be seen only on close inspection but which soon grow in size when the sheet is stretched. Rubber bed sheeting is surprisingly hard to obtain, but the single sample tried was about as good as surgical rubber. War-surplus weather balloons have given inconsistent performance, but those which had not deteriorated from age have been more permanent than anything else tried. This material has a higher modulus of elasticity than surgical rubber, and this, too, makes it easier to use. Heavier materials, such as gasket rubber, are quite expensive and difficult to stretch. For a permanent setup, it is probably best to use a good heavy frame and the gasket material in $\frac{1}{64}$-inch thickness.

The contour-lighting trick is surprisingly easy to perform. Ruled gratings on glass are available from Edmunds Scientific Corporation, Barrington, N. J. As a first purchase of a single grating, 175 lines per inch is suggested, but these are inexpensive enough to warrant the purchase of several. A grating of 133 lines per inch on film was donated by a photoengraving shop. It has a disadvantage because the lines are formed by a series of touching dots which show up on the rubber sheet.

Of several projectors tried, the easiest to use was a 35-millimeter projector with a color-corrected lens. The one available here has a turret-type slide holder. This permits adjustment of the planes of light and darkness by turning the turret rather than by trying to position the grating accurately in the slide holder.

As a final note of caution, remember that rubber cement in any form will destroy the usefulness of surgical rubber.

REFERENCES

1. Spangenberg, K. R.: "Vacuum Tubes," p. 77, McGraw-Hill Book Company, Inc., New York, 1948.
2. Zworykin, V. K., G. A. Morton, E. G. Ramberg, J. Hillier, and A. W. Vance: "Electron Optics and the Electron Microscope," p. 420, John Wiley & Sons, Inc., New York, 1945.
3. Weber, Ernst: "Electromagnetic Fields," Vol. I, John Wiley & Sons, Inc., New York, 1950.
4. Kleynen, P. H. J. A.: The Motion of an Electron in Two-dimensional Electrostatic Fields, *Philips Tech. Rev.*, Vol. 2, No. 11, pp. 338–345, 1937. Though not widely available, this is a very interesting paper. The author obtained a copy through the interlibrary loan service and found it well worth the trouble.
5. Bewley, L. V.: "Two-dimensional Fields in Electrical Engineering," pp. 196–200, The Macmillan Company, New York, 1948.
6. Pierce, J. R.: "Theory and Design of Electron Beams," p. 56, D. Van Nostrand Company, Inc., New York, 1949.
7. Courant, Richard, and Herbert Robbins: "What Is Mathematics?" pp. 386–396, Oxford University Press, New York, 1941. Those interested in experiments and demonstrations using soap films rather than rubber sheets can profitably begin here.

APPENDIX 2

FLUID MAPPER TECHNIQUES

By A. D. Moore

The flow of a viscous fluid between closely spaced parallel planes is a standard topic in texts on hydrodynamics (or fluid mechanics). For steady lamellar flow, the analysis shows that the average velocity is the gradient of a velocity potential which satisfies Laplace's equation in two dimensions. The paths of the fluid coincide with the stream lines of the velocity vector and can be made visible by the addition of coloring matter. The pioneering demonstrations were made by Hele-Shaw at the turn of the century.

Any two plane surfaces will suffice to define the flow space, but one of them must be transparent. Fortunately, plate glass not only is cheap but is ground quite flat in the manufacturing process. In order to provide the desired boundary conditions, something more workable than plate glass is desirable as the other plane surface. Of the several materials investigated, plaster in slab form has proved versatile with respect to providing sources, sinks, obstacles, and other boundary conditions. Cast against plate glass, the slab can be made as flat as the glass, and holes can be cored as well as drilled. While reference to the literature listed below will provide more details, the following condensed procedure will serve as an initial guide in the use of plaster slabs in fluid mapping.

For plates, get two pieces of plate glass, 10 by 12 inches; grind off edge sharpness by hand, with a wet stone. For spacers, use three brass washers; somewhat flatten them by rubbing each side on grit paper; then grind to equal thickness, this being between 30 and 40 mils. To make three posts, turn aluminum or brass to about 0.5 inch in diameter, and of equal length—about 1 inch. Make two hollow well-core molds on the lathe, 1 inch in diameter and about 0.5 inch long. Turn a slight taper on the outside.

Lay down a plate. On it, form a fence mold to make a 6- by 8-inch slab. The four pieces can be any convenient metal pieces 0.5 inch wide, such as brass strip or angle. Lightly grease the inner surfaces with silicone stopcock grease. Likewise grease the outer surfaces of the core molds, and place them on the plate to form the wells. These molds are to be tapped out through the back of the slab, so arrange the taper accordingly.

Mix a little plaster (Duroc preferred, but any dental stone will do), putting the powder into the water. Apply as holding plaster, some of this inside the core molds and outside the fence molds. When this plaster is fairly firm (or later), the slab can be poured.

Nearly a pint of plaster is needed. Use a pint of powder to about 6 ounces of water. If too stiff, add water. Make it somewhat thicker than pancake batter. Pour in about half, and spread the mix around to cover the plate. Using a small stiff brush, jab down into the plaster, all along the mold surfaces, to remove corner-clinging bubbles. Then pour in enough to fill the mold. Now go all over the pour with a rubber-bladed spatula, rapidly jabbing down in and bumping the plate, to make all bubbles rise off the plate.

When hard set occurs, wet all the plaster. Remove the fence molds, slip the slab off, and tap out the cores. Scrape off any fin on the slab edges, flush all loose plaster bits from the slab, and closely inspect the slab face to be *sure* it is clean. Wipe the plate clean. Place the slab face down on the plate.

Cut celluloid well bottoms, these to extend beyond well edges somewhat. Crimp them at one edge, using heat and bending by the fingers, to fit better over the tubes. Cut two lengths of rubber tubing, each to reach from a well edge to 2 inches beyond the slab edge. Use $\frac{1}{8}$-inch I.D. by $\frac{1}{4}$-inch O.D. handmade tubing.

If the slab has just been finished, it still may be setting and asking for water. Wet it. Mix a small new batch of plaster. Mop off excess water on the slab. Wet the sides of the well end of a tube with plaster and lay it in place. Place a well bottom over a well, with its crimp over the tube. Put plaster all around, and somewhat up over its edge. Tap the bottom lightly to settle the plaster into place. Likewise for the other well.

Near each slab corner, make a plaster pile, piling to more than 1 inch above the plate. Set the posts on the plate, around the slab. Put the other plate down gently, to rest on the posts. This makes accurate feet by the squeeze-out technique. After setting, wet the feet and remove the upper plate. The bottom of the slab should be similar to that illustrated in Fig. A-1.

For a tray, make sideboards of tempered Masonite and use crib lining. The sideboards consist of four pieces, 2.5 inches wide, sawed halfway through near each end, and notched together to make a 14- by 16-inch tray. A yard of crib lining (plastic sheeting from a home-supply store) is laid over the sideboards. Pour in enough water to cover the plate when operating. To dump the water later, pick up the four corners of the lining and go to the sink.

Two tanks are needed, each connected to rubber tubing perhaps 40 inches long. Until permanent tanks with nipples are made, use a couple of Republic Freezettes (flexible plastic food containers) with an Acco Clamp No. 125 (office-supply store) clamped on the edge of each. Run a tube through the holes in the clamp ears, and down into the tank.

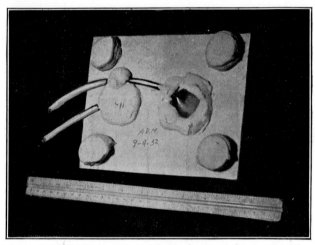

Fig. A.1   A bottom view of a completed fluid-mapper slab, showing the plaster feet in the corners. These will support the bottom of the slab when in operation. The celluloid bottom of the right-hand well and the method of attachment of the rubber tubing may be seen at the center of the slab.

Place a plate on the tray bottom and set the slab on it. Set the posts on the plate, around the slab. Connect each tank tube to a well tube by means of a nipple (preferred nipple: an inch length of thin-walled brass tube, $\frac{1}{8}$ inch I.D.). Put water in each tank. Lift a tube out of a tank, suck on it to start flow, replace the tube in the tank water. Lift both tanks high to be sure air is cleared from the lines. Set the tanks on the table.

Sprinkle the water above the slab with sifted potassium permanganate crystals, these roughly averaging 1 millimeter in length. Gently lower the top plate to rest on the spacers. Lift or lower the tanks to make the wells act as sources or sinks (or one of each) as desired, and watch the patterns form.

This open-edge slab can now be turned into a closed-edge slab by adding an inch-wide plaster barrier by the squeeze-out method. Make a 6- by 4-inch template of bristolboard or cardboard; cut windows in it to match the wells, for registration purposes. Cut a duplicate of the template, from part of a manila folder (used in letter files). This is to be the separator. Cut three extra windows in the separator, where the spacers are to be.

Have the slab soaking wet. Briefly soak the separator, then place it, registered, on the slab face. Mop off excess water. Place the spacers on the slab, within their windows. Lay down a track of thin plaster around the separator edge. When squeezed, it must overrun the separator somewhat and run out near to or over the slab edge. Now squeeze it; lay a plate down gently, and press on it to make sure it rests on the spacers. After hard set, wet the new plaster and remove the plate.

Next, put down the template, registered. This will mark the location of the edges of the separator which are now covered with plaster. Go along the template edge for perhaps 2 inches with a knife having a sharp tip, and score the barrier plaster; score again several times, cutting about halfway through. Continue thus around the template. The separator has kept the overrun from bonding to the flow area part of the face. With the aid of a knife tip, the overrun and the separator can be lifted up with ease.

Prepare to operate again. Crystals falling on the barrier must be flicked off with a brush. The plate now goes directly on the barrier, and the wells must be source and sink of equal value. If there is leakage, lift the plate, dry it, apply a thin smear of silicone grease where it rests on the barrier, replace it, and momentarily press down to spread the grease.

The squeeze-out technique can be used to make part-barriers; also, cast-on plaster obstacles within the flow area; also, to build up a slab to two or more levels, to give two or more flow spaces by which to simulate fields having two or more media.

Well cores of many shapes can be made of plastic modeling compound (Plastelin, Plasticine, etc.). Lay a piece of paper on a plate. Lay a paper template on the paper. Cover the template with an ample lump of warmed Plastelin. Cover the lump with another paper, and roll down to cake form, the thickness being $\frac{1}{2}$ inch, plus. Then squeeze to $\frac{1}{2}$ inch by using an upper plate. Remove the cake, invert it on a plate, remove the first piece of paper, and trim with vertical cuts to the template edge. The cake should be cold when trimmed. Remove the template and the other paper, and stick the core, template side down, to the plate prior to casting.

REFERENCES

1. Moore, A. D.: Fields from Fluid Flow Mappers, *J. Appl. Phys.*, Vol. 20, pp. 790–804, August, 1949.
2. Moore, A. D.: Soap Film and Sandbed Mapper Techniques, *J. Appl. Mechanics* (bound with *Trans. ASME*), Vol. 17, pp. 291–298, September, 1950.

3. Moore, A. D.: Four Electromagnetic Propositions, with Fluid Mapper Verifications, *Elec. Eng.*, Vol. 69, pp. 607–610, July, 1950.

4. Moore, A. D.: The Further Development of Fluid Mappers, *Trans. AIEE*, Vol. 69, Part II, pp. 1615–1624, 1950.

5. Moore, A. D.: Mapping Techniques Applied to Fluid Mapper Patterns, *Trans. AIEE*, Vol. 71, 1952.

6. Moore, A. D.: "Starting a Fluid-mapper Laboratory." A private publication which can be obtained by addressing Prof. A. D. Moore, Department of Electrical Engineering, University of Michigan, Ann Arbor, Mich. As of this writing, a "Fluid-mapper Manual" is in preparation.

INDEX

A Table of Symbols follows the Contents at the front of the book